INDUSTRIAL SAFETY
Third Edition

INDUSTRIAL SAFETY
Third Edition

Edited by

Roland P. Blake

PRENTICE-HALL, INC., ENGLEWOOD CLIFFS, N.J.

PRENTICE-HALL INTERNATIONAL, INC., *London*
PRENTICE-HALL OF AUSTRALIA, PTY, LTD., *Sydney*
PRENTICE-HALL OF CANADA, LTD., *Toronto*
PRENTICE-HALL FRANCE, S.A.R.L., *Paris*
PRENTICE-HALL OF JAPAN, INC., *Tokyo*
PRENTICE-HALL DE MEXICO, S.A., *Mexico City*

Printed in the United States of America

C

Preface

This edition has been extensively revised and broadened in scope to bring it up to date. Excepting only Mr. M. A. Gimbel, the co-authors have turned the work of revision over to me. Mr. Gimbel has shortened his section somewhat and his chapters have been renumbered as 8 to 16 inclusive.

As its title indicates, Chapter One has been rewritten to present an over-all picture of the accident toll for the nation's population as a whole, not for just the working population. I sincerely hope that this chapter will be read with care and serious attention given its findings. Certainly an annual carnage resulting from accidents that at least approaches in number, if it does not exceed, the highest death toll in battle our armed forces have ever suffered in any calendar year amply justifies national concern. Since most of these death- and injury-dealing accidents are preventable, vigorous pre-ventive action should be taken on a nationwide scale.

Chapter Two has been rewritten to present a more lifelike picture of the background of the safety movement in this country and of the manner of its development with particular reference to the factors that have been influential in shaping the present unsatisfactory conditions in the field of occupational safety.

The chapter on the guarding of power transmission machinery has been omitted because direct motor drives have eliminated all but a minor fraction of such equipment. The little that remains is adequately covered by the *American Standard*.

In response to requests from users of this text, the chapter on occupa-tional health in the first edition has been reincluded in considerably ex-panded form to bring it up to date and make it more adequate.

Also, in response to user requests, a chapter on ionizing radiations safety has been added. It is emphasized that this chapter contains only the barest fundamentals and any person making practical use of it should at least become familiar with and understand well, the material in this field that is listed in the bibliography—insofar as it applies to the uses of ionizing radiation with which he is concerned.

Finally, I deem it a great privilege and honor to have had a part in the preparation of *Industrial Safety* and in its revision. Presumably this will be my swan song for I am one of the very few still alive who had a part, small though it was, in organizing the National Safety Council. I am now retired after well over a half century of active participation in the field of occupational safety and health. It has been my good fortune through most of that period to be in a position that enabled, in fact required, me to try to view the occupational safety and health picture as a whole and shape my activities to be of maximum value for the furtherance of the safety cause. If my interpretations of the present situation and the recommendations and opinions as expressed in this book are reasonably sound it is due chiefly to that fact. At any rate, each user of this book is invited to weigh my conclusions and opinions as expressed therein in the light of his own knowledge and experience for whatever value they may have for him.

ROLAND BLAKE

Bethesda, Maryland

Contents

Chapter One

Magnitude of the Accident Toll

Each year since 1934, accidents have killed from 90,000 to 100,000 of our people. The totals for the ten year period 1950-1959 have averaged over 93,000 per year. Injuries that were at least temporarily disabling ran about 100 times as many, that is about 9.3 millions per year. Of these it is estimated that approximately 3% to 4% caused permanent disablement in at least some degree. The money cost to the national economy as a whole has been placed at on the order of 13 billion dollars per year.*

These figures are impressive, staggering, in fact, if we take into account the immeasurable amount of suffering and heartbreak involved in such a tremendous flood of death and injury. Although each such injury is primarily the concern of the accident victim and his family, the entire nation and its leadership should be gravely concerned over so serious a continuing wastage of our human and material resources, particularly since most of its is preventable by time-tried and -proven methods and procedures. The chief problem is to get far more widespread and complete application of the "know how" we already have.

Some progress is being made, however. The death rate per unit of population per year must be going down, else the steadily increasing population totals would yield corresponding increases in the death totals. That is good as far as it goes, but it isn't enough, not nearly enough, unless we are willing to accept such tragic losses indefinitely, which of course we aren't. But what can we do about it? This author believes and fervently hopes that at least part of the answer is to be found in this text.

Available accident data are far too sketchy to show where the gains have been made for the population as a whole. The data on occupational injuries are far more complete than for any other major classification, but even in this area, there are serious gaps, in agriculture, trade and the service

---

* National Safety Council, *Accident Facts*. (Chicago, Illinois, 1962)

industries in particular. Mortality statistics are complete enough, however, to permit reasonably reliable estimates of death rates per 100,000 population. They make it clear that accidents are a major cause of death at all ages. Between ages 1 and 24 inclusive they are by far the commonest cause of death. For the age group 25 to 44 they are second only to heart disease. For the age group 45 to 64 they are exceeded by heart disease, cancer, and lesions of the central nervous system; above 65 they are exceeded by arteriosclerosis in addition to these other diseases. Thus the accident rate does not decrease with age; rather, other diseases increase with age and accidents become a relatively less common cause of death. The accidental death rate is highest for the age group 65 and above and second highest for infants under age 1.

We rightly spend many hundreds of millions of dollars each year on research aimed at the prevention and cure of such diseases as polio, cancer and arteriosclerosis, plus still greater sums on the preservation of health in general, yet our expenditures of time and money and effort to prevent death and injury caused by accidents are slight in comparison. The main reason for this is not too obvious; although we have a deepseated fear of disease and are interested in its prevention, we have little concern for accidents. Many, perhaps most, persons have a serious concern for their health; few feel a similar concern about accidents. Cancer is a dread word; so is polio; others also. But accidents have been a familiar, easily understandable part of life and living throughout the development of the human race. Undoubtedly accidents killed many cavemen.

Another point is of some importance also; i.e., accidents kill so infrequently—one per hundred temporarily disabling injuries. That kind of odds scares no one. Thus we accept accidents and feel little urge to undertake their elimination seriously and systematically. That is bad, very bad, for practically all accidental injuries and deaths are preventable by the unfailing use of methods and practices well within the abilities of every person whose intelligence is above that of a low grade moron, that is, if he will but "put his mind to it."

It is primarily a matter of mental attitude. Anyone who wants to can develop what professional safety men (safety engineers if you prefer) call "safety mindedness." It has been described as an attitude of mind that causes one routinely to consider the possibility of accident in each and every situation and activity in which he is involved and to take suitable preventive action as a matter of course. Safety minded managements all across industry who have succeeded in reducing their injury rates to very low figures consider the development of safety mindedness among all their employees a matter of absolute importance.

Competent management that provides firm, understanding leadership and control does not find this difficult, provided that they fully satisfy all the other essentials of a sound safety program. Developing a similar mental attitude among our entire population is obviously a far bigger undertaking, yet it must be undertaken if we are ever to reduce the shockingly heavy wastage of our human and material resources due to preventable accidents. This wastage will be reduced in proportion to the degree in which the safety mindedness of the American people as a whole improves.

By this time the discriminating reader may be wondering why a text on industrial safety starts off with a chapter giving the accident picture for the entire population. The justification is threefold. First, every student of safety, in fact everyone who has a personal or occupational interest in the advancement of the cause of safety, should have at least an awareness of the overall accident picture. Second, many, perhaps most, of the unsafe conditions and unsafe practices responsible for injuries in industry are more or less common throughout most non-work activities. Knowledge of this should help the safety man promote safe practice far beyond his own little corner in industry. Finally, the more widely an awareness of the magnitude of the yearly accident rate is spread, the more the ranks of those who are working actively to reduce it will be swelled. This author considers that the lack of similar chapters in other safety texts is highly regrettable. The necessary data are available, for they are collected and published annually by the National Safety Council in its book *Accident Facts*. Means should be found for its far wider dissemination, to our educational, political and community leadership in particular.

To further this purpose, the author has included the following break-down of the accidental death and injury totals for a typical year by the four main classifications, Work, Motor-vehicle, Home, Public, with a brief discussion of each.

Class	Deaths	Disabling Injuries
Occupational	13,800	1,950,000
Motor-vehicle	38,000	1,400,000
Home	28,000	4,000,000
Public	17,000	2,000,000
TOTAL	96,800	9,350,000

Motor vehicle

The chief difficulty in this field does not seem to be lack of public awareness. The publicity given to highway slaughter, particularly on week ends and holidays, has made it a matter of general knowledge and has aroused the active interest and participation of many in an effort to reduce it. The nationwide traffic safety program under the combined leadership of the National Safety Council, automotive safety groups, and traffic authorities has brought a progressive lowering of the death rate per million miles travelled, but this gain is being continuously offset by the ever increasing number of cars on the road and mileages driven.

Lack of active safety mindedness resulting in failure to follow commonsense safe practice, is a major factor here as in the other three classifications. However, in the fatal and otherwise more serious crashes the major factors are liquor and speeding. And it is clear that much, perhaps most, of the speeding is due to drinking, as are many of the less serious accidents as well. No exact measure of the importance of drinking as a hgihway killer can be arrived at from the available data, but as to its outstanding importance there is no room for doubt. Reports from 18 states, for example, showed that drinking was obviously involved in over 30% of the fatal crashes. This percentage rose to 48 on Labor Day and 55 at Christmas. What a way to celebrate our Lord's birthday!

Another substantial proportion of the serious and fatal crashes is produced by the irresponsibles, the dare devils and the reckless. Inexperience plays a part also, but the fact that the accident rate for drivers under 20 is not as high as for ages 21 to 45 appears to rank these other faults ahead of inexperience as a causative factor. The age group 20-24 has the highest crash rate of all.

Finally, we have the crashes caused by the occasional lapses of those who normally are safe drivers. These persons are simply not safety minded enough to "play it safe" all the time. Failure to give "full and proper attention," or similarly worded explanations, appear so often in the investigator's reports that it becomes a bit monotonous.

Traffic authorities and traffic safety groups know the problems and are struggling with them, but unless they obtain more active public interest, support, and cooperation than they have been getting, motor vehicles will continue indefinitely to kill around 40,000 victims per year and injure another 1,400,000 or so.

Public safety

This classification is something of a catch-all. It includes accidents in public places and places used in a public way and in all forms of public transportation (Work injuries to persons employed in such places are excepted). Recreation is the chief injury source in this classification.

Water and falls are the chief killers. Drownings formerly ran about 4,000 per year, but for the last several years this number has been on the increase, due presumably to the steady increase in boating, water sports, and waterside recreation. Falls have for years run neck and neck with drowning as a killer but of recent years are lagging behind, increasing in approximate proportion to population increase. Firearms and explosives (exclusive of home accidents) kill another 1000 or so each year.

The lack of even a modicum of safety mindedness is tiresomely apparent in the descriptions of accidents in this classification. Failure to use even a little forethought and commonsense in eliminating or controlling expectable hazards permeates the entire picture.

Home safety

Traditionally the home is the safest place for one to be. But it obviously was not the safest place for the approximately 28,000 persons killed and the over 4,000,000 more injured by accidents in and about their homes during the typical year cited. Falls killed about 13,000, fire about 5400, firearms and poisonings about 1200 each. Here again, lack of safety mindedness is the chief culprit. Home accident-injuries are almost wholly preventable, but it must be an inside job. Definite responsibility must be assumed and continuously discharged by the heads of the household. Every home should establish and maintain a continuous safety program consisting of hazard elimination, safe practice development and maintenance and, most important of all, the development of safety mindedness in all of the children. Old folks can be a problem. Children are teachable; old folks reputedly are not. This is all the more reason why full family teamwork is necessary to insure safety.

Occupational safety

This is by far the brightest part of the overall picture. The methods and techniques of accident prevention in industry have been worked out and thoroughly proved by application. So many establishments all across American industry have practically eliminated work injuries that we can be certain that all are able to do the same regardless of size, branch of industry, or type of operation. The reduction in death and injury rates, particularly in heavy high hazard industry, since the safety movement had its beginnings has been spectacular. It has been far from uniform throughout industry however. Many great plants and great corporations have reduced their injury rates 90% or more, some to figures approaching zero. The entire membership of the National Safety Council had by 1960 reduced their combined injury frequency rate by over 80%. This and other evidence too detailed to include herein shows that big industry has scored by far the major part of the gains.

The 1960 work injury totals were:

Deaths: 13,800.

Non-fatal injuries: 1,960,000. (Of these about 83,000 resulted in permanent impairment to at least some degree.)

Injury data for the early years of the safety movement are so sketchy that no reliable estimate of the totals for those beginning years is possible. However the following evidence collected from a considerable mass of detail is indicative:

1. The National Safety Council began its annual compilations of injury rates for the entire membership with the year 1926. By 1960 the combined membership frequency rate had been reduced by over 80%.

2. An estimate of occupational deaths for the year 1913, by the Bureau of Labor Statistics of the U. S. Dept. of Labor, put the total at approximately 25,000.

3. The steel industry reports (1960) that its steel and blast furnace plants have reduced their combined injury frequency rate over 96% since the start of their safety programs. Their 1960 rate, as reported by the Bureau of Labor Statistics, was 3.3. The combined rate at the start must therefore have been at least 83, that is, their median rate. Obviously, many must have had far higher rates, perhaps twice that figure.

4. Estimates made from old payroll and accident records of frequency rates of a number of large plants in the steel and other heavy, high hazard, branches of industry yielded many rates that approached or exceeded 100, three above 150. One, a steel plant, had averaged 128 over a five year period. The period covered by these estimates was 1911-1918. The injury rate formulae were not developed until much later, but it was possible to calculate the frequency rates with reasonable reliability by using the accident reports required by the workmen's compensation laws.

From this and other similar data it seems conservative to conclude that had frequency rates remained as high in 1960 as they were in those early years, the injury totals for the year 1960 would have been not less than 2½ times greater or on the order of 35,000 deaths and 5,000,000 disabling injuries. Such a saving of life and suffering is tremendously creditable to American industry, but the picture has a dark side too. Despite the great reductions in injury rates that have been scored (chiefly during the first three decades of the safety movement) there has been no substantial reduction in the year by year injury totals since the end of the Second World War. That is, the reductions in injury rates have merely sufficed to offset the continual increases in the employment totals. Unless the rate of gain can somehow be speeded up, there is no hope barring a major depression—a price no one would be willing to pay—of ever reducing the annual death and injury totals substantially. The bar chart and curve showing the relationship between employment and injury totals brings this out clearly.

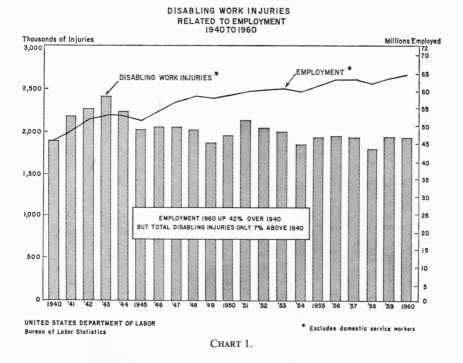

DISABLING WORK INJURIES
RELATED TO EMPLOYMENT
1940 TO 1960

EMPLOYMENT 1960 UP 42% OVER 1940
BUT TOTAL DISABLING INJURIES ONLY 7% ABOVE 1940

UNITED STATES DEPARTMENT OF LABOR
Bureau of Labor Statistics

* Excludes domestic service workers

CHART 1.

Injury breakdown by branch of industry

The purpose of this breakdown is to show the relative importance of the major branches of industry as injury producers. It also makes it evident that small businesses and small workplaces in general, are producing the great majority of the injuries. A great mass of supporting evidence could be adduced, but this table should suffice. Evidently the problem that must be solved if the totals are to be reduced much, is how to get the "know how" and practice of safety, characteristic of big industry, carried effectively to the millions of small employers and their tens of millions of employees as well.

It will be a very big undertaking, not only because there are so many such employers, but also because it will involve changing their viewpoint toward the safety of their own businesses. They don't know that they aren't doing a good enough safety job. It takes an extremely high injury rate in a small workforce, or a run of serious injuries to arouse the concern of the "not yet" safety minded employer. For example, a frequency rate of ten times the combined National Safety Council membership for 1960, would yield only about ten disabling injuries in a year in a work-force of 100. Of these about six would terminate within seven days and therefore wouldn't be compensable in most states. Good safety performance in a business of that size wouldn't permit more than one disabling injury per year on the average nor more than four compensable injuries in ten years, but such employers don't know that.

BREAKDOWN OF INJURIES BY INDUSTRY FOR TYPICAL YEARS *

Branch of industry	1958	1959	1960
Agriculture	300,000	300,000	290,000
Mining	46,000	45,000	47,500
Manufacturing	340,000	400,000	380,000
Contract construction	195,000	217,000	207,000
Public utilities and transportation	178,000	192,000	198,000
Trade	340,000	366,000	375,000
Finance, service, government and misc. ind.	421,000	450,000	471,000
TOTALS	1,820,000	1,970,000	1,960,500

* U.S. Bureau of Labor Statistics.

Even a cursory study of the above breakdown will show that a pre-ponderance of the injury totals is from small business, small employ-ments. Agriculture consists of small establishments in terms of size of work force. A small number of employees is used on most jobs in the con-struction industry; even the big engineering jobs involve much sub-contract-ing to small contractors. The trade and service industries are made up mostly of small employers. All others in the above groups are small and very small firms. In view of the low injury rates that characterize big business, it is clear that little reduction in the injury totals can come from that source; many of them have reached or are near an irreducible minimum already.

Safety leadership has long recognized the existence of this situation but has not faced up to it with anything approaching adequacy con-sidering the magnitude of the job. This will be discussed further in the next chapter, and suggestions based on such progress as has been made will be offered. That progress, small though it has been, shows that great gains can be made if sufficient effort is applied in the right way.

The occupational injury picture in manufacturing

The injury reductions made by big industry have been emphasized. The manufacturing industries as a whole have also greatly reduced their injury rates, as well as their totals, since the war, despite a considerable increase in employment and, more important, in injury possibilities, which is due to a vast proliferation of activities, processes, and products. In fact it appears from chart #2 (showing the relationship between injury frequency rate and injury totals in manufacturing) that but for the reductions

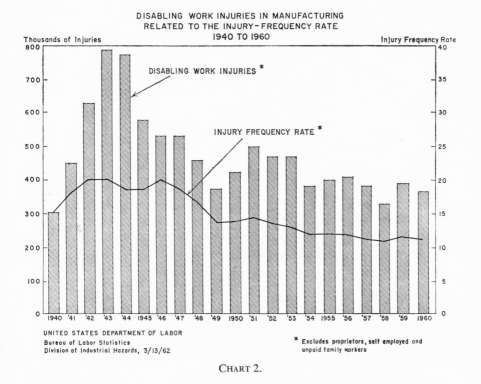

CHART 2.

by manufacturing, the over-all totals of disabling work injuries would have trended upward. Evidently the totals in at least some of the other major classifications must be on the increase.

In conclusion

The following conclusions, drawn from safety accomplishment to date, present lessons of major importance for those who are seeking to continue and greatly advance the work of injury prevention.

1. The accomplishments of numerous establishments in every major branch of industry prove that disabling injuries can be reduced to a figure closely approaching elimination in any industrial establishment, in any branch of industry.

2. It pays to do so.

3. The expenditures required are relatively small.

4. Some degree of hazard is associated with every form of activity; therefore, the highest degree of injury elimination can be achieved only by careful, painstaking attention to safety in every form of activity carried on in the establishment or undertaking in question.

5. Injury prevention does not rest upon involved theory or special technical skill. Instead it depends chiefly upon keen safety mindedness by both management and workers. Safety mindedness has been described in this connection as "ever active attention to safety in every detail of each day's work on the part of every person involved in it in any way."

6. If properly applied, the knowledge and resourcefulness possessed by every industrial organization, large or small, is adequate to bring its safety performance into accord with best practice and keep it there.

7. Any management, regardless of the size of its business or establish- ment, type of industry or undertaking, or its financial condition, can eliminate almost all work injuries.

8. Most injuries result from the combination of physical hazard and faulty behavior. The correction of either will usually prevent the injury, but top rate safety performance in terms of minimum injury rate can be achieved and held only by eliminating or reducing physical hazards to the maximum extent that is practically possible; and, in addition, and with similar thoroughness, promoting and fostering the development and maintenance of safe practice and safety mindedness among the entire work force.

9. Safety leaders have long been aware of the seriousness of off-the-job accidents. Finally, some of them undertook to reduce such injuries among their work forces by expanding their safety programs to include educa- tional and promotional activities suited to this purpose. They have scored enough gains to justify the prediction that if such action becomes wide- spread throughout industry, it can be of major value in spreading the safety mindedness so urgently needed by our entire population. It would also reduce the off-the-job injuries of the work forces. Without such pro- grams most workers appear to shuck off their safety mindedness along with their work clothes and leave it in their lockers or at the time clock when they check out each day.

Final comment

The author has frequently been asked which branch of industry in his opinion has done the best safety job. My answer has invariably been—

the steel industry, and, in that industry, the United States Steel Corporation. Under the personal leadership of Judge Elbert H. Gary, it set up a corporation-wide safety department in 1906, at the same time officially stating safety to be a fundamental of corporation policy. By 1961, its combined injury rate had been reduced by 98%; the combined injury rate of the steel industry by 96%. Other companies and other branches of industry, notably Portland cement, chemicals, heavy manufacturing, and mining, have made similar reductions but when the factor of inherent hazard is taken into account, none in my opinion have equalled the performance of steel.

Chapter Two

Development of Industrial Safety

This chapter will tell in very brief form how the safety movement in American industry developed, and will also call attention to certain things in the manner of its development that will add to an understanding of the situation as it stands after a half century of effort by at first hundreds, then thousands, then tens of thousands of devoted and splendidly motivated participants. Much that is faulty or lacking in the safety movement today is due, in large part at least, to mistakes made in the formative years, mistakes that arose largely out of bitterness carried over from the long years of struggle that finally brought corrective action by state governments and an organized safety movement by, and in, private industry.

As pointed out in the preceding chapter, accidental injuries have always been a familiar part of life and living and working. Since obviously unsafe behavior was involved in nearly every case of such injury, the injury was regarded as primarily the accident victim's own fault. This did not matter much in the handicraft era. Home workshops were the rule; such plants as there were were powered by waterwheels, if at all. Injury rates could not have been high or many of the injuries serious, so when an injury did occur, it was taken as a matter of course. The employer felt no responsibility for it nor did his employees expect him to.

The advent of the steam engine, followed by the electric motor and the tremendous increase in the use of power driven machinery that it made possible, soon brought an increasing stream of serious and fatal injuries. This soon brought a change in the worker's attitude. It was easy to see that when a workman was killed or injured by a hazardous condition that could obviously have been safeguarded, or eliminated, the employer was at least partly at fault. This change in thinking was sped by the shocking nature of many of these occurrences; workmen whirled to death when their clothing was caught by projecting set screws on line shafting; crushed flat between belt and pulley; flesh eaten away upon falling into an unprotected floor-level acid vat; chewed up inch by inch when caught in massive gears or screw conveyers, etc.

The great industrial expansion, particularly of heavy, high hazard industry, that followed the depression of the 70's, accelerated the upward trend of serious and fatal injuries. The newspapers became interested and tended more and more to print the gory details of the more serious cases. Public interest grew. Organized labor, though weak in those days, used every means at its command to develop public support for its demands for corrective action.

Labor fought for two things: the guarding of hazardous machinery and correction of other serious hazards, and, recompense for the accident victims and their dependents, particularly in cases of serious permanent disablement or death. Leading clergymen and other humanitarian minded leaders joined in the struggle, and, gradually, public demand for correction grew.

The first law requiring the guarding of hazardous machinery was enacted in Massachusetts in 1877 in response to widespread indignation and concern over an especially sympathy-arousing type of injury—the fingers of young girls were being cut off or mangled by the gears of spinning machines in textile plants. The girls had to work with their fingers very close to the in-running sides of these gears and the toll of fingers was heavy. In spite of this, it took many years of agitation to get this law passed. How many young fingers and mangled hands it cost will never be known; such records were not kept until workmen's compensation legislation made them necessary, but there can be no doubt that over the long years before the guarding was installed the total number of such accidents ran into very large figures. Gradually other states followed with guarding laws. By 1900 most of the heavily industrialized states had at least some form of safeguarding legislation with factory inspection to enforce it.

Labor's other demand, compensation for the accident victims, was gained only after a much longer and even harder struggle. Employer resistance was augmented by the fact that this demand became identified with the larger struggle for higher wages, shorter hours, and better working conditions. Unrestrained immigration kept wages at bare subsistence levels. Working conditions were deplorable. Very few plants paid any attention at all to the health and safety of the workers. Ventilation received no attention whatever. Light came usually only from windows and these were often small. Sanitation was minimal. The struggle was long and bitter, largely because the realization that employers would profit by having well-paid, contented workers was slow in coming.

The passage of legislation requiring employers to provide safeguards against certain specified hazards furnished at least some legal basis for the thesis, now thoroughly established by both law and custom, that the employer is responsible for all injuries to his employees while at their work for him. Many employers early in our industrial development accepted this view to the extent of assuming the costs of medical treatment for injured employees and the burial expenses of those killed by accidents. Some provision was often made for the widow, perhaps as a domestic in the home of the employer or through a rent-free cottage. Frequently the employer had a collection taken up for a widow or a permanently disabled victim to which he contributed according to the generosity of his spirit.

The utter inadequacy of such relief measures brought about the practice of suing for damages under common law. Some of these suits were succesful, but, as court decisions multiplied and lawyers retained by the employers developed the technique of defending them, it became increasingly difficult to obtain awards. The courts came to recognize three common-law defenses. The first was "contributory negligence," namely, that the worker injured had by some action or lack of action contributed to the accident. This was an extremely difficult defense to overcome because faulty behavior in some degree is a contributory factor in nearly every case. The second defense, "fellow servant negligence," was effective when it could be shown that the action of a fellow employee had contributed to the accident. The third defense, the theory of "the assumption of risk," held that when a worker accepted employment he knew or should have known the risks involved in the work and assumed them. To overcome this defense, it was usually necessary to show that the hazard was out of the ordinary for the employment in question or that the employer was grossly negligent.

Under this system a vicious racket known as "ambulance chasing" developed. Lawyers following this practice would get to an accident victim (or his heir in case of a fatality) as quickly as possible and get his signature on a retainer agreement. The lawyer would drive as hard a bargain as he could but would always take care to get a substantial share of the award, if any. Usually his share plus expenses left little or nothing for the accident victim. These lawyers soon discovered that, while in most cases they could not overcome the common-law defenses and win an award for the accident victim, they could frequently get a small settlement from the employer by threatening to take the case to court. Seldom, however, did the unfortunate client get more than a small fraction of any such settlement. Ambulance chasers were also retained by many employers to induce the accident victim to accept a small payment and sign a release instead of going to court. Such employers sometimes went to great lengths to insure that such releases would be obtained. It is obvious that under such conditions the accident victims fared badly indeed.

Employer liability laws

The intent of this type of legislation was to make it easier for the accident victim to obtain an award when employer negligence could be shown. However, such legislation proved of little value because of the difficulty of proving the employer negligent. Also, it left the ambulance chaser undisturbed. So labor and its supporters turned to a type of legislation that had been developed under Bismarck in Germany in 1885 and which had soon spread across most of Europe and to England, namely, *workmen's compensation legislation.*

Workmen's compensation laws

This type of law eliminates the question of fault. Its purpose is, roughly, "to provide for the compensation of all injuries arising out of, or in connection with, employment." It requires the employer to pay the injured worker's medical and hospital expenses plus compensation which will furnish to him and his dependents, if any, at least a minimum subsistence during his period of disability. Also, under proper administration the worker who has a legitimate claim need not be put to any expense in order to secure the compensation due him.

The first such compensation law in this country was enacted by Congress in 1908, but the benefits were very meager and they were limited to certain special classes of federal workers. Several states passed laws of this type about this time but they were held unconstitutional. Finally, in 1911, New Jersey passed a law that was upheld. Other states rapidly followed this lead; seven in 1911, three in 1912, eleven in 1913, two in 1914, and ten in 1915. In 1948 Mississippi, the 48th state to act, passed a workmen's compensation law. The territories of Alaska and Hawaii had passed such laws in 1915. In 1919 employees of the District of Columbia government were covered by such a law. In 1928 the coverage was extended to private industry in the District.

No state law covers all its employed persons, however. Some exclude a very substantial proportion of them. Domestic service is not covered in any state, nor, with few exceptions, are any farm workers. Most laws exclude very small employers and a few exclude minor branches of industry that are characterized by small workforces; for example, logging is excluded in some southern states.

The various laws differ in other ways also, but, in addition to eliminating the factor of fault, all of them:

1. Provide for at least a substantial part of the medical expense involved in each case of injury.

2. Establish a definite method of computing the compensation to be paid an injured workman, tying the amount of the payment to the wages of the injured workman and setting a minimum intended to approximate a subsistence income.

3. Provide that in cases of total permanent disability or death, benefits shall continue at least during a period of readjustment. The more liberal acts provide benefits during the entire period of disability or, in case of death, during the entire period of dependency of the widow and children.

By making work injuries immediately and inescapably expensive to employers, workmen's compensation laws have done more to promote their interest in safety than all other influences put together. As the worker's knowledge of his rights under these laws spread, claims increased rapidly in number and the cost to the employers grew to such substantial figures, particularly in large, high injury plants, that many of them initiated extensive programs of hazard elimination. They usually were very expensive because of the heavy cost of guarding the machinery, particularly the power transmission machinery, but it soon became clear that the saving of a few deaths or serious permanent disabilities would pay for a lot of guards. A few socially minded employers had begun the correction of obviously serious hazards long before the passage of workmen's compensation legislation, but the great majority had done little or nothing. Incidentally, the cost of guarding extensive systems of mechanical power transmission was a major factor in the rapid development and adoption of direct motor drives for the individual machines.

The first continuing plant safety program of record was started in the Joliet works of the Illinois Steel Company in 1892 by the formation of a committee of plant executives with authority to act. Their first action was to order the inspection and testing of all flywheels in the plant because of a disastrous flywheel explosion. Soon a full-time safety director was appointed and safety thus became a recognized part of plant operation. One by one other plants in steel and other high injury rate industries took similar action, but it wasn't until enough states had passed compensation laws to make it clear that they would become general, that the possibility of holding costs down by the establishment of definite programs of accident prevention received serious attention by most managements.

The first move toward an organized safety movement in industry came at a convention of the Association of the Iron and Steel Electrical Engineers at Milwaukee in 1912. A session devoted to safety formed a committee that was charged with the duty of arranging for a larger meeting devoted wholly to safety, and to which all persons and groups with an interest in safety were to be invited. This meeting was held in New York City in

October 1913. It formed an organization named the National Council for Industrial Safety whose scope was limited to the promotion of safety in industry, but at its 1915 convention the name was changed to National Safety Council and its scope broadened to include accident prevention for the entire population, on the streets and highways, in the schools, homes, everywhere.

National Safety Council

Interest in safety is the primary requirement for Council membership as well as for attendance at its Congresses. Most of its members are manufacturing companies, public utility companies, compensation and liability insurance companies, local safety councils, chambers of commerce, automobile clubs, and, by courtesy, schools and governmental agencies.

The Council seeks to promote safety largely through the compilation and dissemination of information on the causes of accidents and methods of preventing them. Much of the information is received directly from reports made by Council members, while other information is obtained by special surveys and studies made in industrial plants, on the highways, in specific branches of industry, etc. The information thus gathered is made available to Council members and others in publications, through graphic posters, or by the development of detailed plans and programs for accident prevention. The Council does not manufacture, test, sell, or approve safety devices; neither does it inspect factories or write insurance. It maintains a staff of safety men of professional calibre who give information to the members. Its library on safety is the largest and most comprehensive in the nation.

The Council publishes a number of monthly magazines, each devoted to a branch of safety. The oldest and best known of these, *National Safety News,* started publication in 1919. Only the privately published *Safety Engineering* antedated the *News. Safety Engineering* began publication a couple of years earlier, but after the Second World War it was merged with a magazine on production and the name became *Safety Maintenance and Production.*

The high point of the Council's activities each year is its National Safety Congress. These congresses have grown steadily in the scope and coverage of their programs, in attendance, and in standing, nationally and internationally. They have been at the heart of the safety movement in America ever since their inception. Although there is great value in providing such a meeting-place and discussion center for all persons and groups interested in safety, their major contribution, particularly in the early formative years, has been to provide a source of inspiration for all who participated.

Although as already stated, top-level management interest was inspired chiefly by a desire to minimize cost, the real safety doers, the men on the firing line of the safety movement, were motivated primarily by their humanitarian instincts. Few top executives, directing their businesses from their big-city offices, ever saw the accident-caused human wreckage and suffering at firsthand. But their subordinates in the plants had to live with these things. No normal person could fail to be profoundly affected by what these men in high injury rate plants saw and experienced. They quickly became the core of the safety movement in private industry. Most of the rapid progress made during the first two decades of the safety movement, in working out and learning how to apply the practical methods and techniques of accident prevention, was the fruit of their dedicated fervor and untiring effort.

The Council leadership quickly realized that the value and effectiveness of its work would depend chiefly on the extent to which interest and participation was developed at the local levels throughout the country, that is, in individual plants and in the respective communities. Accordingly, it continually urged and actively promoted the formation of community councils and the development of continuing safety programs in each and every plant and establishment throughout industry.

Community councils

The first community councils depended wholly on the voluntary services of already busy men, but it was soon found that for effective functioning, at least some full-time personnel were necessary. The Pittsburgh, Pennsylvania, council employed the first full-time salaried manager in 1917.

The council movement grew steadily, so that by 1950 there were some 500 community, area, or state councils of which about half had full-time salaried personnel. In some cases, for example, in the Greater New York Safety Council, the staffs were of substantial size.

The activities of these councils cover in toto a very broad field, of course tailored more or less to the needs and conditions in their respective communities or areas. Their basic purpose is the promotion of safety interest and safety activities together with the spreading of good safety practices. A complete detailed listing would require too much space for inclusion herein, but their chief activity is the promotion of, planning for, and the servicing of safety meetings for any and all groups and interests, ranging from small evening or luncheon meetings to annual congresses patterned after the annual National Congress. In short, each such council functions, as far as its facilities permit, as the center of safety activities in its area.

Other agencies rendering safety services

There are literally hundreds of these agencies. A large number of trade and industry associations render a safety service primarily to their membership, but in some cases they go well beyond that, usually in the form of cooperative effort with safety councils or other groups. A few, notably The Portland Cement Association, have participated in the organized safety movement since its inception and have also been very active in promoting and servicing continuing safety programs in individual establishments in the various branches of industry. The notable reductions in combined membership injury rates that some of the industries so served have scored have been largely due to these Association programs.

Many agencies of the Federal government render services in the field of industrial safety. Chief among these are:

1. United States Bureau of Mines, Washington, D. C.

2. Bureau of Labor Statistics, United States Dept. of Labor, Washington, D. C.

3. National Bureau of Standards, Washington, D. C.

4. Bureau of Labor Standards, United States Dept. of Labor, Washington, D. C.

United States Bureau of Mines

This bureau was established in 1910 in the Department of the Interior. One of its major functions is to study the causes of accidents and ill health among miners and to promote the application of preventive measures. Its work has been and continues to be outstanding in its field. A very large part of the reduction in the injury rate in the mining industry is certainly to be credited to the work of the Bureau. Its most spectacular accomplishment has been in coal mining. That industry, formerly marked by frequent explosions involving heavy loss of life and very high injury rates from other accidents as well, has become a relatively safe industry when its intrinsically hazardous nature is taken into account. The Bureau soon discovered the causes of coal mine explosions and proved them preventable. It developed rescue methods and provided trained crews with the specialized equipment necessary. Its first aid courses have helped to promote interest in safety, not only in the coal mining industry, but throughout industry in general. The Bureau also maintains a coal mine inspection service, primarily informational and consultative in nature, but since its inspectors are highly competent and armed with authority to enter and inspect, their findings and recommendations are taken very seriously indeed.

Bureau of Labor Statistics

Established in 1913, this bureau among other things collects, tabulates, and disseminates statistical information about occupation-injuries. It issues annual reports on them, giving estimated annual totals and breakdowns by branch of industry. It supplements these with reports on specific branches of industry.

National Bureau of Standards

An important function of this bureau, established in the Department of the Interior in 1910, is to develop safety standards for various materials and equipment and to formulate testing methods for determining their safety. The total volume of its accomplishments in the fields of fire and accident prevention bulks large. It works very closely with the American Standards Association, sponsoring many of the standards itself.

Bureau of Labor Standards

The objectives of this bureau, established as a division in 1934 and later raised to bureau status, are to formulate labor standards in labor legislation and labor law administration, and also to promote the improvement of working conditions. Its safety activities as a part of this general purpose include cooperating in the development and promotion of American Safety Standards through ASA procedure, furnishing consulting service on safety to labor administrative agencies and labor organizations, aiding states, upon request, to improve the competency of their safety personnel, and, in general, cooperating in the movement to reduce the toll of occupational injuries. The Bureau played a major part in the formation of the Federal Safety Council whose function is the promotion of safety in federal employment. In 1940 the Bureau organized the Committee for the Conservation of Manpower in the War Industries, whose basic purpose was to make available to plants lacking adequately trained safety personnel, and unable to afford it, a competent safety advisory service through the part-time use of safety engineers loaned for the purpose by large plants able to spare them for perhaps a day per week as a contribution to the war effort.

Safety training courses

In-plant safety training has long been recognized as a basic element in any well-rounded safety program, but our educational authorities have been slow to add safety courses to their curricula, partly because they are loath to add to already overcrowded schedules and partly because of lack of demand from industry, which in general prefers to merge its safety training and indoctrination with the job training. Despite many years of promotional effort by a committee of the American Society of Safety Engineers, only a handful of schools of any nature were offering safety courses by 1940. In that year the accelerating demand for technically trained personnel led to initiation of the nationwide program of engineering-science-management training known as the ESMDT courses. These were federally financed, administered by the United States Office of Education, and given by the colleges and technical schools. The first course on industrial safety under this program was a 150-classroom-hour course given by the University of Pennsylvania, with the cooperation of the Philadelphia Safety Council, the Philadelphia Chapter of the American Society of Safety Engineers and the Bureau of Labor Standards of the U. S. Dept. of Labor. It was so successful, and there was so much demand for such courses, that a 96-classroom-hour course based on it was made available on a national basis. Over 150 colleges and technical schools cooperated in this program, and by its termination at war's end over 70,000 industrial personnel had completed its 96-hour course and many of them an advanced course of similar length as well.

Although these courses were for key men, foremen, job bosses, safety committeemen, etc., in industry and required only a grade school education, the experience influenced many of the colleges to seriously consider adding safety courses to their curricula. The National Safety Council made grants to four colleges to help them to make a start. These and a few others added experienced safety engineers to their faculties to organize the courses and teach them, thus meeting the problem of lack of safety knowledge by their regular teaching staff. This arrangement was acceptable since these were not credit courses. After the war a few colleges developed qualified instructors, and with the help of a committee of A.S.S.E.,* obtained the accreditation of safety courses to be offered as electives, particularly in their engineering curricula. The number of colleges offering accredited safety courses has grown slowly. Future growth will be governed by demand from industry, primarily.

This author has long been of the opinion that the integration of safety instruction to the maximum extent practical, into our educational system, would, in the long run, prove to be the most productive course. There are two reasons for this. Despite the general use of the term engineer in this connection, there is little engineering in the safety field. Very few problems the safety man meets in the practice of his profession require a knowledge of basic engineering theory or formulae. Perhaps the more

---

* American Society of Safety Engineers. 5 N. Wabash Ave., Chicago 2, Ill.

important reason is the fact that the overriding need is for a higher level of safety mindedness throughout our entire population. What better way can there be? In plants we use a wide variety of safety promotional and educational activities and should use them more, but young minds are far more easily influenced than are older ones. The great success a leading church has in holding its membership is credited by its spokesmen as very largely due to the teaching of its basic tenets in its schools. Why not follow a similar course for safety? It is a worthy cause also.

Some of the vocational schools have made encouraging progress along this line. Their work points the way to complete safety integration in our entire school system. It would be a big job but not an unduly difficult one. A prerequisite is to get adequate and suitable safety material into the texts and other teaching materials. Only a very few college texts, even those on production and engineering, contain any safety material whatever, and those that do usually present it as a separate chapter, so brief and superficial as to be of little value. This is not the fault of the authors. No author of a text will include material for which he receives little or no demand, nor will he devote sufficient time and effort to it to enable him to present its essentials in a sound and well balanced fashion—one of the most difficult jobs such an author can undertake. However there is a way that is intensely practical. If only a few schools, preferably engineering colleges, would join forces with ASSE to make detailed studies of their texts, teaching materials and courses, decide where, and what, safety material should be included, few, if any, authors would fail to cooperate. Also, the ASSE would gladly recruit the services of safety engineers in the areas of the participating colleges to act as consultants to the faculty members on an "on call" basis. The integration structure should be capped by a tie-together and summation course offered as at least an elective in the senior year. For students wishing to make safety their profession, safety should either be a required major, or made the subject of a postgraduate year leading to a master's degree.

State safety services

Every state has created some agency charged with at least some responsibility for the safety of at least some of the employed persons in the state. Some have very broad and far reaching responsibility, but as is the case with Workmen's Compensation, none include all. The names of these agencies vary among the different states, being referred to as Department of Labor, Department of Labor and Industry, Industrial Commission, etc. The first agency of this type in this country was the Department of Factory Inspection created in Massachusetts in 1867.

As previously pointed out, such agencies were created to enforce laws aimed at the correction of bad conditions or abuses connected with employment. The campaign that ultimately brought the widespread passage of workmen's compensation laws also usually brought companion legislation requiring the safeguarding of hazardous machinery and equipment. The basic approach was to secure correction through laws enforced by inspectors armed with police power. Penalty for non-compliance with corrective orders issued by the inspection agency is generally a fine, but in many states it can, in flagrant cases, include imprisonment also. Also in many states, the offending employer may be forbidden to operate the machine or equipment in question, or if the hazard is general, forbidden to operate the entire plant until the condition has been corrected.

In their early years, the state factory inspection services made a major contribution to the safety movement by getting machinery guarded and many other serious hazards corrected in plants whose managements would not do it of their own volition. The flow of injuries from such hazards decreased as the work of safeguarding progressed. By about 1930, the country-wide level of safeguarding was reasonably good, in the establishments subject to safety inspection, primarily in the manufacturing industries. Although machinery continued to be and still is, a relatively important injury source, machinery injuries are now mostly due to faulty operation and maintenance and failure to comply with well-known rules of safe practice.

It may seem surprising to the objective minded onlooker, but instead of expanding their services to include phases of injury prevention other than mere guarding, most of the inspection agencies pushed for ever more extensive and detailed regulatory requirements. They lost sight of the fact that the sole purpose of the safety regulations and the inspection services that enforced them was to cut down the flow of injuries. They failed to keep sufficiently in touch with safety progress in even the plants they inspected, to realize that at least part of their efforts could be more productive if properly applied to activities other than the mere enforcement of safety regulations. Nor did they learn to think in terms of injury rates and how to find and reduce those rates that were higher than good practice permits. Instead, most of them gauged the value and quality of their inspection service chiefly by the number of inspections made and corrective orders issued and complied with year by year. Many of them still follow this course and justify their budgetary requests by such data, absurd as that appears to the prevention minded analyst.

A few inspection agencies have experimented with the so-called educational approach, holding safety meetings, sending out safety literature, etc., much as the community councils do, usually carrying on their enforcement work as a parallel activity but in at least one state practically giving it up. They failed to see the limitations of this approach, i.e., that only those already interested in safety will attend safety meetings, seek safety information, or read and make use of safety literature sent them unsolicited. Apparently they also failed to analyze the injury data in their respective states sufficiently to discover that by far the greater part of each year's injury total is contributed by small and very small employers, few of whom are sufficiently safety minded to want to find out the quality of their safety performance. These agency heads failed to realize that their problem was, and still is, to find ways and means of carrying the know how and practice of safety to those employers who do not have it and do not know that they lack it. Whatever gains the agencies using this approach may have scored have not been great enough to be discernible in the year by year injury totals of their respective states.

At least one state however, made a clear-headed analysis of its situation and has been experimenting with what it calls the "consultative approach." This involves broadening the plant inspection to a thoroughgoing appraisal of all phases of safety, such as guarding, safety of plant and equipment, of processes, of operating procedures, attention given to the development and observance of safe practice, safety promotional activities and so forth. Using the findings as a basis, the inspector functions as a consultant to the management, helping it to correct the weaknesses found and to develop and prosecute a well-rounded and sound safety program suited to its needs.

Enforcement authority is not surrendered; it is merely held in abeyance for use if a management fails to cooperate. In such case its direct value is, of course, limited to the correction of the hazards covered by the state safety regulations. Even with such uncooperative employers, however, this approach has considerable value because the recommendations of a competent man clothed with authority to enforce the applicable regulations will usually be treated with greater respect than they would if he had no such authority, or if they knew he wouldn't use it.

The right to enter and inspect at any reasonable hour is essential to the success of the consultative approach. If he cannot inquire into every phase of plant operation that might have a bearing on safety, the inspector-consultant will be seriously handicapped in advising soundly as to the kind and extent of corrective action that should be taken.

Enough success has been scored with this approach to show that if properly applied it can be very effective with high injury rate plants. In most states however, many difficulties will have to be overcome before it can be used extensively or with anything approaching full effectiveness. First of all, it takes very good men. The inspector-consultant must have a thorough knowledge of the hazards connected with the branches of industry in his area of responsibility and the means of their control. He must also have a similarly thorough knowledge of the methods and techniques of accident prevention in general. He must be able to present his findings clearly and convincingly. Finally, he must be a sound and effective salesman.

There are few such men in the state inspection services. This is not said in a spirit of criticism. Men of the competence required to make effective use of the consultative approach would be wasted as mere inspectors, nor could they be hired or long held for the salaries inspectors receive. In addition to the low salaries, there is in many states a still more serious obstacle, political appointment. Where political preference is requisite to get and hold such a job an effective service of this type is simply not possible. Should a fully competent man be appointed, which is highly unlikely, his first allegiance would be to his party or sponsor; his work would be a poor second.

Also, the safety laws of many states are faulty in one or more important respects. Most of them require at least an annual inspection of every establishment covered by them regardless of the quality of their safety performance. None recognize injury rate. From the standpoint of the injury preventionist it is obviously absurd for a state safety inspector to make his routine inspection of a great plant that through long years of systematic safety effort has brought its injury rate down to figures approaching zero, yet it is still the usual practice because "it is the law." Such laws were necessary and proper when they were enacted, mostly around the turn of the century, but they do not fit present conditions and should be amended to authorize the state inspection service to place its effort wherever it can get maximum results. Some state laws do not give adequate right of entry for the consultative approach or are too limited in their coverage. In effect, they say that an occupational injury in an establishment not covered by the law is of no concern to the state.

The lack of injury data adequate to furnish a measure of performance in any effort to cut down the year by year injury totals is another obstacle. In most states, injury reporting is required only for the administration of the workmen's compensation laws. The agencies administering them have the primary duty of seeing to it that the injured worker's interests are fully protected. They have no official concern whatever with prevention and usually their quite natural practice is to hold to themselves all injury reports and all injury data until they are of no further use. By that time such data are of little value as a guide for preventive efforts. In some states, the law requires that such data be kept secret except for presentation in summary form in annual or biennial reports of the agency. Although the data on compensated injuries would not include employment data and therefore would not alone furnish a year by year or month by month measure of the over-all safety performance for the state, they could be made to do so if correlated properly with the employment data for the corresponding periods, usually compiled by another state agency or by the federal government or both.

Safety movement a complex of activities

The foregoing description of the development of the safety movement in industry gives only the highlights and even these in brief form only. Any reasonably complete description would require far too much space for inclusion herein. And for the same reason, the description of its current makeup has been held to the minimum deemed essential to the purposes of this text. Actually, it consists of an extensive complex of activities carried on by an even greater complex of groups and agencies of government (state, federal, municipal) safety councils, trade and industry organizations, professional engineering and technical societies, in-plant safety programs, and labor unions and groups. Each such agency or group or association is busily carrying on its own activities, often traditional rather than realistically suited to existing conditions, in its own little corner with no apparent interest in, or concern for, the magnitude or trend of the year by year injury totals.

This hodgepodge is the predictable result of the failure of management, labor, and the state agencies charged with the administration of safety and workmen's compensation laws to join hands in the formative years of the safety movement and work together toward a common goal. Had they done so and provided for joint, objective minded leadership with provisions for an annual appraisal of progress made and needs yet to be met, surely action would have been taken long since to extend good safety performance to the areas lacking it; and the annual injury and death totals would be far smaller than they are, probably halved, at least if we may judge from the progress made in areas where joint cooperative effort has been vigorously applied.

Neither the state safety agencies nor organized labor had any part in developing the methods and techniques of accident prevention or even any direct means of keeping in touch with the progress that was being made by, and within, the organized safety program in private industry. Of course, the National Safety Congresses and similar meetings have always been open to anyone who cared to attend and pay the moderate fees, if any. But such attendance would ordinarily be as individuals at their own expense. Few, either from the state agencies or organized labor, were in a position to attend had they wanted to in view of the fact that neither they nor their agencies could have any voice in policy matters. This was most unfortunate, for joint participation of these three major groups, management, labor, and state and federal government, would have been highly constructive particularly during those early formative years.

Their failure to get together was due chiefly to the mutual bitterness and hostility engendered by the long struggle that finally brought state safety and workmen's compensation laws. Labor was bitter because of the long and sometimes ruthless resistance to its demands for what it regarded as the minimum of simple justice for the injured workers and their dependents.

It is only fair to point out here that there was relatively little employer opposition to workmen's compensation for several reasons. Perhaps the most important was that it was quickly realized that the cost would bear on each employer in accordance with his accident experience and, as such experience accumulated, would become a calculable cost item. Also it would become insurable on an actuarially sound basis. Furthermore, many employers were sick of the ambulance chasing setup, the uncertainty of it all as well as the unfavorable publicity that was so frequently involved. They were willing to accept almost anything that would bring relief from these annoyances. Finally, and by no means least, many employers sympathized with the accident victims and were in favor of suitable corrective action.

Employers naturally fought safety laws that included requirements they thought unnecessary or unduly expensive, thoroughgoing power transmission machinery guarding in particular. In those days a large plant using a large number of power driven machines might have literally thousands of feet of shafting and many hundreds of drive belts. In such a plant guarding all the power transmission machinery would be a major expense of itself; usually, too, there were other hazards that required expensive safeguarding, for few had given any worthwhile attention to hazard elimination. Since an unsafe act, or at least not adequately safe action, by the accident victim was almost always an obvious factor, employers were slow to accept the now well-established principle that it is the employer's duty to do everything he reasonably can to keep his employees free of injury while at their work for him regardless of faulty behavior on their part.

Some employers fought inspection laws for another important reason that was perhaps justified at the time. It was before the advent of merit service in state agencies and they feared inspection by political appointees who would be unlikely to have any practical knowledge of industrial plants and equipment and who, therefore, might issue orders that were impractical, unnecessary, or unduly expensive. In those days, too, many plant managements were openly in politics; inspectors of the opposite party could make things difficult indeed. Thus, many employers fought the passage of the laws in the first place, and later fought many of the orders issued under them. All this created an attitude of mutual dislike and hostility between the inspection services and many, perhaps most, of the employers. In some areas at least, it persists in some degree to this day.

In some states the quality of the inspection service fully justified management fears but in others the service was reasonably efficient and objective from the start and such weaknesses as appeared were soon corrected, although such corrections were usually in the direction of ever stricter enforcement. Other faults, such as ambiguity, impractical requirements, and conflicting provisions, caused much trouble also. Often, orders issued by different inspectors on the same hazard were at variance or even in direct conflict. This applied also as between different states, a matter of very real importance to a company having plants in more than one state. Some good came out of this situation, however. It highlighted the value of uniform guarding requirements and led to the setting up of a means for their development under American Standards Association procedure.

The President's conference on industrial safety

In 1949 a safety engineer whose work over a long period of years had enabled him to watch the development of the safety movement and particularly the functioning of the state safety services suggested the calling of a conference under the sponsorship of the President of the United States to study the situation in the occupational safety field and bring in recommendations justified by the findings. The suggestion was taken to the Secretary of Labor who secured Presidential authority to go ahead with it. Presidential invitations to a meeting in Washington were sent to the leadership of the major organizations, agencies and groups that would presumably wish to participate in such an undertaking.

The safety engineer in question strongly urged that the next step after organization should be to have an objective appraisal made of the occupational safety picture for the nation as a whole, including particularly the effectiveness of the various kinds of safety activities being carried on and the areas where more effort was needed and the kind of activity or service it should be. Such an appraisal, properly made, would unquestionably have enabled the development of a realistic action program with every prospect of worthwhile accomplishment. The appraisal would not have been difficult or unduly expensive or time consuming. In fact a half dozen men chosen for their suitability for the undertaking, could have put most of it together seated around a table, needing only a moderate amount of field work to check their tentative findings and fill in any gaps. The safety engineer in question had previously discussed the making of such an appraisal with several key men in his profession but decided against attempting it for two reasons. First, the cost, relatively moderate though it would be, would require a wealthy, public spirited donor. Second, and far more important, an appraisal made by such a self-constituted group would have little standing and would receive little attention. But the findings of a committee of men appointed by the President's Conference to make such an appraisal would have received nationwide attention. And an action program realistically based on the findings, and presented to the country with Presidential endorsement, would have been taken seriously indeed.

Unfortunately the conference leaders, able men though they were, were so far removed from the safety firing line that they had little or no knowledge of the actual situation and thought that all that was needed was more of the sort of inspirational appeal that long since had almost reached its limit of effectiveness in the promotion of safety. So, they rejected the appraisal idea in favor of a series of biennial conferences under the nominal leadership of the President in order to, in the words of the permanent chairman of the conference, "prove to the whole country that the Federal government and the President in particular, are truly interested in the safety and health of the nation's workers."

Conference committees, appointed for the purpose, did bring in a very large number of detailed recommendations but they were aimed almost wholly at the refinement of already reasonably effective methods and techniques and offered almost no suggestions as to how good safety practice might be promoted in the areas where it is lacking.

Evidently the conference leadership failed to realize that the millions of not yet safety minded employers, whose establishments yield the greater part of each year's injury total, care little or nothing about either the President's or the Federal government's attitude toward worker safety, simply because they are not aware of being derelict in that respect.

Presumably these conferences are of some value, because they bring representatives of labor, management, and state and Federal government together to interchange viewpoints and ideas far more fully than is possible at the annual safety congresses. They have, however, had no discernible effect on annual death and injury totals. Their cost in travel and other expenses is considerable when weighed against accomplishments.

It is most unfortunate that the Conference leadership did not see fit to come to grips with the real problem, i.e., how best to improve shoddy safety performance in the millions of workplaces, mostly small and very small, from which by far the greater part of each year's injury total comes; or what would amount to the same thing, how to turn the trend of the annual injury totals decisively downward. Had they faced the facts and come up with an action program realistically based on the existing situation, it is difficult to believe that very worthwhile progress would not have resulted.

Statewide safety programs

The failure of the President's Conference to develop a nationwide program need not mean that there is no hope of accelerating the present slow rate of progress in cutting injury rates and totals. Undoubtedly any sound national safety program would be based on action at the state level, that is, statewide programs operated by the respective states with the national organization functioning in an advisory and service capacity. But many individual states can, if they will, set up statewide programs that would get results if properly organized and vigorously prosecuted.

It has been clearly shown, by results attained, that if the consultative approach is properly applied by competent men who have authority to enter, inspect, and enforce where necessary, it is very effective in improving safety performance in high injury rate establishments and businesses. Since only the state factory inspection agencies have such authority and also have, or could well be given, the necessary manpower, the setting-up of statewide programs based on these considerations is the best and most promising plan of action.

The consultative approach is time consuming; the great number of employers that must be effectively reached in even the lesser states means that, in most states at least, an impossibly large field force would be needed to service them all in anything short of several years. But experience has shown that properly led and serviced safety activities by volunteers on a part time or off-hour basis or both, can make many conversions also. Therefore, each state program should be made up of a well-knit complex of these two kinds of activities combined in a manner suited to the needs and conditions of the state in question.

Presumably the organizational setup of a state program may vary considerably as to detail, but three things are viewed as essential to successful performance, i.e., (a) that the full-time personnel, including the executive head, be under merit service, (b) that the organizational leadership be sound and objective minded, (c) that it have sufficient standing to get the needed non-partisan political and public support to, first, establish the program and then to carry it "on faith" until it has proved itself.

There have been several attempts to set up such statewide safety programs but none have endured, partly because the necessary preliminary steps were not taken and partly because of the failure of the key groups, labor, employers, the state inspection services and the safety leadership in the state to compose their traditional differences and, in some cases, dislikes sufficiently to cooperate wholeheartedly in developing and prosecuting such a project. Nevertheless, enough progress has been made to make it clear that such programs, properly set up and pushed, would get very worthwhile results.

An objectively made safety appraisal is an absolute necessity if the action program is to be much more than guesswork. The high injury rate establishments and branches of industry must be discovered and the means of reaching them most effectively determined. Existing safety services must be evaluated and those of maximum effectiveness for this work expanded if possible. Agencies and groups able to expand their current safety activities that are productive or take on additional ones should be urged to do so and aided thereto.

Predictions as to the future

Prediction is a hazardous pastime. This is particularly true for industry in times of rapid change and expanding technology. A steady, high rate of orderly industrial activity favors safety. Fluctuations in volume of production, changes in methods and processes, shifting employment, unrest—these things and the like, bring higher injury rates. On the other hand, there is considerable evidence that public awareness and concern over the seriousness of our accident wastage is growing. Safety in its varied forms is slowly but surely being integrated into our educational system; it is increasingly included in radio and television programs; professional safety engineers are increasing in number and in degree of professional organization; the American Society of Safety Engineers grows steadily in size and standing.

Perhaps the greatest hope of reducing the annual injury and death totals lies in the growing interest and participation in safety activities by organized labor. Labor unions are progressively increasing their safety activities, particularly by establishing safety departments having the dual purpose of promoting safety interest and safety know how among the membership and transforming the currently mostly passive support into active interest and participation on as wide a scale as possible. Organized labor with its millions of workers at the firing-line source of work injuries and its tremendous political strength could unquestionably do much to improve the situation in at least every state and community where it is strong and soundly led. However, unless such action and the policies under which it is prosecuted, are based on an objective, clear-headed appraisal of the conditions and needs in each state in question, and, further, unless any and all traditional animosities and prejudices between the participating groups can be buried and forgotten for the good of the cause, accomplishment will be limited at best. In other words, it is a job that *can* be done but will it be? What do you think?

Chapter Three

Accident Costs

As stated in the preceding chapter, the desire of the management to minimize compensation and medical costs brought the organized safety movement in private industry into being under the inspirational and promotional leadership of the National Safety Council. The realization that it pays to prevent accidents and the injuries they bring is still the driving force behind the safety movement, both in private industry and in government. In those early years, only the so-called direct costs (compensation plus medical) were given more than passing attention, but as knowledge of the circumstances normally surrounding accidents accumulated, it became clear that other substantial costs are usually involved also. During the decade or so following the First World War these other indirect costs were the subject of considerable investigation by plant safety men and at least one firm of management consultants. Finally, in 1927 H. W. Heinrich presented a paper at the National Safety Congress of that year, based on studies he and his associates had made in plants insured by his company. He placed the indirect cost at on an average 4 times the direct cost. This was the origin of the much discussed and highly controversial 4 to 1 ratio.

It happened that this author had made a number of such studies for his firm in the plants of its clients. These studies yielded ratios ranging from 8 to 1 to 1 to 1, but, in general, they supported the Heinrich findings. Probably the chief reason for the wide range found in these studies was the smallness of several of the accident samples. Had it been practical in each and every case to continue the study long enough to satisfy the law of averages, the findings would undoubtedly have been in much better agreement.

In this author's opinion, the 4 to 1 ratio was reasonably valid at that time for the type of plants he selected for study. All were small or relatively small, with high injury rates and without definite safety programs.

In each case, the primary purpose was to develop information that would show whether or not a definite organized safety program would be justified in terms of probable cost savings. In each case the management had failed to respond to the humanitarian appeal because in none were the injuries numerous or serious enough to make it effective. All of the company heads were keenly cost conscious, however.

The executive head of a plant similar to these almost invariably thinks of his compensation insurance premium as solely or at least very nearly his entire accident cost. Further, unless there has been an obviously costly injury or two, he is likely to think that the insurance company is making an undue profit on his account. He is slow to believe, even if told, that merely to break even on small accounts such as his, the insurer has to allow about 40% of the premium for overhead and sales expense. But this same doubting executive will give serious attention to a showing of substantial uninsured accident costs.

The author has used cost studies for this purpose many times and has found them so effective that he favors them as a routine procedure for promoting management safety effort provided a preliminary analysis finds the situation promising. The safety promoter must be highly competent, able to appraise plant conditions and operations with reasonable accuracy without going into great detail, but he must have management permission to inspect the plant and dig as far as he finds necessary into operating methods and procedures pertinent to safety. He must then convince the plant chief executive that a cost study is fully justified. Unless the executive is sufficiently interested to make it clear to his staff that he wants the study carried out and written up in reliable form, regardless of what facts are uncovered, other matters are likely to be allowed to interfere and the study to go unfinished or be inconclusive. An abortive study is worse than none for it lends support to the attitude that "things are good enough as they are," an attiude responsible for a very large proportion of the sum total of substandard safety practices by management.

Such a failure is really the fault of the safety promoter consultant who urged it. He should not recommend such a study unless he can be reasonably sure that it will be properly handled and carried to conclusion; also that it will show substantial uninsured costs. He cannot, of course, read the executive's mind, but if the latter takes hold of the idea, works out a plan of action (presumably with the consultant's advice), calls together the key personnel to explain the project to them, makes specific assignments of responsibility and makes it clear that he wants the job done and done right, the consultant can be sure that it will be.

It is emphasized that the size of the ratio arrived at in such a study is not important. The thing that *is* important is to show that the accident costs not covered by the insurance policy are substantial, if in fact they are. If the study shows them to be, the consultant will usually be able to get suitable executive action.

The early studies made with the author as consultant were in high frequency rate plants. After the Second World War, he participated in five more, two of them in large plants with full time safety staffs and low injury rates. In one of these, the uninsured cost was only slightly greater than the insured cost; in the other it was nearly three times as great. Neither of these studies led to any substantial additional expenditures for safety because careful appraisals of plant operations and conditions did not justify them. The appraisals did show, however, that in both plants the safety programs should be tightened up and strengthened here and there, with particular emphasis on more systematic and more extensive training of new employees and more use of job safety analysis.

The other three plants studied were in the 200 to 500 employee range each. Their frequency rates averaged over a five year period, were 18, 27 and 28 respectively. These frequency rates would have been relatively very low at the time of the early studies, but the rates in manufacturing in general had been reduced so much in the intervening quarter century, that these rates had become relatively high. The uninsured costs shown by these studies ranged from 1½ to 2½ times the insurance premium. In two of these cases the studies led to executive action that brought very sizeable reductions in injury rates within three years. The third plant, the most poorly managed, incidentally, ran into financial difficulties and was taken over by a larger competitor.

For the purpose of such cost studies, accidents are defined as "unintended occurrences arising out of or connected with plant operations that interfere with or hinder efficient operation." Some involve worker injury; the great majority do not. Some may be costly; for the majority the cost is small or very small, but all involve some cost. Competent, safety minded management views accidents and the injuries they yield as a needless waste and regards their prevention as an essential element of efficient plant operation. Thus, a high injury rate averaged over a long enough period to cancel out chance fluctuations, constitutes valid evidence of inefficient management. Usually it is a matter of loose operating methods and practices. It may indicate the need for closer executive control, further foremen training, a stronger safety program, or all of these things.

One would expect the uninsured cost in high injury rate plants to be high because in such plants many things go wrong. The findings of the studies the author has been connected with support this opinion, in that almost without exception, the higher the frequency rate, the higher the uninsured cost as compared to the insured cost.

Items of uninsured cost

The author made no attempt to develop a standard list of the items of uninsured costs, but Heinrich did.* His list has been so widely used that it deserves presentation here. It is:

1. Cost of lost time of injured employee.
2. Cost of time lost by other employees who stop work;
   a. Out of curiosity.
   b. Out of sympathy.
   c. To assist injured employee.
   d. For other reasons.
3. Cost of time lost by foreman, supervisors, or other executives as as follows:
   a. Assisting injured employee.
   b. Investigating the cause of the accident.
   c. Arranging for the injured employee's production to be continued by some other worker.
   d. Selecting, training, or breaking-in a new worker to replace the injured man.
   e. Preparing state accident reports, or attending hearings before state officials.
4. Cost of time spent on the case by first-aid attendant and hospital department staff, when not paid for by the insurance carrier.
5. Cost due to damage to the machine, tools, or other property, or to the spoilage of material.
6. Incidental cost due to interference with production, failure to fill orders on time, loss of bonuses, payment of forfeits, and other similar causes.
7. Cost to employer under employee welfare and benefit systems.
8. Cost to employer in continuing the wages of the injured worker in full, after his return—even though the services of worker (who is not yet fully recovered) may, for a time, be worth only about half of their normal value.
9. Cost due to the loss of profit on the injured worker's productivity and on idle machines.
10. Cost of subsequent injuries that occur in consequence of the excitement or weakened morale due to the original accident.
11. Overhead cost per injured worker—the expense of light, heat, rent

---

* *Industrial Accident Prevention.* 4th ed. New York: McGraw-Hill Book Company, Inc., 1959.

and other such items, which continue while the injured employee is a non-producer.

As Heinrich puts it, "This list does not include all the points that might well receive consideration, although it does clearly outline the vicious and seemingly endless cycle of events that follow in the train of accidents." Although some safety engineers consider some of the above items too inconsequential or of too infrequent occurrence to justify inclusion, and some cost accountants consider certain of them unevaluatable, this list does give a reasonably adequate picture of uninsured accident costs.

Examples of findings of accident cost studies

The following two examples are reasonably representative of the summarized findings of a number of studies made in each case by a plant cost clerk under the personal supervision of the plant chief executive with the author as consultant. In these studies, the first-aid attendant was instructed to notify the cost clerk promptly whenever a call came in or a worker came in for first aid. The cost clerk was required to drop whatever he was doing and make a thorough investigation, keeping the record of each case open as long as might be necessary to arrive at the total cost. At the end of the period set for the study, the summation was made.

Example 1. *Foundry and Machine Shop.* One year period. Average work force 185. Lost-time injuries 11, first aid cases 203. The accident occurrences were typical, the most serious being the spillage of a ladleful of molten iron due to cable breakage. This accident, in which two men were burned, involved most of the compensation paid:

Compensation payments	$ 203.00
Medical expense	$ 134.00
Total insured cost	$ 337.00
Lost time:	
By lost-time cases	$ 34.68
By first-aid cases	$ 156.80
By fellow workmen	$ 102.00
Supervisory (judgment estimate)	$ 80.00
Clean-up of ladle spill on overtime	$ 64.00
Production loss:	
Down time	$ 92.50
Lessened production rate	$ 65.00
Material spoilage	$ 36.00
Machine and equipment damage	$ 343.00
Overhead and administrative expense	$ 150.00
Total uninsured cost	$1123.98

Example 2. *Woodworking plant.* One year period. Average work force 374. Disabling injuries 30, non-disabling 407. There were 3 compensation cases—a broken leg, a crushed foot, and a back strain. In summation:

Compensation payments .... $ 465.00
Medical (including first-aid dressings) .... $ 585.00
 Total insured cost $1050.00

Lost time:
 By lost time cases .... $ 292.00
 By first aid cases .... $ 575.00
 By fellow employes .... $ 195.00
 By supervisory personnel .... $ 240.00
*Production loss (general) .... $ 250.00
 Machine and equipment damage .... $ 575.00
 Material spoilage .... $ 90.00
 Total uninsured cost $2217.00

In neither of the above studies was any definite provision made to discover and determine the cost of the no-injury accidents. The amount that should be added for them would be a mere guess. That no-injury accidents are relatively numerous in such shops there is no doubt, but few are individually costly. Expensive occurrences such as fires, explosions, major machinery breakdowns, collapse of overloaded floors and the like, are accidents under the definition given above, but as such they are hardly germane to this presentation because management views them as hazards inherent in plant operation and to be guarded against as general policy rather than as a part of the safety program. Anyway, they are so infrequent in any given plant that should one occur during the period of a study it would distort the findings and should be thrown out. Also, insurance in one form or another is normally carried against such occurrences, but of course there is always some uninsured cost, sometimes heavy.

It is emphasized that many of the details of uninsured accident cost will not be brought to light by the usual cost system. This is particularly true of time loss, but it usually applies to material spoilage and machine and equipment damage as well. Therefore, in order to get reasonably accurate results it is necessary that a competent cost man make a prompt, detailed investigation of each accident and determine each item of cost. If this is consistently done for all accidents in a given establishment for a period long enough to establish an average (a year, say, in a small plant), the findings will be reasonably reliable, otherwise not.

---

* This was caused by the only no-injury accident, a sticker breakdown.

The Simonds method

Basic to this approach is the establishment of standard average uninsured costs for the plant in question, for each of four classes of accidents. The averages thus established are applied to the total of accidents in each class for a given year to arrive at the total uninsured cost for that year. Once established, these averages are to be used year by year until changes in plant or operating conditions or processes would be likely to impair their accuracy.

The four accident classes are:

Class 1: Permanent partial disabilities and temporary total disabilities.

Class 2: Medical treatment cases requiring the attention of a physician outside the plant.

Class 3: Medical treatment cases requiring only first-aid or local dispensary treatment and resulting in property damage of less than $20.00 or loss of less than 8 hours' working time.

Class 4: Accidents which either cause no injury or cause minor injury not requiring the attention of a physician, and which result in property damage of $20.00 or more, or loss of 8 or more manhours.

These cost items and the procedure for the use of this method are discussed in the Accident Prevention Manual for Industrial Operations published by the National Safety Council. A pilot study to determine an average cost for each Class is recommended and the procedure described at length. Two forms are presented, "Department Supervisor's Accident Cost Report" and "Investigator's Cost Data Sheet." An example of the findings of such a pilot study is given. It arrived at average costs of $60.00, $19.30, $2.80, and $191.30 respectively for the four Classes. The accident experience was, *Class 1*: 34, *Class 2*: 148, *Class 3*: 4,000. About the same number of *Class 4* accidents were found in the pilot study as of *Class 1,* therefore the same number, 34, was used for them. The summary was:

Class 1:	total cost	$ 2,040.00
Class 2:	total cost	$ 2,856.00
Class 3:	total cost	$11,200.00
Class 4:	total cost	$ 4,124.00
	Total uninsured cost	$20,220.00
	Insurance premiums	$13,000.00

Thus the total accident cost for that year was $33,220.00.

As this commentator sees it, the actual method used to determine uninsured accident costs is of little importance. What *is* important is that it appeal to the plant management as sound enough to yield reasonably reliable figures, and, of course, it must be properly carried out. As already pointed out, the sole justification for determining the uninsured accident costs is to enable management to decide whether or not more money or effort or both, should be spent to reduce them. In the author's experience such cost studies have proved very useful in high injury rate plants, but in plants that through long years of effort have reduced their injury rates to levels representative of first rate performance, an annually determined figure of uninsured accident cost is likely to become a mere bookkeeping statistic because such managements are usually doing all they can to eliminate accidents. If, however, a management is inclined to be niggardly in its expenditures for safety, the safety director, under whatever title, may find that a study to bring the uninsured costs to light will furnish needed support for his budgetary requests. The Simonds method, however, would be poorly suited to a plant whose accident sample was too small to furnish reasonably reliable averages. It would have been satisfactory for hardly any of the plants with which the author was concerned.

Occupational injury cost totals for 1960

The year 1960 was typical of recent years; any differences from other current years are merely fractional. The National Safety Council estimated the cost of work connected injuries for 1960 as follows:

Total cost $4,400,000
Visible costs $2,200,000
Other costs $2,200,000

The Council estimate of the time loss occasioned by that year's injury total was:

Total time loss .... 230,000,000 man-days
By injured workers .... 40,000,000 man-days
By others .... 190,000,000 man-days

In this estimate a charge of 150 man-days was made for each death.

Cost to accident victims

The author prefers the following presentation as being more meaningful:

*Total wage loss $1,200,000,000.00
†Total compensation payments 855,000,000.00

Net wage loss to injured workers 345,000,000.00

---

* *Accident Facts*, National Safety Council.
† Data from annual reports of Social Security Administration.

An indeterminable amount should be added for work-connected injuries not covered by workmen's compenastion laws. Their wage loss when injured is usually total for the full period of disability. As already pointed out, the total of such unprotected workers is substantial and even though most of them work in low hazard kinds of work, their injury total is very considerable each year and their total wage loss must be very substantial. It seems safely conservative to add 20% for their wage loss, making the workers net loss for the 1960 injuries $585,000,000.00. Nor does this take account of the fact that unless covered by insurance, and probably few are, such workers have to pay their own medical and hospital costs. But the money cost is by no means all the cost to the accident victims. When we take into account the tremendous inescapable sequelae of suffering, hardship, and deprivation caused by each year's injury and death totals, it is obvious that despite workmen's compensation laws, work-connected injuries bear heavily indeed on their victims.

Cost to employers

Compensation and medical costs are covered by the insurance premium. The difference between the sum of these costs and the insurance premium is spoken of as insurance overhead. Although the spread in this overhead cost as between the various insurance underwriters is considerable, the average appears to be about 40% of the total. On this basis, the total insurance premiums for 1960 would come to about $2,150,000,000.00.

The National Safety Council estimates that on the average, the ratio between insurance premium and uninsured cost is about 1 to 1. If the cost studies cited above are at all representative, that ratio is conservative indeed, but accepting it, the total cost to the employers of the nation as a whole comes to $4,300,000,000.00, or more.

Cost to society

Work-connected injuries also place a very considerable burden on society as a whole. Even though most of the victims receive compensation, a not inconsiderable proportion require additional help from such agencies as hospital associations, community chests, and other forms of relief assistance. Obviously for those not under compensation provisions or laws, the need for help is far greater. Finally, employers necessarily include their accident costs in the selling prices of their products. Therefore, accidents increase the cost of just about everything and everybody pays, inescapably.

Chapter Four

Appraising Safety Performance

An accident is an unexpected occurrence. When human injury is involved, we have an "accidental injury." The use of the term "injury" as meaning "accidental injury" was officially approved as American Standard on April 19, 1937 (now revised as American Standard Method of Recording and Measuring Work Injury Experience, Z16.1–1954). It is used in that sense throughout this discussion.

The old saying, "The proof of the pudding is in the eating," applies to plant safety. Each injury is, in itself, proof that some hazard or combination of hazards has not been adequately controlled. Therefore, the flow of injuries in any plant or operation constitutes the only final measure of safety in that plant or operation. A bad injury record is proof of unsafety. Perfection in safety could only be claimed for entirely injury-free operation. To use the injury record as a measure of safety performance, however, it is necessary to know how *often* the injuries occur (that is, the rate at which they occur) and how *serious* they are.

We must, of course, say exactly what injuries are to be used in measuring safety performance. Shall we include all those that require dressing or only those that cause temporary disability? The accepted practice (American Standard) is to include, as a basis of measurment, only those injuries which disable the injured worker for more than the day or shift during which he is injured. Anything less is not regarded as a lost-time injury and is not counted in figuring injury rates. When minor injuries are included in measuring safety performance, the desire to make a good showing conflicts with the effort to get workers to report minor injuries for treatment, with infections as a result.

41

Injury frequency rate

The injury frequency rate answers the question, "How often do injuries occur?" and it is defined as the number of disabling * injuries per 1,000,000 man-hours worked. Expressed as a mathematical formula:

$$\text{Injury frequency rate} = \frac{\text{number of disabling injuries} \times 1,000,000.}{\text{total number of man-hours worked}}$$

Injury severity rate

The injury severity rate answers the question, "How serious are the injuries?" and is defined as the number of days of lost time per 1,000,000 man-hours worked.†

$$\text{Injury severity rate} = \frac{\text{number of days lost} \times 1,000,000}{\text{total number of man-hours worked}}.$$

Use of injury rates

The chief values of injury rates are:

1. To measure the injury experience of a given department, branch, or firm.

2. To determine from month to month or year to year whether that experience is getting better or worse.

3. To compare the experience of one operating unit with one or more other units.

4. To serve as a basis for an accident-prevention contest between two or more operating units.

In general, injury rates answer the question, "Is additional accident prevention effort needed?" Such rates naturally do not indicate definitely what needs to be done. This question requires further study and calls for other procedures.

Examples

Obviously, injury rates can be calculated for a week, a month, or a year, or for any period of time by using the same formulas. Furthermore, the

---

* A disabling injury as usually defined in practice is one causing loss of working time beyond the day, shift, or turn during which the injury was received. For exact definition see the "American Standard" Method of Compiling Industrial Injury Rates, published by the American Standards Association, 70 E. 45th Street, New York City.

† An arbitrary time charge is made for death or permanent disability. See page 35 for these charges.

same formulas are used to compare the records of two or more plants, even though they are dissimilar in size.

Example 1. What are the injury frequency and severity rates for a firm with 80 workers averaging 40 hours a week each, if in 6 months 4 workers were injured and if they lost jointly 103 days from work?

Injury frequency rate =
$$\frac{4 \text{ injuries} \times 1,000,000}{80 \text{ workers} \times 40 \text{ hrs. per week} \times 26 \text{ weeks}} = 48. +.$$

Injury severity rate =
$$\frac{103 \text{ days lost} \times 1,000,000}{80 \text{ workers} \times 40 \text{ hrs. per week} \times 26 \text{ weeks}} = 1238. +.$$

Suppose for one of the above 4 injuries involving, say, 13 days lost time, we substitute an injury in which thumb and forefinger were amputated. The time charge would be 1,200 days. The example then becomes:

$$\frac{1,290 \text{ days lost} \times 1,000,000}{80 \text{ workers} \times 40 \text{ hrs. per week} \times 26 \text{ weeks}} = 15,500. +.$$

Note that, when an injury involves a time charge, the actual time the injured person is off is ignored.

Example 2. Firm A has 115 workers averaging 40 hours a week each. In 9 months, 3 workers were injured. Firm B has 132 workers averaging 37 hours a week each. In 10 months, 3 workers were injured. Which firm has the better frequency rate?

A frequency rate = $\dfrac{3 \text{ injuries} \times 1,000,000}{115 \text{ workers} \times 40 \text{ hrs. per week} \times 39 \text{ weeks}} = 16.2.$

B frequency rate = $\dfrac{3 \text{ injuries} \times 1,000,000}{132 \text{ workers} \times 37 \text{ hrs. per week} \times 43.3 \text{ weeks}} = 14.2.$

Firm B has the better injury frequency rate.

Definitions and rulings

For the sake of uniformity, all injury-rate data should be compiled and the rates computed in accordance with the provisions of the "American Standard" Method of Compiling Industrial Injury Rates.

Scale of time charges

The American Standard Scale is:

Death 6,000
Permanent total disability 6,000

```
Arm, at or above elbow ....................... 4,500
Arm below elbow .......................... 3,600
Hand ..................................... 3,000
Thumb ....................................  600
Any one finger ............................  300
Two fingers, same hand ......................  750
Three fingers, same hand .................... 1,200
Four fingers, same hand ..................... 1,800
Thumb and one finger, same hand .............. 1,200
Thumb and two fingers, same hand ............. 1,500
Thumb and three fingers, same hand ........... 2,000
Thumb and four fingers, same hand ............ 2,400
Leg, at or above knee ........................ 4,500
Leg, below knee ........................... 3,000
Foot ...................................... 2,400
Great toe or any two or more toes, same foot .....  300
Two great toes ............................  600
One eye, loss of sight ....................... 1,800
Both eyes, loss of sight ...................... 6,000
One ear, loss of hearing .....................  600
Both ears, loss of hearing .................... 3,000
```

The loss of 6,000 days assigned to death in the above scale is not an arbitrary figure as might be assumed, nor is it related to the Workmen's Compensation payments which, incidentally, differ widely among the various states. Instead, the scale, when it was devised, was based on statistics furnished by the life insurance companies, which showed that, during the period covered by the data in question, the average man killed in an industrial accident had a working life expectancy of approximately 20 years, or 6,000 days. Permanent total disability is given the same lost-time weighting as is death, and other permanent disabilities are charged with fractions of the 6,000-day total.

Why not include first-aid cases when calculating injury rates?

By definition, first-aid cases are injuries just as are fatality or permanent injury cases, and some persons argue that these should be included in the calculation of injury-frequency and severity rates. Some safety engineers have followed this suggestion and have been surprised to see an increase in the number of infections. This is the usual result of including minor injuries in the basis of comparison. Such inclusion creates an incentive to let minor injuries go unreported, hence, untreated, and the consequence is infections. Under pressure to reduce accident records, some supervisors will restrain injured employees from reporting for first aid. In the heat of a contest, the workers themselves are likely to hide nondis-abling injuries even from their foreman. First-aid treatment of all injuries is vitally important, and any procedure that works against it should be avoided.

Which rate to use

There is a great difference of opinion among safety engineers as to which rate is the better measuring stick, and good arguments are advanced on both sides of the question. It seems obvious that a large reduction in the injury-severity rate indicates a sizable reduction in deaths and other serious injuries; and after all, this is more important from both the humanitarian and financial points of view than is a reduction of the less serious injuries that necessitate the loss of only a few days' time each. Conversely, if the severity rate were to increase even though the frequency rates were to go down, it might indicate a definite need for more intensive engineering work to eliminate some especially hazardous conditions that otherwise might not be given sufficiently serious consideration.

Luck—a big factor in severity

Severity is much more a matter of good luck or bad luck than is frequency. For example: In plant *A,* a hammer may fall from an elevated platform, hit a worker directly on the head, cause his death, and call for a charge of 6,000 lost days. Another accident of the same type may occur in plant *B,* but this time the hammer falls directly to the ground, luckily hitting no one, and not calling for any time charge whatever. From an accident-prevention point of view, both accidents are of equal importance, but the factor of chance brought plant *A* a severity charge of 6,000, which plant *B* escaped. This accident added only one injury to plant *A's* frequency base, however, and of course nothing to plant *B's.* Obviously, then, when comparing the records of the two plants, the frequency rate eliminates the luck factor much more than does the severity rate. This is the basis for the slogan, "Take care of the frequency rate and the severity rate will take care of itself."

Frequency best for contest purposes

If two or more operating units are competing, as in an accident-prevention contest, it therefore is wise to use the injury-frequency rate as the basis for comparison. If the severity rate is used, and if one competitor is unfortunate enough to have a death or other heavy time-charge case, the workers in that group immediately lose interest because they know they are out of the running.

Adjusted frequency rate for contest purposes

Straight frequency rates do not provide a perfect basis for comparing the injury experience of competitors in an accident-prevention contest if there is a considerable difference in the hazards with which the workers are confronted. For example, it does not seem fair to compare a foundry directly with a cigar factory. Under such circumstances, it may be advisable to provide adjusting factors that make suitable allowance for the difference in hazards. The adjusting factors used most frequently are the manual rates quoted by insurance companies for carrying the workmen's compensation insurance of the various competitors. Another set of adjusting factors might well be the average frequency rate for each industry represented by the competing units.

Other bases for injury-prevention contests

In some contests, that competitor is declared to be the winner who achieves the greatest percentage reduction in his frequency rate as compared with his own former average. This plan, however, is likely to give too great an advantage to those competitors who had the worst former averages, because it is usually much harder to reduce a frequency rate of, say 6, one third than it is to secure a similar reduction in a rate five times that figure.

After a number of competing units have proved their ability to go for long periods of time without any disabling injuries—that is, when many of the competitors are tied for first place with perfect injury records—it may be advisable to change the plan of contest so that the winner will be that unit which succeeds in operating the greatest number of man-hours without any disabling injuries.

Other means of quick appraisal

It sometimes is said, "Show me an establishment in which there is good housekeeping, and I'll know that that outfit has a good injury record." This, of course, is not an infallible method of appraising the injury experience of any firm, but there is no doubt that it is difficult if not impossible to have a good injury record without simultaneously maintaining good housekeeping conditions.

In a similar way, other quick means of appraisal are provided by rating such factors as plant maintenance, machine guarding, lighting, ventilation, operating methods, supervision, and the attitude of the top executives. These and other factors are so closely related to good safety performance that jointly they provide a thoroughly reliable gauge of results to experts who have considerable knowledge in the whole field of safety. Even such experts, however, have learned that they cannot place complete reliance upon an analysis of these factors unless their judgment is backed up also by a knowledge of the injury-frequency and severity rates.

How to present injury rates

The safety engineer should make sure that all executives and supervisors in his firm understand the method of calculating injury-frequency and severity rates so that they will be able to interpret the reports that he submits for their consideration. On the other hand, however, he will often want to supplement his statistical data with bar charts, curves, and other visual interpretations of the injury record so that his associates can grasp the outstanding facts at a glance.

Credibility of injury rates

The exposure (total number of man-hours worked) on which to calculate injury rates should be as large as possible. More credibility is attached to rates covering large exposures than to those covering small exposures. Some authorities consider 1,000,000 man-hours the minimum exposure whose frequency rate may be accepted as a reliable gauge of safety performance during the period in question. Others believe that considerably smaller exposures are satisfactory for the purpose. It is obvious that the fewer the man-hours the greater the need of careful appraisal of such indicative plant and operating conditions as housekeeping, maintenance, machinery safeguarding, attitude of management, and so on.

Since chance plays so large a part in determining severity and, further, since the time charges are individually so large, it is evident that the number of injuries involved—that is, the size of the sample—is more important than the man-hour exposure. The sample used on page 43 to illustrate the calculation of severity brings this point out clearly. One authority gives the figure of 1,000 lost-time injuries as about the minimum that can be accepted as an entirely reliable base for severity. Others would accept 100 injuries as reasonably satisfactory. However, in so small a sample as 100 injuries, the addition or subtraction of a single fatality will usually multiply or divide the severity rate several times.

The following conclusions appear to be justified:

1. Use frequency rates based on large exposures (over 1,000,000 man-hours) as reasonably reliable gauges of safety performance.

2. Use severity rate as a satisfactory gauge of the seriousness of injuries characteristic of specific industries or occupations, provided the base is large, preferably on the order of 1,000 injuries or more.

3. The smaller the exposure on which the frequency rate is based and the smaller the sample for which the severity rate is calculated, the greater the need for supplemental evidence obtained by analysis of the accident record, operating conditions, and the types of hazards involved.

Rates to use for comparison

An executive, when considering his own injury rates, wants to make two comparisons: how his rates compare with those of others in the same industry, and how his rates compare with those representative of best practice. The second comparison is obviously the vital one to every executive who wishes to be better than "just average."

Both the Bureau of Labor Statistics of the U.S. Dept. of Labor and the National Safety Council compile frequency rates annually by branch of industry. The Bureau uses a sampling process designed to give reasonably reliable averages for each such branch of industry as a whole. The Council rates are "based principally on the experience of its members and members of associations having safety programs." Should a given executive be content to be "just average" he would presumably use either the Council figure or that of the Bureau, whichever made his record look better. Actually, of course, best practice would be that of the leader of the branch of industry in question, that is, the establishment or business having the lowest injury rates. Although such data are not available for industry as a whole, enough are available from the numerous safety contests that have been an important and fruitful part of the safety movement almost since its inception, to prove that only zero injury rates for at least one million man hours at a stretch can be regarded as best practice in any branch of industry.

It should be kept in mind that these Council rates are not averages for *all* the firms in any classification; that is, they are *not* national averages. They cover a very large number of establishments, but even this large number constitutes but a small percentage of American industry. Furthermore, the percentage of each industry covered varies widely as among the various industries. It should be obvious that Council membership or even voluntary reporting of injury data to the Council is evidence of greater than average interest in safety and, therefore, that these figures represent better than average performance. This conclusion is borne out by the fact that the average frequency rates given by the Council run generally lower than those given by the Bureau of Labor Statistics. Although comparisons are not exact, because these two agencies do not use identical classifications, the evidence does in general justify the above conclusion.

Statistically adequate data as to just what frequency rates represent top safety performance in each of the various industries are not available, and we must, therefore, base our judgment on the accomplishment of individual firms. Fortunately such data, while scattered, nevertheless cover numerous establishments throughout American industry. Specifically reported accomplishments abundantly justify the conclusion that even for such high-hazard industries as steelmaking, heavy construction, and mining, good practice yields frequency rates well below 10, whereas for the bulk of industry, top performance is below 2.

Three outstanding facts seem to be proved by the National Safety Council and Bureau of Labor Statistics data:

1. Those industries in which large firms predominate have achieved relatively low frequencies; for example, the steel and automobile industries.

2. Those industries in which small firms predominate still have relatively high frequencies; for example, the food industry.

3. Even some of the so-called hazardous industries that have been doing safety work for a number of years on an industry-wide basis have achieved remarkably low frequencies; examples, steel versus construction; cement versus wood products.

In-plant appraisal methods

Just as production executives must continually watch and check the quality of the product, the safety director must continually watch and appraise both the effectiveness of the safety program and the quality of the safety performance throughout the establishment. Since the primary purpose is the elimination of employee injuries, the frequency rate is almost universally used as a gauge of performance. However, as already indicated, unless the man-hour exposure is relatively large (at least a half million and, preferably, twice that), chance plays too big a part for the frequency rate to be a reliable indicator. Even in a plant having several thousand employees, the month-by-month frequency rates have limited reliability. And, of course, the lower the frequency rates, the wider the fluctuations due to chance are likely to be.

In order to reduce the fluctuations, some safety directors include all non-disabling injuries in their frequency figures. However, as already pointed out, if frequency rates so derived are used to stimulate employee effort to reduce the rate, it is very likely to cause both foreman and workers to fail to report minor injuries. It is difficult at best to get good reporting of the little injuries, such as finger nicks, blisters, and bruises. Any course that adds to the difficulty is at least questionable.

The safety director should keep a close watch on his first-aid cases, however, because they can give him valuable clues, particularly if the first-aid attendants have a good knowledge of the plant operations, and the hazards involved, and get the pertinent information about the accident or exposure that yields each injury. If, for example, there is a rush of minor injuries in a day or for a few days, the departments or operations or crews contributing an unusual number should be ascertained, and the causative factors determined in whatever degree of detail the findings might justify.

Close watch should be kept of the accident types, and all cases in which there is a reasonable chance that the occurrence could have yielded a serious injury should be carefully investigated.

Since successful management must be highly cost-conscious, many safety directors emphasize accident costs, and the savings obtainable by preventing accidents. For this purpose, the month-by-month direct cost (compensation plus medical expense) is generally used. Some apply the 4-to-1 ratio (Chapter 3) to make a more impressive showing. A very few have carried on cost studies to develop a ratio for their own plants that would be more convincing to their managements.

Insurance companies think in terms of the costs to them of each risk they underwrite. This means compensation payments plus medical expense, in addition to the various sales, administrative and service costs involved. All of the injury cases that involve compensation or medical expense to the insurance company are included in computing the base rates. Frequency rates, therefore, mean little to the insurer. Their chief concern is with the total insured cost and the proportion of the total premium it uses up.

There have been efforts to apply statistical quality control methods to accidental injuries. The upper and lower limits within which variations are normal in accord with Poisson's law of variability due to chance are determined, using as a base the most recent year deemed to be normal. All injuries, both disabling and minor, are included, and a frequency rate for each week is calculated using 40,000 man-hours as the unit of exposure. These data, plotted as a curve with frequency values as ordinates and the weeks as abscissae, yield a curve whose peaks running above the upper limits of the normal show the need for corrective action.

An experienced safety engineer using this method has found it a very valuable indicator.* However, pending further test by trial, the following points would appear to be pertinent: (a) it is difficult to select a normal year; (b) Poisson's law has limited validity as to human behavior covering the wide range of activities involved in any given plant of any size; (c) the use of a norm with upper and lower limits tends to draw attention away from the only proper goal, namely, a frequency rate of zero.

Another interesting but likewise controversial method of appraisal is based on the assumption that there is a definite relationship between the

---

* H. M. Saltz, "Occupational Hazards—A Brand New Analysis Method." *Factory Management and Maintenance,* November 1950, page 13.

total flow or rate of safety activities and the injury-frequency rate. Obviously a lag or let-down in any activity or activities whose full and effective functioning are essential to good safety performance would soon result in an increase in accidents. Therefore, a reliable barometer of safety activities should enable corrective action to be applied before the injury rate goes up. In this method, as reported,* a safety activity rate is determined by the formula:

$$\text{activity rate} = \frac{\text{safety activity} \times 5{,}000{,}000}{\text{man-hours worked} \times \text{avg. number of employees}}$$

"Safety activity" is the sum (during the unit period) of: (1) safety recommendations made; (2) unsafe practices reported; (3) unsafe conditions reported; (4) the number of safety meetings held. Thus, a safety activity rate curve using the same elapsed time periods (weekly, monthly, etc.) as those used for the frequency rate curve permits a direct comparison. A large steel company using this method finds it helpful in that, when its activity rate is high, its injury-frequency rate is low, and vice versa.

In judging the value of this method, the following questions would appear to be pertinent: (a) Which types of safety activities are in fact effective? (b) Are mere numbers of safety recommendations or reported unsafe conditions valid criteria? (c) Will not the effort to raise the safety activity rate, or at least to hold it high, reduce its validity by bringing in items of little or no value; (d) Should the emphasis be put on number of safety meetings without consideration of how "well done" they are?

In summation, it is emphasized that no such methods of in-plant appraisal of safety performance should be allowed to divert attention from the one ultimate goal of safety programs, namely, the elimination of human injury arising out of or connected with the employment. It is also pointed out that such methods will have little value or validity in an establishment whose safety performance is not good. A high injury rate is proof of the lack of an adequate safety program. Until a program suited to the conditions in the establishment in question is set up, and its various activities are functioning effectively, the only gauge of performance needed is the injury rate supplemented by a consideration of the seriousness of the injuries themselves, and the total costs involved. But reports by users of such refinements as the above appear to justify the conclusion that the safety engineer who wishes to keep abreast of progress in his profession should at least keep himself informed about them. When the frequency rate flattens out at a figure that seems to approach the irreducible minimum, he may find them useful.

---

* E. C. Hinckley and G. E. Stolberg, "Safety Activity Chart." *Factory Management and Maintenance,* July 1948, pages 84-85,

Other methods of appraisal

Injury frequency rates based on adequate man-hour exposure provide a reasonably accurate measure of safety performance in any establishment. The safety of a plant can also be gauged by analysis of its physical conditions and operating methods. However, this requires wide knowledge of conditions that produce accidents and of methods for their control. Furthermore, so many factors are involved in accident causation and accident prevention that even the most experienced safety engineer should be cautious in his reliance upon such analysis unless it is supported by injury rates based on an adequate exposure.

The injury frequency rate is valuable chiefly in enabling the executive to compare his present safety performance with his own previous performance and especially with best, or at least good, practice. Analysis of plant conditions and operating methods is valuable chiefly as a guide to preventive action. The distinction is important. A high frequency rate is proof that action to reduce it is needed, but it gives no hint as to *what* action. Analysis of plant conditions and operating methods (including, of course, the accidents involved), supported by the injury rate data, shows both what should be done and how much improvement should be sought to bring the safety performance up to a level of good practice.

The following factors are particularly valuable as a basis for appraising plant conditions:

1. Housekeeping.
2. Machinery safeguarding.
3. Maintenance.
4. Adequacy of equipment essential to safety.
5. Provisions for worker comfort.
6. Definite program of safety training.

Housekeeping. Bad housekeeping is a major factor in accident causation. Good housekeeping is a major factor in the efficient production of goods of high quality. The relationship is so intimate that it can safely be said that a management's standard of housekeeping is an excellent gauge of its competency.

Machinery Safeguarding. Since the elimination of physical hazards to the maximum practicable degree is requisite to first-grade safety performance, the attention paid to the safeguarding of machinery furnishes a valuable clue as to management knowledge of accident prevention. And since machinery yields a high proportion of serious disabilities, inadequate machinery safeguarding means that the probability of serious injuries is high.

Maintenance. Good maintenance of plant and equipment, like good housekeeping, is an essential part of good management. Furthermore, the condition of all equipment, safeguards, etc., essential to worker safety is a valuable guide to the probability of injury.

Safety Equipment. In every establishment or undertaking there are activities or conditions for which specific equipment is essential to worker safety. Goggles, safety shoes, and other items of personal protective equipment fall in this group. Also, there is a wide range of accessory plant equipment whose design, adequacy, and condition are vital to safety. Portable ladders, extension cords, lifting tackle, and handtools are important examples.

Provisions for Worker Comfort. The provisions made for the comfort of the workers in a plant are so strongly indicative of the management's concern for their well-being that they are included in this list. It would be difficult to appraise the relationship between accidents and the adequacy or inadequacy of such facilities as toilets, washrooms, clothes lockers, drinking water, lunchrooms, etc., but good management pays careful attention to these things. Employee attitude is powerfully affected by them.

Safety Training Program. Training in safe work practices is an essential of good safety performance. To be effective, a definite program of safety training should be set up. The appraiser should find out what provisions have been made for safety training and the extent to which the program is carried out.

Management attitude toward safety

Since the management must accept responsibility for safety and must actively lead and direct the preventive effort, any worthwhile appraisal of future plant safety performance must take into account the attitude of the management toward safety. The items commented on in the preceding paragraphs throw light on the management's attitude toward the control of physical hazards, but little on its attention to the safety of work methods and practices. The safety appraiser should endeavor to determine at least:

1. The knowledge of accident prevention possessed by the chief executive.
2. The amount of executive leadership he gives to the safety work.
3. The means he uses to stimulate employee safety-mindedness.

This appraisal should not be limited to top management. Foremen are the key men in the control of work methods and practices, and therefore the attention paid to their training in safety methods and their means of imparting safety knowledge and safety consciousness to the men under them should also be looked into.

Use of accident records

Accident reports are useless if their only purpose is to tell the story statistically. The accident preventionist can and should use them as a tool to help control the hazards that are causing injuries.

A detailed study of accident reports over a period of time should bring out such information as the following:

1. The relative importance of the various injury sources.
2. The conditions, processes or activities that produce injuries.
3. Extent of recurrence of each kind of injury or accident in each type of activity or operation.
4. Repeaters (individuals repeatedly injured).
5. Information leading to means of preventing recurrence.

Since all information necessary to prevention could eventually be obtained from a complete account of the details leading up to the accident, each accident should be carefully investigated and the findings recorded in full. The details of accident investigation are covered in another chapter.

Chapter Five

Injury Sources and Causes

There has been much confusion in the use of the word "cause" as applied to accidents. To the preventionist, the cause of an accident is the unsafe condition or unsafe act or other faulty action that should be corrected to prevent a recurrence. Such terms as handling materials, falls, burns, etc., are commonly misused. Handling materials is an important injury source but in each case the cause is a hazardous condition or something that some person does or fails to do, or in many cases, a combination of two or more of these things. Burns are a type of injury. Falls are accidents that cause many injuries. The preventionist wants to find out what condition, act or omission led to the fall.

As used herein the term "accident" is defined as "an unplanned or unintended occurrence that interrupts or interferes with a work activity." Many accidents, in fact the great majority, yield no injury and receive only passing attention, if any, unless they do considerable damage or are otherwise costly. The term "accidental injury," as used herein, denotes an injury to a workman due to an accident. It does not include an injury to a worker's health unless it results directly from an accident, as, for example, a poisoning due to the rupture of a cylinder of toxic gas. The reason for using this definition is to direct attention to the fact that injuries excepting occupational disease cases are the unhappy fruit of accidents, and therefore the basic approach, so far as possible, should be that of accident elimination rather than merely injury prevention. For example, protective headgear suited to the nature of the hazard and correctly and unfailingly worn will in almost all cases prevent head injury, but the proper approach is to use every practical means to eliminate or reduce the hazard and resort to such equipment only where the hazard cannot be eliminated by any practicable means. Accident elimination together with hazard elimination are fundamentals in sound production methods and procedures and particularly so in preventive maintenance, so essential to continued uninterrupted production at minimum cost.

The American Standard * defines the term "work injury" as "any injury suffered by a person which arises out of and in the course of his employment," thus including both accident and health injuries.

The second reason for the above broad definition of "accident" is to dissipate confusion as to the correct meaning of the term. It is widely used as synonymous with injury, a usage at least as old as the safety movement, presumably because only those accidents that caused injuries coming under the terms of the workmen's compensation laws had to be recorded and reported. This incorrect usage was furthered by a definition presented at a national safety congress early in the safety movement and used for many years thereafter in Council publications. It went, "an event or rapidly occurring series of events arising out of an unsafe act or an unsafe condition and culminating in an unpremeditated injury." Its literal application would, of course, necessitate the use of the term "no-injury accident" or its equivalent. That is not important, but the word "or" excludes cases in which both an unsafe act and an unsafe condition are involved, an obviously undesirable and presumably unnoticed omission.

Heinrich's domino sequence † accords with this unsatisfactory definition. He compared the series of events in an accident to a row of dominoes standing on end and so arranged that when the first is pushed over it will cause the others to fall successively. The final domino is labeled "injury," the preceding one "accident" as for example, the fall of a person. Preceding the accident there is the cause domino bearing the label "unsafe act or unsafe condition." Preceding this are subcauses—reasons for the causes.

The domino sequence has been widely used with suitable visual aids to explain accident sequence. It shows that if the key domino, unsafe act or unsafe condition, is removed, the dominoes labeled "accident" and "injury" do not fall. It is effective for this purpose, but the presentation should also bring out strongly the fact that in each case of injury both the factor of hazard and that of faulty behaviour are inescapably present. In fact in many cases, there are multiple causative factors both as regards physical hazards and action hazards. Also there should be a clear distinction between "hazard" and "correctible hazard." If all practicable means of reducing the factor of hazard have been applied, the only action possible is to seek by all practicable means to develop and maintain faultless behaviour. Too often, however, these fundamentals are overlooked and sole attention is given to the unsafe act. The correction of

---

* American Recommended Practices for Compiling Industrial Accident Causes.
† Industrial Accident Prevention.

physical hazards is likely to be expensive, and to workers who know of correctible hazards in their workplaces such a course is almost surely to be regarded as evidence that their employer is in favor of safety if it costs him little or nothing.

Accident cause analysis

In order to promote uniformity in accident cause analysis whereby the findings of the various analysts would be comparable, the interested groups and agencies joined forces and under American Standards Association procedure, developed a standard method. This Standard has received good acceptance both by private industry and the Federal government. Its application by state authorities to the data they collect from private industry in the administration of workmen's compensation laws is practically limited to the states which have adapted their report forms to use it and which also maintain statistical units adequate to process it. Actually, unless a state sets up and prosecutes a state-wide safety program such as is advocated in Chapter 2, it is difficult to see much value in such processing of the data, for although it would show the relative importance numerically of the various agencies and other factors, it would give no information whatever on the vitally important thing—injury rates, either as regards man hours or machine hours. But an adequate state program will of necessity include means of getting the additional information for this purpose.

Accident factors

In the American Standard each essential point about an accident or an exposure causing a work injury is classified as an accident factor. These accident factors are grouped in six major classifications as follows:

1. The agency (object or substance most closely related to the injury).
2. The agency part.
3. The unsafe condition.
4. The accident type.
5. The unsafe act.
6. The unsafe personal factor.

The "Agency."   The "agency" is the object or substance that is most closely associated with the injury, and which, in general, could have been properly guarded or corrected. Agencies, with some examples, are listed below:

Machines (lathe, punch press, saw, drill press, buffer, stamper).
Prime movers and pumps (engine, pump, compressor, fan and blower).

Elevators (passenger or freight, electric, steam, hydraulic, hand-operated).

Hoisting apparatus (crane, derrick, dredge).

Conveyors (belt, sprocket, chain, and other types).

Boilers and pressure vessels (steam boiler, superheater, condenser, digester, pressure piping).

Vehicles (motor, animal-drawn, railway, water, aircraft).

Animals (domestic animal, insect, snake, wild animal, fish).

Mechanical power transmission apparatus (main shaft, countershaft, bearings, pulleys).

Electrical apparatus (motor, generator, conductor, rheostat, lamp).

Hand tools (axe, cleaver, chisel, crowbar, file, mallet, knife).

Chemicals (explosives, vapors, fumes, corrosives, poisonous vegetation).

Highly inflammable and hot substances (lacquer, film, petroleum, steam).

Dusts (explosive, organic, inorganic).

Radiations and radiating substances (radium, ultraviolet, X-ray).

Working surfaces not elsewhere classified (floor, ramp, road, shelf, stair).

Miscellaneous agencies (ladder, floor opening, window, tank, can, box).

The "Agency Part." The "agency part" is the particular part of the selected agency that is most closely associated with the injury, and which, in general, could have been properly guarded or corrected. The list of agency parts is, of course, almost endless. On a simple machine such as a drill press, the agency parts would include such things as the chuck, drill, table, spindle, belt, gears, etc.

The "Unsafe Mechanical or Physical Condition." The "unsafe mechanical or physical condition" is the condition of the selected agency which could have been guarded or corrected. Such conditions can usually be grouped under one of the following:

Improperly guarded agencies (unguarded or inadequately guarded).

Defective agencies (rough, slippery, sharp, inferior in composition).

Hazardous arrangements or procedures in, on, or around the selected agency (unsafe storage, congestion, overloading).

Improper illumination (insufficient light, glare).

Improper ventilation (insufficient air change, impure air source).

Unsafe dress or apparel (lack of or defective gloves, aprons, shoes, respirator; loose clothing).

Unsafe mechanical or physical conditions not elsewhere classified.

No defective agency.

The "Accident Type." The "accident type" is the manner of contact of the injured person with the object or substance, or the exposure or the movement of the injured person which resulted in the injury. Accident types are listed as:

Striking against (refers generally to contacts with sharp or rough objects, resulting in cuts, slivers, punctures, etc. due to striking against, kneeling on or slipping on objects).

Struck by (falling, flying, sliding, or moving objects).

Caught in, on, or between.

Fall on same level.

Fall to different level.

Slip (not fall) *or overexertion* (resulting in strain, hernia, etc.).

Exposure to temperature extremes (resulting in burning, scalding, freezing, heat exhaustion, sunstroke, frostbite, etc.)

Inhalation, absorption, ingestion (asphyxiation, poisoning, drowning, etc., but excluding contact with temperature extremes).

Contact with electric current (such as results in electrocution, shock, etc.).

Accident type not elsewhere classified.

The "Unsafe Act." The "unsafe act" is that violation of a commonly accepted safe procedure which causes the selected accident type. Examples of unsafe acts are:

Operating without authority, failure to secure or warn.

Operating or working at unsafe speeds (too slow, too fast, throwing materials).

Making safety devices inoperative (removing, misadjusting, disconnecting).

Using unsafe equipment, using hands instead of equipment, or using equipment unsafely (unsafe loading, placing, mixing, combining).

Taking unsafe position or posture (standing or working under suspended loads, lifting with back bent).

Working on moving or dangerous equipment (cleaning, adjusting, oiling).

Distracting, teasing, abusing, startling (quarreling, horseplay).

Failing to use safe attire or personal protective devices (goggles).

Unsafe acts not elsewhere classified.

No unsafe act.

The "Unsafe Personal Factor." The "unsafe personal factor" is the mental or bodily characteristic which permits or occasions the selected unsafe act. The following are examples of unsafe personal factors:

Improper attitude (disregard of instructions, failure to understand instructions, nervousness, excitability).

Lack of knowledge or skill (unaware of safe practice, unskilled, etc.).

Bodily defects (defective eyesight or hearing, fatigue, intoxication, existing hernia, weak heart).

Unsafe personal factor not elsewhere classified.

No unsafe personal factor.

Environmental vs. behaviouristic causes

Many studies have been made to determine the proportion of injuries due to enviromental hazards as against those chargeable to unsafe acts. The most widely quoted study * used 12,000 cases taken at random from closed, claim-file insurance records and 63,000 from plant accident records. In the words of the author, "major responsibility for each injury was charged either to the unsafe act of a person or to an unsafe mechanical condition, but in *no* case were both personal and mechanical causes charged." The conclusion reached was that 10% were due to "dangerous physical or mechanical conditions" and "88 % of all accidents were caused primarily by the unsafe acts of persons." The remaining 2% were classed as unpreventable. This study either led to or supported the widely held 15-85% fallacy, i.e., that in general, not over 15% of all injuries are due to unsafe conditions and the remaining 85% are due to unsafe acts.

It is evident that reasonably complete causative information could not have been available for more than a small proportion of the 75,000 cases. Also the method of classification eliminated all causative factors deemed by the analysts to have been of secondary importance. The classification was always either one thing or the other, never both. This was over-simplification for the purpose of establishing a ratio whose only practical value is to emphasize the fact that unsafe action is a major factor in injury causation. It has, however, had the very unforunate effect of drawing attention away from the even more important fact that the first and basic approach to injury prevention is and always should be one of hazard reduction or, if possible, complete elimination. The less the factor of hazard, the less the chance of injury. It is obvious that if unsafe acts are responsible for so overwhelming a proportion of all injuries, preventive effort should be almost wholly devoted to their elimination and, further, if the so-called accident-prone workers have most of the accidents, a belief held by many, their detection and elimination from any but the least hazardous kinds of work would, even if nothing else was done, greatly reduce the injury rate. Actual experience however, strongly negates both these conclusions. Safety programs based chiefly on them do not get good results.

The ratio idea is fallacious because it rests on a false assumption, that work connected injuries are, in almost all cases, the result of *either* unsafe

---

* H. W. Heinrich, *Industrial Accident Prevention* (New York: McGraw-Hill Book Co., 1959), 4th ed.

conditions *or* unsafe acts. The findings of thorough accident investigations, however, give a very different picture. They show that except for the relatively few establishments in which the practical minimum of hazard has been attained or closely approached, a goodly proportion, in some cases a majority, of the injuries result from a combination of correctible unsafe condition and faulty behaviour. Frequently there are multiple factors of both as the following example from a plant, whose injury rate was about average for its branch of industry, shows:

A workman feeding strip to a blanking press through a limited opening type guard was struck on the heel by a small casting that fell from a passing hand truck. He threw his hand up and away from himself just as the ram reached the top of its stroke and his fingers went in over the top of the guard. The descending ram caught them and mangled them against the guard.

The person who investigated this accident regarded it as a freak but he did recommend action to prevent too-full loading of trucks. A checkup by others brought out the following conditions:

1. The truck was the four-wheel box type being pushed. Its box was so high that the man pushing it could not see over it. *Corrective action*— a pull type truck was substituted.

2. There was a deep wear-hole in the floor which had probably caused the truck to jounce. *Corrective action*—The floor was repaired and a checkup inspection of all floors was ordered.

3. The press was so set that the operator's back was to the aisle and too close to it. *Corrective action*—The press was turned around and an inspection for similar hazards ordered. Several were found and corrected.

4. A guard fully enclosing the ram for its full stroke would have saved the workman's fingers. *Corrective action*—Such a guard was provided for this press and all others of this type as well.

To this author it seems surprising that the ratio idea gained as wide acceptance as it evidently did. A modicum of careful thought should lead to the realization that there are two essentials in every case of injury— there must be some degree of hazard and there must also be faulty behaviour by someone. If the factor of hazard could be eliminated there could be no injury. Similarly, if behaviour could be made and kept perfect the result would be the same. Since neither is possible it follows that the maximum in injury elimination can be had only by doing everything possible to minimize the hazard and, with equal thoroughness, apply every practicable means of developing and maintaining as nearly fault-free behaviour as possible. Incidentally, it may be that failure to distinguish between "hazard" and "correctible hazard" has been responsible for some of the fuzzy thinking in this connection.

A study conducted by a National Safety Council committee yielded the following conclusions:

18% of injuries due wholly to mechanical causes.
19% of injuries due wholly to personal causes.
63% due to a combination of both of these causes.

An analysis by the statistical unit of the Department of Labor and Industry of the State of Pennsylvania yielded the following:

3% due wholly to mechanical causes.
2% due wholly to unsafe acts.
95% due to a combination of both causes.

The authoritative presentation of the ratio idea undoubtedly did much harm because the not yet safety minded employer accepting the 15-85% or similar ratio naturally reasons, to quote a specific instance out of the author's experience, "I'll go after the 85% first and take care of the 15% after I get the carelessness thing licked. Why spend a lot of money first off on only 15% of the job? I'm not that kind of a sucker."

It should be noticeable by now that at no time thus far has there been mention of carelessness as a cause of accidents. And yet we often hear people make such statements as "80% of all accidents are due to carelessness." It is most unfortunate that so many persons believe this sort of thing. Carelessness is *not* an accident cause as the safety man sees it. To him it indicates lack of safety mindedness and safety know-how, calling for more thorough instruction and training in safe practice. He knows too, from experience, that as used by executives, foremen and other supervisory personnel, it is usually an alibi for failure to instruct, train or supervise adequately and competently, or it is strong evidence of incompetence for leadership responsibility.

Analyzing the causes

Whenever an accident occurs, even though no one is injured, it is very important that it be carefully investigated and the findings analyzed as a guide for action to prevent a recurrence. The fact that every accident of any kind, anywhere, any time, carries an injury potential should never be lost sight of or ignored. The proper approach is much like that of a doctor who is called upon to diagnose a possibly serious but elusive illness. He will not prescribe a remedy until he has thoroughly examined the patient, analyzed all the symptoms, had suitable laboratory tests made, delved into the person's history, assembled all the facts, and finally arrived at a diagnosis he can be reasonably sure is correct. In a somewhat similar way the safety engineer's procedure in analyzing the causes of accidents can be outlined in ten steps as follows:

1. Obtain the foreman's report of the accident.
2. Obtain the injured (or involved if no injury) worker's report.
3. Obtain the reports of witnesses if any.
4. Obtain the report of the nurse or doctor (if an injury).
5. Investigate the accident.
6. Record all the facts.
7. Tabulate the essential facts of the given accident together with those of other accidents.
8. Study all the facts.
9. Decide what action should be taken.
10. Assign responsibility (or secure its assignment) for carrying out the action decided on.

Tabulating the facts

If the American Standard is used as a guide in tabulating the findings of each accident in turn, the record will, in time, build up a picture of the pattern of accident occurrence in the given plant or establishment that will be helpful in guiding the over-all safety program. The following list of facts found worth recording in a typical large plant is probably reasonably representative:

1. Nationality.
2. Speak English.
3. Occupation.
4. Department.
5. Name of foreman.
6. Years employed by company.
7. Length of time on job.
8. Agency.
9. Type of accident.
10. Environmental cause.
11. Unsafe act.
12. Behavioristic cause.
13. Cost.
14. Time lost.

Such a tabulation is valuable for the following reasons:

1. When it is studied by the safety engineer, it may suggest to his mind certain preventive measures that might otherwise be overlooked.

2. It sometimes is difficult or impossible to secure immediate action on certain recommendations that are suggested for preventing the recurrence of a single accident. Tabulations of many accidents may provide cumulative evidence that such action is increasingly essential.

3. Tabulations clearly indicate the relative importance of certain facts and enable the safety engineer to select those machines, substances, hazards, causes, departments, foremen, workers, and other individuals on whom the safety engineer should concentrate more effort.

4. Such tabulations are used as a basis for accident prevention contests, for tracing trends, for determining if the accident record is getting better or worse, for preparing reports for executives, foremen, and workers, and for determining what preventive activities are most needed to secure the best results.

TABLE 9

ENVIRONMENTAL CAUSES OF ACCIDENTS, HOW TO ELIMINATE THEM, AND
FUNCTIONAL RESPONSIBILITY FOR CORRECTIVE ACTION *

A	B	C
Environmental Causes of Accidents:	How to Eliminate the Causes of Accidents; Suggestions for Corrective Action:	Who Can Eliminate the Causes; Functional Responsibility for Corrective Action in a Typical Plant:
1. Improper guarding (unguarded, inadequately guarded, guard removed by someone other than injured worker, etc.).	**a.** Inspection. **b.** Checking plans, blueprints, purchase orders, and contracts for safety. **c.** Include guards in original design, order, and contract. **d.** Provide guards for existing hazards.	**a.** Safety director, foreman, and maintenance man. **b.** Chief engineer and purchasing agent. **c.** Chief engineer and purchasing agent. **d.** Maintenance man and foreman.
2. Substances or equipment defective through use or abuse (worn out, cracked, broken, etc. through no fault of injured worker).	**a.** Inspection. **b.** Proper maintenance.	**a.** Safety director, foreman, and maintenance man. **b.** Maintenance man.
3. Substances or equipment defective through design or construction (too large, too small, not strong enough, made with flaws, etc.)	**a.** Source of supply must be reliable. **b.** Inspection for defects in plans and materials. **c.** Correction of defects.	**a.** Purchasing agent. **b.** Chief engineer. **c.** Chief engineer.
4. Unsafe procedure (hazardous process, management failed to make adequate plans for safety).	**a.** Job analysis. **b.** Formulation of safe procedure. **c.** Job training.	**a.** Production manager. **b.** Production manager and foreman. **c.** Foreman.
5. Unsafe housekeeping facilities (unsuitable shelves, bins, racks; no aisle markings, etc.).	**a.** Provide suitable layout and equipment necessary for good housekeeping.	**a.** Chief engineer, production manager, and foreman.

* *Courtesy* Lumbermen's Mutual Casualty Company.

TABLE 9 (*continued*)

A	B	C
6. Improper illumination (poor, none, glaring headlights, etc.).	a. Improve the illumination.	a. Chief engineer and production manager.
7. Improper ventilation (poor, dusty, gaseous, high humidity, etc.).	a. Improve the ventilation.	a. Chief engineer and production manager.
8. Improper dress or apparel (management's failure to provide or specify use).	a. Provide safe dress or apparel or personnel protective equipment if management could reasonably be expected to provide it. b. Specify the use of certain protective equipment on certain jobs.	a. Plant manager. b. Plant manager.

TABLE 10

BEHAVIORISTIC CAUSES OF ACCIDENTS, HOW TO ELIMINATE THEM, AND FUNCTIONAL RESPONSIBILITY FOR CORRECTIVE ACTION *

Behavioristic Causes of Accidents:	How to Eliminate These Causes of Accidents; Suggestions for Corrective Action:	Who Can Eliminate These Causes; Functional Responsibility for Corrective Action in a Typical Plant:
1. Improper attitude (deliberate chance-taking, disregard of instructions, injured man knew how to do his job safely but failed to follow safe procedure; absent-minded, etc.).	a. Supervision. b. Discipline. c. Personnel work.	a. Foreman. b. Foreman and personnel man. c. Personnel man.
2. Lack of knowledge or skill (injured man did not know how to do his job safely, too new on the job, unpracticed, unskilled, etc.).	a. Job analysis. b. Job training.	a. Production manager and foreman. b. Foreman.
3. Physical or mental defect (one arm, deaf, epilepsy, partially blind, etc.).	a. Pre-employment. Physical examinations. b. Periodic physical examinations. c. Proper placement of men.	a. Physician. b. Physician. c. Physician and personnel man.

* *Courtesy* Lumbermen's Mutual Casualty Company.

Studying the facts

It is essential for the safety engineer to study all the facts before deciding on the action that should be taken. Even though the accident may seem to be a simple one, and even though the necessary action may seem to be perfectly obvious, it is wise to go through the entire diagnosing procedure to make sure that nothing of value has been overlooked.

Prescribing remedies

After studying all of the facts, the safety engineer should start to jot down all possible things that might be done to prevent recurrence. If he follows this procedure, he will be surprised at the number of things he can think of that might be done. It may then become difficult for him to decide which of these suggestions, if any, he should discard, and which he should write up in recommendation form for official approval and follow-through.

When endeavoring to prescribe remedies, the safety engineer will frequently derive many especially valuable ideas from his study of the behavioristic and environmental causes listed under Tables 9 and 10, particularly if two other columns are added to these lists, one column indicating suggested remedies, the other indicating the functional responsibilities for putting these suggestions into force.

Examples. Let us consider briefly a few actual accident cases.

Case 1. A worker who had been six years on the job as machine operator "slipped" on the concrete floor and caught his hand in a set of improperly guarded gears, losing 3 fingers. There was nothing on the floor to cause him to slip.

Cause: Improperly guarded machine.

Suggested action: Completely enclose gears.

Persons to carry out suggestion: Chief engineer and maintenance man.

Case 2. A crane chain in service an unknown number of years broke and dropped a load, crushing the toes of a worker. The chain was of proper size for the load. The employer did not encourage or require workers to wear safety shoes.

Causes:
1. Equipment defective through use.
2. Improper apparel.

Suggested action:
1. Institute program for periodic inspection of all crane chains and see that defective chains are destroyed or made safe.
2. Specify that workers on certain jobs must wear safety shoes.

Persons to carry out suggestions:
1. Chief engineer.
2. Plant manager.

Case 3. A worker three years on the job was running down stairs. He stumbled and fell, breaking an arm. The stairs were well lighted, in good condition, and provided with hand rails on both sides. All workers had been cautioned not to run in the mill, particularly when going up or down stairs.

Cause: Wrong attitude.

Suggested action:
1. Determine reason for running and correct by disciplinary action if necessary.
2. Repeat caution to all workers.
3. Tighten up on supervision.

Persons to carry out suggestions:
1. Worker's foreman.
2. Plant manager and foremen.
3. Plant manager and foremen.

Case 4. A man was assigned to operate a drill press. On the first day of work he wore gloves. His glove caught on the drill and two of his fingers were broken.

Cause: Lack of knowledge. Did not understand danger of wearing gloves when operating drill press.

Suggested action: Improve job training and supervision.

Person to carry out suggestion: Foreman.

Case 5. An oiler, after entering a room where oil was stored, slipped on oil on the floor, fell, and sprained his wrist. One oil faucet had been leaking for several days. No one had cleaned up the oil from the floor.

Causes:
1. Equipment defective through use.
2. Unsafe housekeeping facilities.
3. Improper attitude.

Suggested action:
1. Inspect and repair leaky faucets.
2. Provide drip pan to catch oil in case of leakage.
3. Supervise and discipline oilers.

Persons to carry out suggestions:
1. Foreman.
2. Foreman.
3. Foreman.

Chapter Six

Injury Distribution

The factors that determine who will be injured through accidents, and when and why, have been the subject of almost endless discussion. Many research studies have been made in efforts to discover and appraise these factors, and although much has been learned and many findings have been announced by the researchers, there is far from general agreement about the validity of many of them.

Three theories of injury distribution have been widely discussed. Each has its adherents. Stated very simply these three theories are:

1. Chance distribution. According to this theory, each hazard or unsafe act, however slight the degree of hazard involved, will, if a sufficient number of exposures occur, yield an injury. Which exposure will do so is, in each instance, purely a matter of chance.

Examples:

(a) A repairman left a large bolt on the flange of a crane girder in a steel plant. Later the motion of the crane dislodged it and it struck a workman on the head, killing him. That it fell at just the right moment to hit anyone was pure chance. That it hit the workman in the right way to kill him was also a matter of chance.

(b) A workman nailing up a heavy crate hit the nail a glancing blow. The nail flew across the aisle striking another workman in the cheek, narrowly missing his eye. That the nail flew instead of bending over was largely chance. That it hit the only other person in range was chance. That it missed his eye was chance again.

2. Biased distribution. This theory assumes that a person once hurt is thereby likely to be either more or less apt to become an accident victim again. His susceptibility to accidents will have been increased by nervousness or fear, or decreased by greater caution and improved judgment.

Examples:

(a) A window cleaner in a plant, whose windows could be cleaned from a step ladder, failed one day to set his ladder properly. It fell, and he received a brain concussion. He recovered, but thereafter became so nervous on a ladder that he had to be placed on other work.

(b) The time-honored practice of requiring a student aviator who makes a bad landing to go up again at once if he is uninjured indicates the applicability of this theory to high hazard situations.

3. Unequal liability. This theory assumes that some persons are much more liable to be involved in accidents than others, that is, they are "accident prone."

Examples:

This can be physical, psychological, or both, as the following three examples exemplify:

(a) A laborer was, because of faithful work, promoted to crane hooker-on. He suffered a crushed finger on his second day on this job. Two more minor injuries and several close calls quickly followed his return to work. An eye test showed that he lacked binocular vision and that the defect was not correctible. He was changed to another job that did not require it and received no more injuries.

(b) A young man who had been an armature winder was hired as a motor repairman. He learned the more diverse work quickly and, since the repair work did not take his full time, he was soon being used in the maintenance of the electrical equipment generally, some of which work was done "hot." All went well until he had a violent quarrel with his teammate. This was patched up, but he remained sullen and uncommunicative. He met with two accidents (electric shock) on succeeding days—the second of which necessitated artificial resuscitation. Investigation showed that he had a record of being hot tempered and that a period of moodiness and inattention followed each outburst. He was kept on the motor repair work but his spare time was changed to work he could do safely alone. The whole matter was discussed with him privately and helpfully. He accepted the change. No further trouble developed.

(c) A man who, because of his industry and willingness, was used as a man of all work in a machine shop, seemed always to be getting hurt, though not seriously. He pinched his fingers handling the steel parts, he bumped his shins, and dropped things on his toes. He fell down stairs. He ran into a column. Finally a thorough examination, physical and psychological, showed that his distance perception was poor, his muscular coordination very poor, his mental reactions were slow, his reasoning power was of a very low order, and he had a terrific inferiority complex (small wonder). He was fitted with glasses that corrected his vision and was assigned to the stockroom keeper, a kindly, elderly man who needed help because of the increasing work load and his own declining strength. Under his sympathetic supervision, this man became valuable because of his industry and good memory.

Analysis of accidents in establishments selected to typify a wide range of safety performance, from excellent to poor, shows that all three theories apply, but that the extent to which they do so varies widely not only as between establishments or activities, but within a given establishment as well. It should be obvious that in an establishment where little has been done to eliminate the hazards, chance will play an important part. It is equally obvious that in activities in which many factors may enter, some of which are not practically controllable by the person or persons directly involved, the working of blind chance may be crucial. For example, a pop bottle thrown by an urchin at a roadside picnic struck the driver of an open car passing by, stunning him. The "wild" car swerved across the road, glanced off a tree and back on the road just in time to collide with an oncoming truck. That the bottle hit the driver at all was chance. The direction of swerve was also chance, as were both the location of the tree and the fact that the car hit it a glancing blow. Finally, the oncoming truck having been at just the right position and speed on a little-traveled road was a chance coincidence of remote probability. Although exactly the above sequence of events may never occur again, this example is no more remarkable than cases that accident investigation in industry turns up so frequently that they appear almost commonplace. Careful analyses of reports based on thorough accident investigation by competent persons show that in most cases chance plays a part, usually the major part, in determining whether or not in each accident someone is hurt, and if so, how seriously.

Every foreman or supervisor who has had long experience in directing and training men in high hazard work knows that biased distribution applies rather frequently. Injuries and "close calls" do make men more careful or more nervous as the case may be. In fact, any person who cannot learn from such experiences should, when this is discovered, be at once transferred to low hazard work. Similarly, the person who cannot keep his head clear and his nerves steady in the face of danger should not remain in work in which dangerous situations are likely to occur.

The theory of unequal liability or accident proneness has aroused a great deal of controversy, much of which persists. Part of this is undoubtedly due to lack of agreement as to what the term "accident proneness" means. Also, it is evident that confusion as to the basic factors in accident causation undoubtedly contributes to the differences in opinion. In other words, back of the controversy over accident distribution there is another controversy, namely, that concerning the relationship between unsafe conditions and unsafe acts in causing work-connected injuries. This was discussed in the preceding chapter.

Ratio of minor to disabling injuries

Another misconception has a bearing on the subject of accident proneness. This is the belief that the ratio between disabling injuries and minor injuries is fairly constant and, further, that a person who has relatively frequent minor injuries is particularly likely to suffer a serious injury. Actually, though this belief has some basis in fact, it is far from being invariably true. Inherent hazard may be defined as "the possibility of serious or fatal injury." The extent to which minor accidents and injuries indicate the likelihood of serious ones varies in accordance with the inherent hazard of the work itself, with the activities of others that may affect the job in question, and with any exposures there may be in the working environment. For example, a lack of digital dexterity might cause a bench worker using a variety of hand tools to receive many little finger and hand injuries. Yet the possibility of a disabling injury in such work is remote. He would, however, to some extent, be subject to the inherent hazards of his environment. If, on the other hand, a worker handling heavy materials by hand lacked depth perception, he would be likely to suffer finger injuries with a good chance of getting a crushed hand or finger.

The variation in the ratio between disabling and non-disabling injuries is indicated by the following ratios from injury samples, each of which included upwards of 500 cases:

Occupation	Disabling	Non-Disabling
Logging (Pacific Northwest)	1	6
Building Construction	1	8
Woodworking	1	27
Steel Manufacture	1	51
Bench Work (Metal Parts)	1	204
Light assembly	1	371
Light hand work (Inspection sorting, etc.)	1	447

It should be remembered that each of these ratios has a margin of error due to the difficulty in getting full reports of minor injuries. This margin of error would presumably be largest in the woods, or in heavy construction, and least in light indoor work. Also, these ratios, covering in each case a wide variety of activities and situations, would apply to any given job and any given activity only by sheer chance.

The widely-quoted ratio of 1 disabling injury to 29 minor injuries is a generalization of value indicating that, given a large enough mass of accident data covering a broad range of injuries, minor injuries are on the order of 30 times as frequent as disabling ones. Expanding this relationship to include occurrences that have an injury potential is useful in justifying safe practice. The estimate of 300 of such occurrences per 29 minor injuries and 1 disabling injury has received wide acceptance as being accurate enough for propaganda purposes, but not enough to be presented as factual.

Accident proneness

That workers do vary widely in their proneness to injury cannot be doubted, nor can the fact that a large proportion of the accidental injuries in any given working force of considerable size will be suffered by a relatively small proportion of the workers. Very early in the organized safety movement, both of these facts became apparent as a result of a study of the accident experience of individual plants maintaining complete accident records. One unfortunate and very unsound practice, rather widely followed, resulted from this discovery. This was the tendency to discharge workers who had "too many accidents." With plentiful labor supply, this was the easiest way out. Justification for this practice was also found in the acceptance of the 85%—15% ratio. The reasoning was that if so high a proportion of accidental injuries was due to unsafe acts, and if a small proportion of workers was particularly prone to commit unsafe acts, it was best for the worker, for fellow workers, and the company to get him off the working force, where he could damage neither himself nor his fellow workers. Actually, of course, in the long run, discharge was the most objectionable course, not only because it was inhuman, but also because the discharged worker would merely take his unsafe behavior to less-discriminating employers with the increased probability that he would injure himself, or others, or both.

The idea of accident proneness was given wide publicity, and various research workers in this country and abroad have undertaken to explore the subject, measure and appraise its importance, and develop means of detecting it in advance.* They established that, in the working forces studied, the injury distribution could not be accounted for by the "chance" theory alone. A small proportion, usually 10 to 30% of the group, suffered from 40 to 60% of the injuries. Furthermore, a high proportion of these repeaters continued to be so year after year. However, attempts to determine just what pattern of personality factors adds up to accident proneness failed. Although progress has unquestionably been made in this direction, the findings give small hope that any simple and generally applicable means of determining the accident-prone personality in advance will be found. Probably reasonably reliable prediction will require much more complete

---

* Vernon, Farmer, Newbold, Viteles, and others.

psychological and aptitude testing than is now practically possible on any broad scale.

In general, these research studies failed to take into account the importance of eliminating the factor of hazard, as far as possible, the importance of careful and thorough training, and above all the practical impossibility of eliminating or taking adequate account of the variations in hazard in the work activities so that the factor of proneness could be measured with reasonable accuracy. For the most part, they assumed that if the work performed by the group studied was of the same general nature, the conditions would be sufficiently uniform for the purpose. If they appreciated the vital importance of careful analysis of each of the operations performed to discover the hazard points, the application of all practicable means of eliminating or controlling these hazard points by such means as guards, rearrangement, changes in design, and the like, and the development of safe work methods to avoid the otherwise uncorrectible hazards, the reports on their findings give little evidence of it. Also, they appear to have assumed that a tendency to have minor injuries is a reliable indicator of the tendency to have more serious ones, a conclusion that is, at best, far from having been established.

Another point that these researchers, for the most part, appear to have overlooked is that the accident data they were able to collect for their studies necessarily came from establishments whose safety performance was at least relatively good, otherwise the data would not have been available. In this connection, relatively good safety performance implies careful attention, usually over a considerable period of years, to the elimination of hazards, and the development of safe work practices with at least a reasonably adequate system of training in safe work practices. In other words, the data came mostly from establishments who, by consistent safety effort over a period of years, had reduced their injury rates to a small fraction, usually not over 5 to 10% of what they had been at the start of their safety programs. Conclusions based on samples of this nature would obviously not have general applicability. They would be applicable only to establishments whose safety performance was similarly good.

Accident pattern of poor safety performance

The type of accident distribution typical of an establishment that has not advanced far in its effort to prevent worker injuries is shown by the following data from a combined machine and sheet metal shop. It employed an average of 420 men. The record covered a full year. There were 19 disabling injuries and 399 non-disabling. The frequency rate was 22.5, the severity rate was .95. The ratio of disabling to non-disabling was 1-21.

The distribution of injuries by men was:

Number of Men	Number of Injuries Each
2	11
2	9
1	8
4	5
7	4
19	3
16	2
233	1
136	0
420	418

Nine of the 19 disabling injuries were to men who had only one injury each, 5 were to men who had 2 injuries each, 1 was to 1 of the men who had 5 injuries each, 2 were to men who had 3 injuries each, and the remaining 2 were to the men who had 11 injuries each.

The distribution of injuries by kinds of work was:

Occupation	No. of Men	No. of Injuries	Injuries per Man
Materials handlers	14	66	4
Maintenance Men	24	76	3
Cleaners, Stockroom, Tool Crib	16	18	1
Production	366	258	0.7
	420	418	

The five men who had eight or more injuries each were materials handlers working chiefly with steel sheets and parts stamped or cut from these. Cuts from the sharp corners and from fins left by worn dies accounted for all but seven of these 48 injuries. Five of the remainder were due to particles in the eyes, presumably cinders from passing trains. The other two were due to falls from cars.

The 19 disabling injuries comprised:

Type of Injury	No. of Injuries
Cuts from the sheet metal	3
Crushed feet or toes	5
Falls	3
Infections of minor wounds	3
Caught in machine	2
Eye	2
Finger crushed by a hammer	1

These data support both the chance distribution theory and that of unequal liability. The plant was full of hazards that were subject to correction by readily available means, materials handling procedures were not good, personal protective equipment—hand protectors, goggles, safety shoes—were little used, little effort had been made to get all minor injuries reported, housekeeping was poor, and there was no definite system of safety training. The extent to which accident proneness was a factor is not determinable in such a situation. However, had a properly organized and effectively directed preventive program been set up and maintained whereby the conditions mentioned had been corrected, the frequency rate would probably have been cut by two-thirds or three-quarters without much trouble. The accident-prone individuals would then begin to show up and could be dealt with on an individual basis. This should not be construed to mean that accident proneness should be left untouched until then. Quite the contrary. The watch for accident proneness should be an intimate part of every safety program, but so should the watch for the accident-prone job, condition, process, tool, or machine.

The practical approach

Objective appraisal of the methods used and results obtained by establishments who have achieved low injury rates emphasizes the importance of the following:

1. The job or activity in question must be made as safe as is practicably possible. If job safety analysis has not been applied, that is the first step to take.

2. Based upon the findings of job safety analysis, whatever safeguards may be practicably applied and whatever changes in design, arrangement, equipment, and the like that can be applied to correct the hazard points should be made.

3. The safe work methods should be worked out and clearly described.

4. Complete job standards, including such items as physical requirements, mental and temperamental characteristics, if important, and personal protective equipment if needed, should be developed.

5. The applicant for the job, or the incumbent, should be appraised in the light of these findings.

6. The worker should be trained in the work procedure, using the accepted 4-step method or a suitable modification of it.

With this procedure carefully applied, it will be found that almost all of the accident repeating will disappear. The very few individuals who still have accidents will be found to be those who do not respond to ordinary training methods. They must be treated on an individual basis, by shifting to low hazard work or by suitable medical–psychological treatment. Discharge should be resorted to only in extreme cases.

The proof of the effectiveness of this approach is to be found in that it is being practicably applied in numerous establishments throughout the country that have, in fact, reduced their injury rates to an extremely low figure and are still showing improvement.

If by accident proneness we mean broadly the likelihood of injury in any given kind of work, it is evident that proneness is not alone a matter of attitude or of mental or psychological lacks or defects. Any person assigned to a job or activity whose hazards he does not know fully, who has not been trained in or does not know the safe practices that should be followed, will, of course, be liable to injury. Therefore, before a worker should be considered accident prone, the job should be made as safe as possible, his physical suitability for the work involved should be ascertained, and he should be properly trained in the safe procedures required.

Summation

Each of the three theories of accident distribution applies to a greater or lesser extent in every establishment or undertaking. Determining their relative importance for American industry in general is not practically possible because of the very wide range in safety performance among the multitude of establishments that make up American industry as a whole, nor would it be of much value if it could be done. Unsound pronouncements resulting from research not properly conceived, executed, and evaluated are proving harmful to the cause of prevention because they mislead. Accident proneness has been shown to be a rather important causative factor in establishments that have, through consistent effort, reduced their accident rates to a low figure, but its importance is less for establishments whose preventive effort is indifferent or poor. Analysis of injury sources shows that at least 70%, and probably as many as 85%, of the annual total of approximately two million occupational injuries and deaths come from establishments of this type. Any attempt by these employers to reduce the accidents largely by getting rid of accident prone workers is certain to fail. Low accident rates can be reached and maintained only by thoroughgoing programs of prevention which effectively reduce the hazard factor in all work activities and concurrently develop safe and adequate employee behavior. Discovering and dealing with accident proneness is merely one of the numerous activities that are necessarily included in such a program. The relative importance of these various activities is not determinable and is not important. That each and all of them should be well coordinated and effectively prosecuted is extremely important.

Chapter Seven

The Elements of an Effective Safety Program

The essentials of top-rate safety performance in any given establishment may be summarized as follows:

1. There must be forceful, continuous executive leadership.
2. Plant and equipment must be made safe.
3. Supervision must be competent and intensely safety minded.
4. Full employee cooperation in accident prevention must be secured and maintained.

For any continuing project as extensive as is implied in the above and necessarily also involving and influencing the work activities of the entire employed personnel, a definite planned program is necessary. Although the details will vary in different establishments, there are certain time-tried and proven activities that are found so consistently in establishments whose injury rates are of the best, that it seems safe to pronounce all of them essential to top-rate performance.

The safety program and the activities carried on under it have the purpose of (a) reducing the hazard factor (b) developing safe and adequate behavior by every employee. A point previously made is emphasized; that in every case of work-connected injury there must be some degree of hazard (chance of injury) *and* unsafe or otherwise faulty behavior. But no work activities can ever be made entirely hazard free. Perfect behavior by everyone cannot be attained. Therefore, top-rate safety performance (the maximum in injury elimination) can be had only by reducing the factor of hazard to the minimum, and concurrently developing employee behavior to the maximum degree of excellence.

Finding and correcting the hazards

Activities whose major purpose is hazard elimination are:

1. Planning
2. Safety in purchasing
3. Inspection
4. Job safety (or hazard) analysis
5. Accident investigation

Planning for the prevention of accidents should, of course, be an intimate part of the planning and development of the entire undertaking. If this procedure is followed, a new plant or project of any kind can have so low a factor of hazard that, with reasonably good management and attention to the development of safe behavior, human injury can be practically eliminated in its operation. However, given a plant already in operation, planning is still important because of the almost continuous changes in process, procedures and the like, and also because of the continuing modifications necessary to keep operations and equipment abreast of industrial progress. Each such change, new operation, or modification should be carefully planned to eliminate as much of the hazard factor as is possible.

A definite system of *inspection* should be set up to cover all of the plant and everything in it. Not only may hazards have been overlooked in the planning, erection, and equipment of the plant, but more important, the daily wear and tear and the changes made cause hazards to develop, which are likely, in the absence of adequate inspection, to come to light only when they yield injury. Therefore, every management should set up a system of inspection suitable to its needs.

Quantity production has been made possible only by very thorough planning of each operation and piece of equipment involved, as well as the maintenance of control adequate to insure that the work will go as planned even if the initial planning proves to be faulty, and suitable modifications must be made. This process eliminates most of the hazards and develops reliable, skilled behavior, thereby eliminating most of the injuries. However, in even our most modern, up-to-date establishments, this sort of planning and control is ordinarily extended only to the production jobs and has not been applied to such non-productive work as shipping and receiving, maintenance, repairs, and the like. These are high hazard activities, but if the safest methods of work for such jobs are worked out, the hazard points discovered, the advisable safeguards determined and provided for, and proper training provided, injuries can be eliminated as effectively from them as from quantity production work. Thus, safety men have modified the ordinary type of job analysis used for production and are applying it as *job safety* analysis to eliminate accidents in work that has not been subjected to quantity production procedures.

Both *inspection* and *job safety analysis* bring many unsafe practices to light, but that is not their chief function. The control of worker action is primarily a supervisory function. Whatever unsafe acts and practices are turned up by the three activities mentioned above should be made known to supervision promptly as a sort of extra dividend.

In spite of all that is done, some hazards will remain overlooked or not adequately safeguarded, and some behavior faults will continue. Therefore, there will be some accidents resulting in human injury. Obviously, each of these should be investigated. *Accident investigation,* therefore, is in the nature of a post-mortem whereby the investigator seeks to discover information that will be helpful in preventing a repetition.

All of these activities will be of no avail unless the proper and fully adequate corrective action is provided for throughout. Planning that does not eliminate or reduce hazards is valueless. Inspection that does not discover conditions subject to correction or improvement is useless. Job safety analysis that does not develop better working methods and information that will be helpful in placing and training workers has been wasted. Finally, an accident investigation that results in no useful information or any recommendations for corrective action might as well not have been made.

Developing safe behavior

The techniques that have proved effective in dealing with unsafe acts are perhaps not so definite and clear-cut as those by which the hazards may be found, because they involve, for the most part, merely the adaptation of methods widely used in advertising, education, and training. An adequate program of developing and maintaining safe behavior must include the continuance of safety advertising whereby all employees are favorably conditioned to receive specific ideas and participate in specific safety activities. Along with and as a part of this advertising program must go informational material whereby the employees will receive a general education in safety principles and safety measures. However, just as advertising alone, without face to face contact between salesmen and customers, will sell few goods, the advertising and educational program of itself will cause few employees to develop safe methods of work because it is only the unusual individual who will apply to his own day-by-day thinking and actions the general information and ideas that he receives through an advertising and educational program of a general nature. Therefore, all of this must be supplemented by on-the-job training in specific procedures on an individual basis. Except for vestibule or other specific training preparatory for the firing line job, the training must be given by the foreman, or under his direction.

Specific activities whose primary purpose is to develop safe and adequate behavior are:

Placement. Job safety analysis will have determined the human qualifications needed for each specific job. Proper pre-employment physical and aptitude tests and, in some cases, psychological analysis make it possible to place the job applicant in work best suited to his abilities. Haphazard placement is undoubtedly at the root of many injuries.

Training. Job analysis will have determined the safe methods of work and will have developed the information the worker needs. However, in training him for proper functioning, the detailed method of training expressed so well by the simple formula "Tell him, show him, have him do it, correct him until he has it, supervise him to see that he keeps it," expresses the fundamentals of adequate job training.

Supervision. It should be obvious that if it is true (and it certainly is) that the foreman is the key man in safety, the most careful attention should be given to the selection and training of foremen so that they can function competently in their positions of key responsibility. Therefore, a carefully worked out schedule of foreman training in safety should be a part of every safety program.

Education. A clearer distinction should be made between education and training. By education, we mean the increasing of a person's general knowledge in the fields in which he works, and in allied fields. By training, we mean the development of skill in the doing of specific tasks or types of work. Safety education should be related to the work men do and should be presented in a manner that will stimulate their thinking.

Employee Participation. Since the great majority of people learn mainly "in the doing," and since also their interest is enlisted chiefly by personal participation, the maximum in employee participation in safety activities and allied undertakings should be sought. It is possible in the well-organized and adequate safety program to assign some specific part to every employee in the organization.

Keeping the program up to the mark

Methods of appraisal of safety performance have already been discussed. It is emphasized that every safety program requires continuous supervision and appraisal if performance is to be kept up to the mark. Careful watch must be kept on quality of performance in each of the various activities, even though appraisal may be difficult: definite standards or benchmarks are, for the most part, infeasible, and one must take into consideration the circumstances of the individual case. The important point is that the safety director or other executive having primary responsibility for the functioning of the safety program must set suitable goals and must adopt means of gauging performance in the program as a whole and in each of its various parts.

Chapter Eight

Job Safety Analysis

Job analysis is an essential part of production control and as such its technique has become well developed and widely established in American manufacturing practice. It involves the accurate and detailed description of each job in terms of duties, safety, tools required, methods, sequence of operations, and working conditions. As would be expected, such a procedure of itself eliminates a high proportion of accident hazards. When, to adequate job analysis, the other necessary factors of successful mass production are added, namely, planning, supervision, training, and continuous control, we get a high degree of safety as an inherent part (we might say as "a by-product") of quantity production. Production is not efficient unless it is safe. If this fact were fully appreciated by management generally, it would widen tremendously managerial interest in accident elimination.

The safety man's knowledge of job analysis need not include all the steps in mass production technique, but he should be reasonably familiar with the procedures involved in order to concentrate on the prevention of accidents in a manner that will be practical and of maximum effectiveness. Although he should not accept the jobs that have been placed under "production control" as free from fault, the major part of his effort will be required on those that have not been so placed.

Not only could industry profitably extend the application of job analysis much more widely to repetitive types of work in general, but similar methods should be applied generally to nonrepetitive work, such as maintenance and short-order production. It is the general experience that this type of work shows a relatively bad accident record. Presumably, this is chiefly due to two factors, namely, relatively high hazard together with the lack of detailed analysis and control.

An example of the value of the application of job analysis is given by the record of one large firm. It had, over a period of years, brought its frequency rate down from over 50 to under 10, where it hovered between 7 and 10 for several years. Detailed study showed a frequency rate under 5 for all production work (job analysis had been applied to nearly all of this) with most of the short-order production jobs and maintenance, materials handling, and incidental construction work showing frequency rates up to 30 or even above. By extending job analysis procedure to most of these activities, their frequency rate was cut by from 50 to 90 per cent, and the overall frequency rate was brought under 5 for the first time in the company's experience. This and other examples appear to justify the conclusion that, if similar procedure were widely followed, a major advance would be scored in the fight to eliminate accidents.

Job analysis includes details of operations

Job analysis or job breakdown requires getting down to the minute details involving all the operations of a job. A detailed description of each step from the time work is started should include the preliminaries of issuing the job tickets, blueprints, and special tools, as well as definition of the skill and other qualifications required for the job.

Selection of employees

This part completed, the manufacturing department is in a position to inform the personnel department what help is required, so that the proper selection may be made at the employment office. If the operations are broken down properly, it is a comparatively simple matter to decide what personal characteristics are necessary in the new employees, such as age, sex, health, education, physique, skill, height, and weight.

It would be undesirable and hazardous to place a 100-pound girl, 5 feet tall, on a punch press which required a person 5 feet, 6 inches, at least, to reach over far enough to place the work properly. Then, too, if the parts are too heavy for a 100-pound girl, fatigue, as well as extra straining due to inadequate reach, would decrease efficiency and increase the hazard of injury.

After the manufacturing department has analyzed the job, it is ready to inform the employment man what to look for in a prospective employee. The request for help would read, for example:

Request for 1 Operator on Large Punch Press, Class A

Occupations Most Nearly Allied Are:
  Hydraulic press operator.
  Weidemann press operator.
  Shearman.

Trade Requirements:

Set up and operate punch presses. Must be able to make set-ups with standard dies; do all types of punch press work within the capacity of the machine. Work from blueprints.

Education—elementary school or better.

Physical Requirements:

Weight . . . . 140 lbs.
Height . . . . 5'6" minimum.
Age . . . . 21 years minimum.
Average strength.
Standing job.
Satisfied with repetitive work.

Rate Established—Piece Work.

Importance of proper instruction

Proper selection of the new employee to suit the requirements of the job is essential. It is at least as important that he receive his instruction and training from an instructor or supervisor who can teach effectively and who has the individual steps in such instruction well planned and organized for the purpose. Much too often the supervisor who thinks he knows the job perfectly fails as an instructor because he does not look at the job from the viewpoint of the new worker. The job breakdown sheet will greatly aid this type of supervisor to correct this weakness. Even the most experienced and effective of supervisors will find it helpful in organizing operations in proper sequence so that the operator will be able to grasp them more readily and learn to perform his work better, faster, more safely, and with a minimum of supervision and follow-up.

Breaking the job down into its component parts

A simple job breakdown sheet for training new men can be made quickly for almost any job.

A simple job such as driving a screw can be analyzed as shown on following page.

It is generally accepted that 80 per cent of most jobs are very simple operations, which any average person can perform with a minimum of training. The balance, or 20 per cent, represent the knacks or skills and tricks of the trade which come through training and experience. These critical or key points must be made clear and emphasized more than are the regular steps in the operation. At the same time, of course, accident hazards are stressed.

JOB BREAKDOWN SHEET FOR TRAINING MAN ON NEW JOB	
Part Door Hinge	Operation $\dfrac{\text{Drive Wood Screw)}}{\text{(Yankee screw driver)}}$
Important Steps in the Operation	"Key Points"—knacks, hazards, "feel," timing, special information
1. Set screw driver at R, "fixed" position	
2. Center bit in screw head	
3. Start screw	Steady screw with fingers. Enough pressure to start. Hold vertically—don't let bit jump out of screw head
4. Set screw driver at R, ratchet position	Slips injure work and fingers
5. Center bit in screw head	
6. Drive screw	Hold bit squarely in screw. Operate vertically. Keep pressure on screw
7. Finish drive	Drive at "closed" position. Extra pressure—even—vertical. Don't let bit jump out. Set driver at "fixed" position if necessary. Solid tight finish—don't split screw

Naturally, there are some nonrepetitive jobs, such as maintenance and repair work, but even these can be analyzed so that a fairly regular sequence can be followed.

The routine versus the nonrepetitive job

The following typical example shows the differences between a routine and a nonroutine job:

In lieu of the routinizing of motions involved in quantity production jobs, stress in nonrepetitive work is on the training of the workmen in safe ways of performing specific operations as lifting, using tools, etc. That is, in planning for and laying out the job, the different operations involved are described and men with the requisite training in them are specified. A comparison between a typical production job and a typical maintenance operation will make the need for this course clearer.

Production job (1 operator)	Maintenance job (Mechanic and Assistant)
Part #2A42 Operation #4	Rebabbitt main bearings mill #47
A. Pick up piece from pan with left hand, place in jig, lock jig.	A. Obtain required tools, equipment and supplies from tool and stock room including safety equipment required.
B. Slide jig under first spindle, drill 2 #40 holes.	B. Clear with department superintendent and foreman and arrange for coöperation necessary to control hazards that might be involved.
C. Slide jig under second spindle, drill 1 #48 hole, turn jig over, drill 2 #48 holes.	C. Set up screens, barriers, warning signs, etc., as needed to protect other workmen and prevent interference with job.
D. Turn jig over, unlock jig, remove finished piece and place in pan for finished work.	D. Go over layout of job in detail with assistant to insure full understanding of procedure and requirements of each part of job.
E. Brush chips from table and jig.	

In planning and setting up the production job, the following provisions should be made for safety:

1. Comfortable seat with proper height relation to table.

2. Chip hopper under or at back of table with grating section in table located for convenience in brushing chips to and through it; suitable brush to be used.

3. Spindles pulled down to working position by hand levers. Spindles and drills enclosed in telescoping cylindrical metal guards arranged to contain drills fully in their raised position and allowing only sufficient projection of drill, when drill is lowered, to permit proper placing of hole.

4. All moving power transmission parts fully enclosed.

5. Machine controls conveniently located and protected against accidental contact.

6. Provide lighting of adequate intensity free from shadows or glare.

The hazards usually present in the maintenance job are:

1. Interference with adjacent operations.

2. Contact with adjacent machines or equipment.

3. Falls in setting up and removing hoisting rig or in working on scaffold or machine frame, etc. (large machine), or from tripping over loose material or from slippery footing due to oil spillage.

4. Flying particles.

5. Hand tool hazards.

6. Those connected with the lifting, hoisting, moving, and placing of mill parts.

7. Explosions of babbitt due to failure to guard adequately against the presence of moisture.

8. Burns.

9. Electric shock or burns if electric powered tools or extension lights are used.

In planning for and laying out the babbitting job, each of the hazards listed will suggest detailed precautions which should be taken. Tools and equipment should be of a proper type and properly maintained; the protective equipment used should be in accordance with good practices; the mechanic and his assistant should be properly trained and instructed; and supervision should be adequate.

Such work as oiling machinery, washing windows, cleaning, painting, etc., involving exposure to a wide variety of hazards, is particularly apt not to be carefully planned or adequately supervised. The slogan, "Follow the oiler," often used by safety men, expresses this fact. It is not necessary and it may not be desirable to routinize such work in great degree. However, it is highly important from a safety standpoint to analyze these jobs adequately. Proper analysis will determine exactly what hazards are involved and will indicate correct control measures. With these things settled, the instruction and training required can be definitely set forth and provided for, together, of course, with all equipment, tools, and safety devices needed.

Safety benefits from analysis

The benefits of job analysis are multitudinous and affect production as well as safe operation. From a safety viewpoint, the advantages are:

1. Discovery of existent physical hazards.

2. Discovery and elimination or safeguarding of motions, positions, or actions that are hazardous.

3. Determination of the qualifications required for the safe performance of the work, such as physical fitness, motor skills, special abilities, and so on.

4. Determination of equipment and tools needed for safety.

5. Establishment of standards needed for safety, including instruction and training of workmen.

6. Proper organization of methods consistent with accepted efficient and safe practices.

7. Preplanning, preparedness, proper performance started by organizing the mind to execute properly the requirements of the operations.

Training new employees

In applying the principles of accident prevention, it is sometimes found better to train an inexperienced individual rather than break up an accumulation of bad habits or practices acquired over a period of time. Sometimes employees are inherently unsuited to the work they are expected to perform. If a job study has been made, it will indicate the characteristics to look for in the men such as strength, height, weight, skill, judgment of distance, speed of hand or eye, versatility, perseverance, and special physical or other qualities.

Added to this, the details of the operations will bring out specific hazards so that in the training process they may be made known and full instructions given on how to avoid injury.

Special cognizance must be given to the fact that a man transferred to a new job may be on a par with a new man. In other words, he may be oriented to the factory but not to his new work. This may mean correcting habits acquired in another department, which may be hazardous on the new job. The old story of having done this work this way for ten years and never having had an accident before is too often heard.

Maintenance and other nonrepetitive work

On repetitive work, if the initial planning is carefully considered, the work goes on smoothly and safely. On nonrepetitive work such as repair or maintenance, a general system of planning each job increases the efficiency, speed, and safety of the irregular activities.

For example, general safe practices in maintenance work should include:

1. Use of proper tools for specific tasks.
2. Planning for proper headroom while working.
3. Placing tools conveniently for reaching.
4. Keeping tools in A-1 condition.
5. Prevention of reaching over moving equipment by establishing a rule to stop all machinery before starting to work, and locking out or tagging the switch.
6. Avoiding off-balance positions while on ladders or above the floor level.
7. Correct positions for lifting.
8. Consideration of other workmen and hazards to others.
9. Reporting hazards noted.

Taking machines apart for repairs requires a regular routine for each kind of machine, which can be analyzed and planned just as a routine production job is. The difference lies in the additional number of operations involved because of the nonrepetitive nature. This calls for a larger number of breakdown sheets.

Chemical operation process and flow sheets

The application of job analysis is normally carried on in the chemical industry much more carefully because of the unpredictable problems that might arise.

The research organization develops the formula for the product, studies the prospects for customer use and demand, the effectiveness of the product, and the desirability of producing the chemical. During this process, notes are made of the various mixtures, reactions, and hazards.

The approved product is then turned over to the *pilot plant* or *semiworks,* where small batches are made under the direction of the chemical engineers, who work out plans for production. The engineers decide on the kind of equipment needed, methods of controlling temperatures, gases, pressures, and manufacturing processes. Costs are established, waste controlled, output noted, and equipment needed for standard production is decided upon as well as the methods needed to control the various hazards.

Before the work is transferred to a production area, process sheets and flow sheets are prepared for the operators. These sheets, which are based on a complete analysis of the job, specify the best, safest methods which must be followed and constitute definite instructions to the department employees.

The engineer assigned to the job goes with it to the production department to supervise the installation or selection of equipment needed for the new work, to assist the foreman and operators in starting the operation, and to make whatever changes and improvements are required.

After the engineer and production department men are satisfied that the operation and equipment are acceptable and safe, the job is turned over to the production department.

The process sheets, which are always available for the operator to consult, include safety precautions required, and for some of the more hazardous chemicals, symptoms of absorption and immediate first-aid treatment to be given. Here is a printed list of the information prepared and submitted to the operating department.

References
Chemistry
Instruction sheets—operating procedures
Specifications
Flow diagram
Equipment required

Material balance and yield expected
Safety precautions and hazards
Reactions to expect
Method of sampling
Heats and cooling required
Disposal of residue and waste
Use of by-products
Action in emergencies such as water failure, power failure, fire control, extreme exothermic reaction
Health hazards—protective equipment required
Running time
Costs
A "Flow Chart."

New man benefited by job study

Careful analysis presupposes:

1. Having a plan.
2. (a) Analyzing the job by breaking it down to the principal steps and listing them. (b) Picking out the key points or knacks to emphasize special action in connection with the principal steps.
3. Having the right tools, equipment, and materials specified.
4. Having the work place properly arranged.

After the above details are carefully worked out, we are ready for the new man. Put him at ease, find out what he knows, and get him interested in the new job.

The next step is the presentation of the operations by:

1. Telling, showing, illustrating, and questioning to make certain your points are understood.
2. Stressing the important parts or knacks with emphasis on the safe way.
3. Giving clear and complete instructions, taking up one point at a time and no more than the new man can master. Drive your points home before proceeding.
4. Check up on what he is learning by asking questions.

After this, the new man is ready to perform the job and to tell and show the instructor how it should be done. The instructor observes carefully, corrects errors, and repeats instructions if necessary. If the learner shows promise, he is put on his own, but he should be followed up and checked until he has proved that he is qualified to work efficiently and safely.

The following of this careful routine is of great value, because thus a person may be trained to do a job right and to utilize methods which experience has proved to be the best and safest.

We must not overlook the fact that when a new operation is introduced or a man is transferred to a different job, the same principles set forth above apply.

On-the-job safety analysis

In the preceding paragraphs, we have dealt with the foreman's part in carrying on production. The safety man does not, as a rule, participate in this analysis, but he might be asked to assist before the new job is started, and it is, therefore, necessary for him to do his part by observing the operations of the man on the job. On-the-job safety analysis is a measuring stick by which the effectiveness of an operation in the shop may be judged with reference to safety and efficiency. We are then observing the movements of the worker with relation to the performance of each cycle in the task.

The safety man in the shop will start by observing closely the movements of the worker and the conditions surrounding the job. If chemicals are involved, he may use specialized instruments for checking air contamination, gas pressure and odors, and be on the alert for leaks and unnecessary exposures to gases and toxic or irritating chemicals. As the movement pattern becomes clear, he can pick out those movements that might be hazardous and eliminate them or provide adequate safety devices.

As an example, take a crimping operation performed on a punch press. The part is placed into the nest of the die with the right hand. Using hand trips located on each side of the press, both hands are out of danger because they are required to trip the press.

The press performs the operation and the operator reaches under the die with the left hand to get the crimped part and places it in a tote box on the floor. Since the left hand is placed between the dies to get the finished piece, there is a hazard, because the hand could be amputated if, for some reason, the press repeated or was tripped. This potential hazard can be recognized only by observing the movements of the operator with reference to the equipment. Bear in mind that we also have another hazard because we load by hand.

Applying our "on-the-job analysis," we can decide to use a mechanical ejector or air ejector to get the piece out and drop or blow it into a chute, which will carry it to the tote box on the floor.

Then, reviewing the method of feeding to remove hazard number two, we can decide to substitute for the use of hands for placing the work on the die a metal chute outside of a *guarded* die so that the work will slide into the die nest by gravity or mechanical feed.

With this improved set-up, we accomplish:

1. A guard completely encloses the die.
2. Neither hand is required to go into the danger zone.
3. A foot trip is substituted for the two hand trips.
4. The operation is simpler, faster, hence less costly.

The change-over costs are relatively low and are soon offset by the saving in time, to say nothing of the potential losses due to accident. This same method could be used on flattening operations. Other simple methods could be applied to meet the various conditions to be found on punch presses and all other machines.

The question may be asked, "Why didn't this hazard show up when the foreman analyzed the job?"

Every safety man knows that millions of jobs are in our shops now that were never analyzed. If a systematic analytical process were established in a shop to do one or two jobs, a day in every department, the dividends would be enormous.

Management realizes that job breakdown or job analysis pays dividends not only in efficiency but also in preventing injury and keeping men on the job and machines and equipment in operation.

A good safety man appreciates the present situation and considers "on-the-job analysis" one of his most effective means of eliminating accidents.

Chapter Nine

Plant Inspection

As was previously pointed out, accidents do not just happen. They definitely are caused by unsafe conditions or unsafe practices in combination or singly. It is obvious, then, that if we are to prevent accidents (and the human injuries they yield), we must discover the causative factors and apply adequate corrective measures before the accidents occur. Well-planned inspection procedure thoroughly and systematically applied is an effective means of discovering hazardous conditions.

We all know that on the average a very considerable amount of time must be expended after each accident merely to restore satisfactory operation. A moderate amount of paid-for time is consumed in the maintenance of an adequate inspection service, but whatever it may cost in time and money to discover the hazards in advance of the accidents is much less than (usually only a small fraction of) the cost of discovering each hazard by the accidents it will inevitably bring if left uncorrected.

A simple and commonly recurrent type of accident is exemplified by empty drums insecurely piled and finally rolling down on a man working near by. The injury was sustained at a definite moment, immediately following the collapse of the pile, but the possibility of injury was created when the drums were piled, which might have been hours, days, weeks, or even months before they actually fell.

Adequate planning, instruction, training, and supervision would obviously prevent the creation of such hazards as that cited above, but even the best performance in these respects is powerfully aided by an effective safety-inspection service. Well-planned systematic inspection by competent personnel will discover almost all hazardous conditions promptly upon their development, and will often anticipate them. Such inspection can also be helpful in discovering unsafe practices and procedures, though, for the most part, these are found and corrected chiefly through supervision and training procedures, job analysis, and the coöperative efforts and suggestions of the workmen themselves.

Two types of safety inspection are commonly made use of:

1. The essentially one-call inspection to appraise safety conditions and safety performance in a plant. This is usually the function of an insurance engineer, a state or other governmental safety inspector, or a consultant who calls at the request, or at least with the approval, of the management.

2. A continuing activity set up and maintained by the management to discover conditions and, so far as practicable, procedures and practices that, if uncorrected, may or will cause accidents.

The one-call type of inspection

It is assumed that the purpose of the visit is to make an appraisal of the safety performance of the plant or undertaking in question and present the facts thus gained to the management for use in improving performance. As already pointed out, management (including all those in a supervisory capacity) must believe in safety, understand and apply safety principles, and insist on safe practice throughout the plant if good safety performance is to be reached and maintained. Since this is true, not only must the safety appraiser reach correct conclusions, but he must also present them effectively. That is, he must be a salesman as well as an engineer. He should not be a "high-pressure" salesman, more concerned with the effect of his salestalk than with its reliability, but a sales engineer who deals only with facts and sound conclusions drawn therefrom and who makes every effort to present his findings in such a way as to make them of maximum value as well as stimulative of adequate corrective action.

Insofar as is practicable, the inspector-appraiser should, just as a salesman does, get as much advance information pertinent to his mission as he can. Such matters as type of industry, size of establishment, size and standing of company, its position in the community, its organizational setup, its safety record, and the personality of its chief operating executive are all likely to be of value, though any of this advance information may need to be revised in the light of the findings during the visit. Since the time available for the appraisal is usually limited, every moment should be carefully spent. The inspector should plan his work as far as possible, but at the very least he should set down in orderly form the conditions, factors, and matters that should definitely be investigated.

Engineers recommend the use of check lists * of items that should be looked into. Each inspector should make up his own lists to suit his own

---

* *Safety Subjects,* Bull. 67 Bureau of Labor Standards, U. S. Department of Labor, Washington, D. C.

needs and methods, for such lists serve as a safeguard against memory lapses and oversight. The following is a foundation list:

1. Housekeeping.
2. Material handling methods.
3. Adequacy of aisle space and working space.
4. Guarding of transmission machinery.
5. Point-of-operation guards.
6. Maintenance.
7. Hand tools.
8. Ladders, portable steps, horses, etc.
9. Hand trucks, power trucks, wheelbarrows, buggies, etc.
10. Floors, platforms, stairs, railings.
11. Cranes, hoists, derricks, plant railways.
12. Lighting.
13. Electrical equipment, particularly extension cords.
14. Elevators.
15. Eye protection.
16. Other personal protective equipment.
17. Dusts, fumes, gases, vapors.
18. Pressure vessels—Insured? Inspected?
19. Any other explosion hazards as volatiles, gases, chemicals.
20. Other dangerous substances.
21. Oiling methods.
22. Inspection of chains, cables, slings and other lifting tackle.
23. Access to overhead equipment.
24. Exits.
25. Yards, roofs, and roadways.
26. Any other conditions suggested by the accident records.

Every one of these things should be considered in every inspection. All will not always apply, but none should be overlooked. The inspector of limited experience will be wise also if he develops pertinent detail under each basic item. For instance, under "Housekeeping" the subitems of chief importance would be:

1. Loose material and objects under foot.
2. Loose material and objects overhead.
3. Piling.
4. Projecting nails.
5. Disposal of scrap and waste.
6. Grease, water, or oil spillage.
7. Tool housekeeping.
8. Marked aisle lines.

9. Window cleanliness.
10. Painting.
11. General cleanliness.
12. Orderliness.
13. Fire hazards.

The initial interview. Since active executive interest in safety is vital to good safety performance, the inspector must appraise this somewhat intangible factor carefully. If interest is lacking in an important degree, his chief duty is to stimulate it, for, without it, even the most accurate of appraisals and soundest of recommendations will usually prove to be of little value. But a sound appraisal where findings are convincingly presented will often stimulate executive interest sufficiently to bring the needed executive action. Therefore, the first person to see, if at all possible, is the chief operating executive. It is even better to see with him the safety director or other person having primary responsibility for safety in the establishment as a whole.

Much will depend on the impression made by this first interview. A sale is seldom made during it, but if the executive does not see something of probable value in the presentation, the sale is probably lost. An amusing example will emphasize this point. A safety director whose talents ran more to high-pressure salesmanship than to safety engineering volunteered his services in calling on establishments to "carry the gospel of safety" to them. On his list was an establishment that (though he didn't know it) was a subsidiary of a firm well known for its excellent safety performance. He asked for and was granted an interview with the manager and presented a carefully worked out salestalk pointing out the seriousness of accidents and the fact that they are mostly preventable by the proper application of proved technique, described briefly the arrangement whereby his firm was donating a part of his services in the cause of safety, and ended up with a definite promise that a frequency rate of ten or better could be had without undue effort. The manager answered with the crushing comment that inasmuch as his frequency rate was already below five, he would be glad to act as consultant to the safety director.

Obviously, this safety director had nothing to offer this manager. Had he, before calling, or even at the start of his interview, found out what the safety status of the firm in question was, he could probably have secured its valuable coöperation in the safety program he was attempting to further.

The initial interview should cover at least the following:

1. Explaining the purpose of the visit. (If calling at the request of the executive in question, get a clear statement as to what is wanted.)

2. Find out what the accident record is like. (If the executive does not have it in terms of injury rates, costs, or causes, a brief statement of the advantages of doing so should be made, and if possible, the accident file should be secured and the reports reviewed with him. The frequency rate should be calculated and a comparison made with good practice. Key accidents should be selected for further investigation.)

3. Settle upon a definite plan for the inspection, covering particularly:

    a. Who is to accompany the inspector.

    b. Personnel to be contacted.

    c. Route to be taken.

    d. Type of inspection, as, general or detailed, or the inspection of specific equipment or processes or operations or combinations of such factors.

    e. Probable time required (or allotted).

4. Arrange for a conference to discuss findings. If possible, decision should be secured as to who should be included, because this may influence the presentation considerably. Also, conditions found might make desirable a conference with the executive alone in advance of one including staff members.

Working out the above points and others that might be pertinent should give the inspector at least a fair understanding of the executive's interest in and grasp of accident prevention. Much of the discussion can, without seeming to, be aimed at his education, provided he needs it. This is particularly true of the analysis of the accident record. If the executive's interest is aroused, he will wish to accompany the inspector on at least a part of the tour of inspection. Unwillingness to do so is evidence that the conference has not been very effective and greatly increases the importance of a convincing presentation of the inspection findings.

The inspection trip. If the establishment is of considerable size, a quick trip through it is usually advisable in advance of a detailed inspection. This is particularly true if the executive goes along, in which case readily noticeable substandard conditions and telltale indications of such factors as inadequate maintenance, supervision, inspection, training, and the like may be pointed out. Also, the accidents selected for investigation may be looked into. Good conditions should receive favorable comment, but such commendation should not be overdone.

This "walk-around" will aid decision as to the order of the inspection. In well-planned, orderly plants, particularly those devoted to straight-line production, it is best to follow this process. In the multi-storied building, it is usually best to start with the roof and work downward.

The inspector should always remember that plant executives do not wish to be instructed on how to operate their business, but, nevertheless, that the alert executive is constantly seeking information and ideas that may be helpful to him. He can ill afford, however, to waste time on unsound ideas or inapplicable theory. He is keenly on watch for indications by which he may judge the soundness of the advice he is given, and of course the competency of the giver. Not only, therefore, should the inspector always be tactful, but his attitude should be that of presenting his ideas and pertinent information in such form that the recipient may add them to his own intimate knowledge of his own business and thereby improve his performance.

For instance, it is usually much better to ask, "Don't you think a guard would be advisable for this machine?" than merely to announce, "This machine should be guarded." If the executive answers "No" to the first question and the inspector is unable to present convincing evidence that it should be guarded, the situation is no worse than before because belief in the need for guarding is essential both to satisfactory guarding and to faithful use of the safeguards themselves.

Recommendations must be practical. A suggestion that looks "silly" to the man "on the firing line" is worse than none, but the idea involved may be accepted and prove helpful if presented in a form that indicates a different method of approach or a different viewpoint. One executive emphasized this point by remarking that a consultant whose services he valued "holds a looking glass up to me so that I can see myself go by."

It is a mistake to rush an inspection. If time does not permit a complete job, it is better to do part of it thoroughly than to cover the whole plant sketchily. The guide should not be permitted to hurry the inspection. If the initial interview has been effective, the guide will be anxious to show the inspector everything and get his ideas, an attitude that will aid the inspector greatly.

Since the foremen are the key men in safety, it is important to meet each foreman when starting the inspection in his department. The foreman should receive as careful consideration as the chief executive and will, in general, react similarly, the main differences being that the foreman deals chiefly with daily detail and the individual supervision and training of his men. He wants facts and practical usable ideas, not theory and not guesses. Each accident selected for investigation should be discussed in adequate detail with the foreman, particularly to discover the corrective measures applied to prevent a recurrence. The care with which a foreman investigates the accidents in his department is of fundamental importance, but the application of corrective measures is of even more importance.

The inspector should make descriptive notes of each department, giving the kind of work done or nature of the process, the department and building number or name, floor number, name of the foreman, and any other information necessary for accurate description and reference. All recommendations and comments on each department should be written down before leaving the department and each should be definite in wording and accurate in description. For example, a machine should be correctly designated by name and number (or whatever other designation is used in the department).

In summary, a successful inspection tour presupposes at least that:

1. The inspector has made a satisfactory impression on the executive in charge.

2. The purpose of the inspection is clearly understood by both the executive and the inspector.

3. The executive is favorably inclined to the inspection.

4. The inspector is competent to cover the ground in question.

5. He has secured, at least in reasonable measure, certain essential information, particularly the kind of manufacture or nature of the operation, the company policy toward safety, the attitude of the chief executive, the accident record, the nature of the hazards involved, and the scope of the safety program.

6. There is as definite a plan of inspection as conditions permit.

The conference on the findings. The presentation of the conclusions reached from the inspection is usually as important as the conclusions themselves, for unless effective corrective action results, the time and effort has been wasted. Therefore, when the inspection is completed, the inspector should take sufficient time to run over his notes carefully and organize his presentation. He must decide what to include, what to generalize on, what to emphasize, what illustrative detail to use, and what recommendations to make, if any. Usually, it is a mistake to present a program based solely on his findings, because some, at least, of his conclusions may have to be modified in the light of information and viewpoints brought out in the conference. He should, however, have a tentative program for presentation if found desirable, but it is usually better to have the corrective program worked out in the conference from the discussion that will develop around his findings. In the first place, a jointly-arrived-at program is likely to be more practically workable than even the most experienced inspector-consultant could develop himself.

In the second place, those present at the conference will presumably have to carry out whatever program is undertaken. It is human nature to exert oneself more to carry out a project one has had a part in developing than something merely "handed down" with the order to "carry on."

The inspection report. The conclusions reached in the conference should be summarized at its close so that everyone present will know what has been agreed upon. Also, each one should know just what is expected of him. It is usually best to have a stenographer present to record the decisions reached and prepare a copy for each participant. In most cases, however, the chief executive will prefer to have the inspector-consultant prepare a report based upon his findings, as modified by the conference and the decisions reached by the executive, and transmit the desired number of copies to the executive. This is the course normally followed when professional consultants are used. It has the great advantage of allowing the consultant to incorporate whatever detailed information and recommendations he believes will be useful. In a report to be studied at leisure, much more can be included than is possible in even the most extended conference.

The preparation of such a report requires much skill and careful work. Every statement should be clear and definite. The report should be primarily factual. Opinions, when given, should include, as far as practicable, the basis on which they rest, so that their soundness can be intelligently evaluated. Every report of any length should contain a summary, so that from it the reader can readily grasp the substance of the whole report. A report that is difficult to weigh rarely receives much attention. Finally, the needs and viewpoints of those for whose use it is intended should be a governing consideration throughout.

Inspection as a continuing plant activity

Inspection as a check on quality of product is a production essential. Inspection to discover conditions that, if uncorrected, may lead to accidents and injuries is similarly essential to first-rate safety performance. Production inspection and testing procedure have been extensively written about and largely standardized; safety inspection has not, except in certain important but specialized fields, such as steam boilers and passenger elevators.

The student wishing detailed information covering specific equipment should consult pertinent technical literature, and, in particular, that dealing with the insurance of such equipment, for of necessity the insurance underwriters have taken a major part in the development of standards and standard procedures designed to control the hazards of the equipment they insure.

Much of the preceding discussion of the one-call type of inspection is applicable to the continued inspection work of an establishment. In fact, the safety engineer or other staff member may frequently be called on or may find it advisable to make such an inspection of his establishment or of another plant of his firm. In such case, he will have the obvious advantage over the outsider that his more intimate knowledge of his own firm and its operations gives, but he will, to some extent at least, lack the outsider's fresh, unbiased viewpoint and varied experience. Also, the outsider usually has considerable prestige. This latter factor accounts for the experience plant engineers commonly have of being unable to secure management action to correct some condition that is promptly corrected upon the recom-

mendation of an outsider. It is, therefore, often advisable for the plant
engineer to make sure that the visiting consultant or inspector does not fail
to discover such conditions.

A typical form of reporting on one-call inspection or reinspection by
the plant safety engineer follows:

INSPECTION: Made by John Jones in company with Henry Smith on
   January 15, 1963.
   Purpose: General observation.
   Report forwarded to: John White, Manager and Henry Brown, Safety
   Engineer.
General Conditions:
   Housekeeping: Fair. Some sections require attention.
   Layout of plant: Satisfactory.
   Equipment: Generally in good condition.
   Hand tools: Fair. Require periodic checking. Some now need re-
   placing.
   Lighting: Good, except as otherwise noted below.
   Ventilation: Good except in paint-spraying area, building No. 1, 4th
   floor.
   Floors: Good.
   Electrical equipment: Recommend special attention be given motors in
   milling machine section. Otherwise generally fair.
   Machine guards: Design satisfactory. Recommend additional guards
   as shown below.
   Attitude of employees toward safety: Excellent so far as could be
   ascertained on a single visit such as this.
Building No. 10—Recommendations:
   Building No. 10, 4th floor, Bay #401: Recommend change of layout
   of drill press area, in order to avoid crowding.
   Bay #406: Flywheel on punch press. It is about four feet above the
   floor. It should be enclosed in a metal guard.
   Bay #410: Milling machine control switches are at various locations
   on the machines. It is recommended that the locations be standardized
   at a point conveniently within the operator's reach. In many cases at
   present it is necessary for him to reach to the back of the machine to
   start or stop it.
   Bay #413: Tool grinders in this area require attention. Tool rests in
   some instances were ½" from the wheel, the glass shields were dirty
   and the men would, therefore, not use them. This could be improved
   by placing a light under the shield so that the men could see their
   work better. Hanging goggles on a machine for general use by all men
   is definitely advised against. Each man who should wear goggles

should be provided with a personal pair carefully fitted to his needs. A test of grinder No. 607 showed that it was operating at 4000 r.p.m. It was equipped with a ten-inch wheel for which the maximum safe speed is 2500 r.p.m. Mr. Smith asked the foreman to correct this condition without delay.

Usually when plant safety inspection is inaugurated in a given establishment, its purpose is chiefly that of bringing previously unnoted or unevaluated hazards to light. However, as these are corrected, its second and major function, that of discovering promptly hazards that develop from day-by-day operations, becomes relatively more important.

The fundamentals necessary to an adequate inspection service may be set down as:

1. Definite schedule as to what to inspect and how frequently.
2. Competent inspection personnel.
3. Adequate systematic procedure.
4. Effective supervision.

The inspection schedule.   Literally everything in the plant should be inspected at some time (or times) by someone. The problem, therefore, becomes one of deciding what to include in the systematic safety inspection. The inspection necessary in the interests of production will cover much of the safety field. The safety inspection is additional and, in theory at least, should be added only where the inspection incidental to production is not adequate for safety. Often the first step should be to strengthen and broaden the scope of the production inspection. With that step functioning as fully in the interest of safety as is practicable, whatever else is needed may readily be added.

For example, the maintenance of an electric overhead traveling crane is essential to production so that the inspection service needed to keep it operating properly is a production essential. However, the safety engineer (or other person having major responsibility for safety) should scrutinize the inspection procedure to make sure that the safety of those who operate the crane or work with it is being, and will continue to be, adequately covered. Examples of the type of equipment that the production inspection setup will, if left to itself, ordinarily deal with inadequately or overlook entirely would be personal protective equipment, machine guards, housekeeping, and hand tool maintenance.

In the light of the above, the safety man will survey the entire establishment in detail, find out just what is covered by inspection and to what extent, and reach (or secure from the proper authority) a decision as to the extent to which the existing inspection procedure should be extended in the interest of safety. With this done, it is a comparatively simple matter to draw up a schedule for the additional inspection services needed. The schedule should show the dates on which inspections are to be made. The safety director receives a copy of each inspection report and checks each off on this inspection calendar as it is received. The schedule thus serves as a check on the up-to-dateness of the inspection work.

The dates selected for the inspection and the frequency of inspection are contingent upon the type and use of the equipment. For example, equipment used 24 hours per day will obviously require more frequent inspection than if it were used only 8 hours daily. Sometimes this fact is overlooked when a shift is added. Also, equipment whose faultless functioning must be relied on for safety requires the more frequent and painstaking inspection. Examples are: Elevator cables, the pull-out type of punch press guard, or respiratory protective equipment for use in a possibly lethal atmosphere. It is not practicable to make up a standard calendar for general use because industrial plants and the operations in them vary too greatly to permit standardization to that extent.

The inspection personnel.   It should be obvious to all that any service on whose continuously effective functioning worker safety depends should be continuously maintained at a high level of effectiveness. Only personnel temperamentally suited to this type of work should be selected. They should be carefully instructed, trained, and supervised. Their interest in and realization of the importance of their work should be kept at a high level. The mere faithful following of prescribed procedure is not enough. Daniel Willard of the Baltimore and Ohio Railroad reported the following illustrative example:

A train he was on stopped at a division point. He got off to look things over. He noticed the thoroughgoing way in which a workman walked along beside each car and hit each wheel a lusty blow with a hammer. He stopped the man and complimented him, and by way of making conversation asked him why he did it. The answer that came back was, "Dom'd if I know, sor."

Specialists are needed for much specialized equipment. Steam generators, elevators, and complicated electrical equipment fall in this class. Insurance underwriters maintain inspection services for their assured, which in general can be depended upon to have a good degree of competence. Also, there are inspection services that may be had on a fee basis. Many manufacturers of specialized equipment furnish such services. Finally, the state inspection services should not be overlooked.

It will be necessary to make some close decisions as to just when to use the specialist and when to undertake to train selected personnel for the inspection. No general rule can be laid down. The internal inspection of a steam boiler, for instance, is obviously a job for the specialist, but a good mechanic can, with the help of the manufacturer's instructions, readily master the inspection and maintenance procedures necessary for electric traveling cranes. The cables used on the crane are, however, highly specialized equipment, and the manufacturer's full advice and instructions as to their safe use and maintenance should be meticulously followed.

Every foreman must of necessity maintain a more or less continuous inspection of the equipment and activities under his charge. He should develop a systematic procedure and follow it consistently. The coöperation between the foremen and the safety-inspection setup should obviously be close, for if it is not, there is likely to be friction, or duplication of effort, or inadequate inspection, or any combination of these three faults. An important part of a foreman's duty is to see that men under his charge operating hazardous equipment not only know what inspection they should include as a part of their operating practice, but also that they accurately and faithfully perform it. This is of particular importance with new men.

Some plants report very satisfactory results from appointing a committee of three to five employees from each department to make an inspection of the department. A new committee or a new member is appointed each month, thus, in time, giving every employee in the department a part in the inspection work. Appointments are made by the foreman, who explains fully what is expected of the committee and emphasizes the need of frankness. Reports are made in writing to the foreman. Prompt and definite action on all recommendations is necessary, or the men soon lose interest. Each recommendation should be carried out with reasonable promptness, or satisfactory reasons why it is not should be given.

Inspection by safety-committee members singly or as committees is chiefly valuable in bringing in additional viewpoints, in bringing additional experience and knowledge to bear, and in checking the inspection work done by others. Safety-committees are also particularly valuable in checking up on such operational matters as housekeeping, the handling of materials, operating methods and work practices, and the use of safety equipment and personal protective equipment.

There is a definite need for adequately trained inspectors possessing the requisite basic knowledge. This is particularly true of unsafe practices and methods of operation. It is a simple matter to teach men how to inspect for the ordinary physical defects of plant and equipment, but detecting unsafe practices requires a good knowledge of the operation involved and particularly of the correct way of performing it. For example, take the drill press, a comparatively simple machine very widely used. The inspector should be so trained and experienced that he can note its hazards quickly, covering at least the following points:

1. Is the table stop bar in place and so used that the work cannot spin if it catches in the drill?

2. Is the hair of the operator close to the unguarded spindle so that it may catch? (Unless the fact is recognized that static electricity attracts the hair, a female worker, even with net hair protection, may be partially scalped.)

3. Is the drill properly sharpened for the job on which it is used? (A drill sharpened for steel should not be used on copper or brass, and vice versa.)

4. On a reaming operation, is the work properly fastened to the table so that it will not ride up on the drill and strike the operator?

5. Are proper jigs and fixtures used to hold the work?

6. Is the operator holding the small piece in his hand and pushing up against the drill instead of placing the piece on the table and pulling the spindle down onto the work?

7. Are long chips forming which should be broken up by a chip breaker before they catch the hand?

8. Pieces piled on the table may be shaken off by the vibration of the machine and drop on the feet of the operator.

9. Does the operator reach behind the drill in order to get his coolant or wrench?

10. Is the operator wearing rings, a tie, a loose shirt, hair unguarded, bandages on fingers, gloves, long sleeves, or long sleeves on sweater rolled up and bunched above the elbow?

11. Is the stop and start button conveniently located, so that the machine can be stopped in an emergency without loss of time?

12. Is the operator in a comfortable position with the proper stool, if one can be used?

13. Is the table too high or too low for the operator?

14. Are his surroundings congested so that he has difficulty in getting the material to the drill and away from the drill?

15. Does he use his hands instead of a brush to remove the chips from the table?

16. Is the condition around the drill slippery, due to splashing of oil and other coolants?

17. Does he wear goggles? If not, should he?

18. Is illumination satisfactory?

The following points would be pertinent to the operation of the ordinary milling machine:

1. Is the pressure on the nut on the arbor satisfactory, so that when the arbor is under strain it will not break off and fly?

2. Is the work secure on the table?

3. What is the condition of the mallet used for tightening the vise? Is the rawhide chipping off so that a piece of it might strike the eye or so that it might glance off the work?

4. If a lead mallet is used, is it in good condition?

5. Are the springs still in the handles used for adjusting the table, or will they be spun around because of the possibility of engaging, due to the absence of the spring?

6. Can a guard be placed over the cutter, and is it properly placed for the operation being performed?

7. Does the operator allow the table to move back far enough from the cutter so that the new piece may be inserted without his being cut?

8. Is he wearing goggles? If not, should he be?

9. If chips are flying, has he placed a guard of some kind to confine them within his own area?

10. Is his platform slippery?

11. Does he apply the wrench on the arbor and start the machine to run the nut up?

12. Does he remove chips by hand or with air instead of with a brush?

13. Does he work too close to the revolving cutter?

14. Is the cutting oil rancid?

15. Are his small tools in good condition?

16. Is he taking too big a cut so that the machine groans?

17. Is his feed too fast for the kind of work being done?

Systematic procedure. Although this starts with the schedule, that is not sufficient. The inspection procedure should be worked out in sufficient detail to make sure that everything of any importance is properly covered. Lack of order in the procedure inevitably results in overlooking some things. Lack of thoroughness leaves hidden defects. Again, no set schedule of details can be given. The principle that should always be applied, however, is to list carefully all the safety defects that a given piece of equipment might develop and work out a practical inspection procedure to check for all of these.

For illustrative purposes, a form used by one well-known firm is shown on the following page. Note that in the "Weekly Inspection Report of Trucks" the instruction and training of the inspector would have to include detailed standards as to just what is satisfactory, for which job-safety analysis is practically a necessity. Note also that this foreman's report is very general and goes to the foreman's superior.

Effective supervision. There is no exception to the general rule that if any activity is to be kept up to a high level of performance, it must be properly supervised. A considerable amount of detail must be established and there must be sufficient routinization to insure reasonably thorough performance. However, routinization tends to beget unimaginative routine

---

WEEKLY INSPECTION REPORT OF TRUCKS

1. TRUCKS:

Condition of:

Steering Mechanism	Brakes ....
Directional Lights	Trailer Brake Mechanism ....
Head and Tail Lights	Horn ....
Marker Lights	Flashlight ....
Rear View Mirror	First-aid Kits ....
Flags available for projecting material (number)	
Fire Extinguishers	Blanket Roll & Hot Pads ....
Towing Cable (or Bar)	Truck Tools ....
Winch and Cable	Jack ....
Extra Head and Tail Light	Chains ....
Globes	Wind Shield Wiper & Defrosters
Preliminary Accident Report	....
Spare Tire	Truck Flares ....
Is all unnecessary material re-	Fuses & Containers ....
moved?	Fuse Kit ....
Remarks	
Miscellaneous	

---

performance that "merely goes through the motions." Supervision, therefore, must be continually alert to detect the signs of this and other lapses in the inspection work.

Chemical plant hazards and inspection

The inspection of a chemical manufacturing plant represents additional difficulties because of the unseen elements that are likely to be present such as corrosion, internal pressures, chemical reactions in material in storage or in process, closed systems for transferring liquids and gases, high temperatures, automatic devices for recording and controlling operations, etc. Examples of what to look into include:

Acid, alkali, and other leaks from piping and equipment.

Presence of toxic gases, fumes, vapors, and dusts.

Hazard of splashes, breakouts, spillages in maintaining and servicing equipment.

Fire and explosion hazards.

Need of mechanical ventilation.

Use of protective personal equipment such as: goggles, gloves, respirators, and rubber clothing.

Proper storage of chemicals: out of sun, cool enough area, proper containers, diked tanks, etc.

Methods of transferring liquids from one container to another: pouring, pumping, use of open and closed systems, etc.

Special precautions taken to store extremely flammable or rapidly oxidizing or corrosive chemicals.

Proper grounding of equipment.

Methods of emptying and cleaning tanks, tank trucks, and railroad cars. Generally, filling and emptying are safest when done through the top of the cars in order to minimize loss of liquid and consequent possibility of injury from defective fittings.

The use of compressed air to transfer, mix and agitate chemicals.

The condition of pumps, pipe lines, tanks, valves, relief valves.

The methods of transporting liquid chemicals and the kinds of containers used.

The condition and location of drains and traps.

Piling and racking of drums and carboys.

Use of railroad flags, derailers and car stops for cars containing dangerous chemicals such as chlorine, ammonia, ethylene oxide, carbon disulphide.

Storage and handling methods of combustible solids, and dust control.

Need and provisions for controlling static by ionizing devices or by carrying to ground the static from belts, pulleys, machines, shafting, and in work with highly sensitive substances.

The installation of automatic fire fighting and control equipment. Many accidents result from fires.

Methods used in filling drums with powders or liquids.

Materials handling is important since considerable hand labor is involved in moving and emptying drums and bags of materials.

The need of compulsory bathing at the end of the day and also of keeping wearing apparel clean.

Provision for safety showers and immediate first-aid treatment in the departments.

Since there are a great many widely used chemicals that present hazards of injury and fire, the reader is referred to the tables of hazardous chemicals found in chemical handbooks for further information. As previously pointed out, accidents (and of course, injuries) can be held to the minimum in any establishment only if their prevention is made an intimate and essential part of all operations. Thus the operating organization is, in fact, the safety organization. To whatever extent each man in the plant is responsible for plant operations, to that extent he is also responsible for the safety of such operations.

Safety Inspection Check List for a Chemical Plant

Pressure Vents on Kettles:
  Indoors
  Outdoors
  Sufficient capacity
Relief Valves:
  Condition
  Sufficient capacity
Control Valves:
  Blocked
  Missing
Condensation:
  Drained properly
Heating Coils:
  Leaking
  Worn
Spargers:
  Condition
Charging Lines:
  Valves
  Leaks
  Construction
  Connections
Charging Chutes:
  Condition
Elevators:
  Safety stops
  Gates
  Doors
  Cabs
  General conditions
Revolvators, Hoist, Crane:
  Safety stops
  Cables
  Chains
  Hooks
Pressure, Vacuum Stills—Vessels:
  Valves
  Gages
  Releases
  Explosion possibilities
  General condition

Condensers:
  Vents
  Blockage, Gages
Receivers:
  Overflow control
  Valves
  Relief valves
  Vents
  Flash arrestors
  Gages
  Pressure control
Vaporizers:
  Heating equipment
  Valves
  Relief valves
  Flash arrestors
  Pressure control
  Vents, Gages
Reactors:
  Heating equipment
  Valves
  Relief valves
  Vents, Gages
  Flash arrestors
  Pressure control
Absorbers:
  Capacity
  Suitability
  Leaks
  Gages
  Vents
  Valves
  Condition
Kettles:
  Pressure control
  Gages
  Heating equipment
  Batch blankets
  CO_2, etc.
  Vents
  Relief valves

Safety Inspection Check List for a Chemical Plant

Kettles (continued):
  Inert gas
  Valves
  Flash arrestors
  Explosion possibilities
Lagging:
  Missing
  Insufficient
  Poor condition
Meters:
  Condition
  Suitability
Recorders:
  Condition
  Suitability
Heat Control Devices:
  Condition
  Suitability
  Signal system
Pressure Control Devices:
  Condition
  Suitability
  Signal system
Float Activated:
  Condition of Valves, Gages
  Suitability
  Signal system
Gages:
  Danger of breakage
  Condition
  Suitability
  Approved type
  Guarded
Switches & Wiring Sytem:
  Location
  Condition
  Suitability
  Explosion-vapor proof
Tanks (blend, storage, holding, flash):
  Location

Connections
Manholes
Gages
Valves
Vents
Heating
Flash arrestors
Tanks:
  Inside of building that should be outside because of hazards.
Flashback arrestors:
  Blocked
  Missing
  Unsuitable type
Exhaust equipment:
  Ventilation of building area
  Sufficient capacity
  Clogged ducts
  Stacks
  Condition
  Leaks
  In repair
  Absorbers
Exhausts outside:
  Atmosphere contamination
  Sufficient capacity
  Leaks
  Condition in repair
  Absorbers or collectors
Drains:
  Sufficient capacity
  Explosion-fire possibilities
  Proper location
  Traps
  Covered
Weigh Tanks and Boxes:
  Location
  Overflow control
  Flashback arrestors
  Return lines
  Valves

Safety Inspection Check List for a Chemical Plant

Weigh Tanks and Boxes (continued):
Vents to outside
Signals
Methods of Transferring Flammable Liquids (Open or Closed Systems):
Hazardous use of buckets—open carriers
Pumps
Gravity feeds
Toxic conditions
Self-closing valves
Changes recommended
Storage:
Poor location
Hazardous location
Quantity too great
Handling problems
Piling methods
Pumps:
Leaks
Condition
Suitability
Automatic shutoff
Location
Recirculating in case of blockage
Manholes:
Kept covered
Tight
Possibility of fire or explosion:
Gas Accumulation, Dust Condition:
Automatic recorders
Leaks
Fire-explosion hazard
Health hazards
Injurious to equipment
Grounds:
Missing
Leaks:
General

Connections:
Suitable
Weather Damage:
Dampness—Moisture
Heat—Possible chemical reaction
Escape Facilities for Emergencies:
Fire
Explosion
Gas
Fumes
Vapors
Bodily contact
Gas Holders:
Location
Automatic control
Fire and explosion possibilities
Connections
Valves
Regulators
Gages
Leaks
Autoclaves:
Location
Pressure control
Vents
Valves
Bearings
Compressors:
Pressure control
Temperature control
Valves
Guards
General:
Containers, Drums, Carboys:
Handling, storage, conditions
Guards for belts and gears
Splash pans
General condition of floors
Housekeeping
Safety showers—masks
Other conditions not listed above.

Corrective action. It should not be necessary to point out that unless prompt and reasonably thorough corrective action follow the inspection findings, the effort, time, and cost expended on inspection is wasted. Yet this situation is all too common and, where it exists, it points directly at the management. It is the almost inevitable result of executive failure.

The adequately safety-minded executive not only knows that effective inspection is necessary, but he also knows that orderly provision must be made for whatever corrective action the inspection shows the need of. Further, he knows that this activity, as every other function under his charge, must continue to receive its needed share of his supervision if it is to be kept up to the mark.

The procedure the safety-minded executive will set up will depend upon his managerial methods. It is his obvious responsibility, after receiving recommendations for corrective action, to discuss them with the staff members involved and make specific assignment for the action decided upon. The safety man should see that the various inspection reports are so presented or summarized, or both, as to conserve the executive's time and facilitate his action. Each report should be kept active until every item on it has received consideration and proper disposal. Some safety men have an individual form filled in for each hazard found. It is placed in a tickler file and kept "live" until the work has been completed. A sample follows:

SAFETY HAZARD TO BE CORRECTED

DEPARTMENT:

LOCATION: Building No. 10, Bay #401.

DATE: January 15, 1963.

MACHINE: Drill Press No. 600.

HAZARD: Stop and start electrical contact buttons, located in back of machine.

CORRECTION NECESSARY: Transfer these contacts from rear of machine to location at ridge of table directly in front of operator.
(*Note:* For location, see assembly of machine next to drill press in question.)

WORK TO BE DONE BY: Order issued on Maintenance Department.

WORK COMPLETED: Satisfactorily—January 21, 1963.

Equipment to be used by an inspector. The manner in which the inspector should be dressed and the equipment he may need is governed entirely by the kind of inspection he makes and the conditions surrounding his work. Each inspector should be properly equipped for the job he has to do, and he must remember that he establishes a standard that others follow. His equipment may include:

1. Safe, snug-fitting clothing (avoid loose sleeves, flowing ties, and rings).

2. Safety shoes.

3. Proper goggles.

4. Hard hat.

5. Respiratory protective equipment (contingent upon the nature of the work and hazards involved).

6. Insulated flashlight.

7. Danger tags to attach to equipment that should not be used.

8. Padlock for locking out switches when inspecting certain machines or cranes.

9. Measuring tape.

10. Revolution counter for checking speeds of grinding wheels, pulleys, shafting, fly wheels, and saws.

11. Stop watch.

12. Camera.

13. Notebook.

14. Portable instruments for testing the atmosphere for toxic, inflammable, or explosive substances.

15. Light meter.

16. Velometer for testing air movement.

17. Pressure gauges.

Chapter Ten

Accident Investigation

Every accident constitutes proof that adequate preventive action was not taken. The safety-minded management plans all its plant and operations to be as safe as possible, trains its workers in safe practices and seeks their sincere cooperation in preventing accidents, supervises them carefully, makes job-safety analyses to determine and establish safe job routines, and maintains plant inspection to discover otherwise undetected hazards. It is obvious, then, that the hazards that slip past all these preventive measures and cause accidents should be discoverable by accident investigation and so they are. But certain fundamentals must be met adequately if maximum value is to be obtained from the time and expense involved. This discussion has been prepared to present these essentials with certain detail of general applicability, but it is not intended to be all inclusive.

The purpose of accident investigation is to discover the causative factors, the hazardous conditions and practices that brought the accident about, *so that the proper action may be taken to prevent a recurrence.* The need is for full information as to causes—all the correctible causes that led to the accident, not just the major cause. This point brings out the importance of eliminating the factor of fixing blame. If part of the purpose is to fix blame, or if workers think it is, vital information will often be withheld or the facts will be distorted. The use of even the milder term "fixing responsibility" is questionable, unless it is made very clear that the purpose is to find out whose performance should have been better and in what way, in order that he may be helped to improve, and not again contribute to an accident.

At times the temptation to punish particularly thoughtless or inconsiderate action is difficult to resist. Experience, however, seems clearly to be on the side of limiting disciplinary action of any kind to instances of action so objectionable that the fellow workmen themselves favor punishment. Many firms leave decision on such cases with the workmen.

Presumably the investigation of accidents became an established procedure to combat damage claims under common law or under employer liability acts. The fixing of blame or responsibility was of major importance. Under workmen's compensation acts, the data needed are those which determine whether or not the injury comes under the act, and if so, what compensation the injured person is entitled to. But the fixing of blame need not and should not enter.

The information gained from accident investigation should be used wherever it may apply throughout the establishment. The corrective action following each investigation is not complete until the question, "Where else might this apply?" is asked and fully answered.

Many causes of accidents

There are many causes of accidents, one or more contributing to every case. The investigator should understand how to pick out these causes and decide where to place responsibility for correction. His purpose should be to strive for a complete picture of the case, "starting from scratch" and working through the details. One authority stated, "There is nothing so eloquent as a fact."

Every operation is subject to three responsibilities:

1. The worker.
2. The foreman.
3. The management.

Since the worker has but one responsibility, the other two require investigation also when endeavoring to learn the underlying causes of an accident.

A complete accident investigation report made by men who report their findings honestly, impartially, and frankly will not contain the term "carelessness" because the term has little meaning. Unless the reason *why* adequate care was not taken is brought out, the *how* of getting it can only be guessed at. The *why* is likely to lead deeply into such management functions as employee selection, training, instruction, and supervision. All possibly pertinent factors should be considered.

The solution of any problem demands fact finding.

Learning where, why, when, how, and to whom accidents are happening means a great deal in learning how to avoid them.

Naturally, a knowledge of the principal causes revealed makes possible well-directed preventive effort.

Who should investigate—give authority?

Among the persons who make an investigation, we should include the man responsible for safety and the foreman or other leader. These men should have authority to go as far as may be necessary to get to the root of the trouble. They must be careful to state the facts exactly as they found them.

Conduct of investigation

The foreman should participate in the investigation of accidents to his men. He should, to whatever extent circumstances seem to him to warrant, carry his own investigation further. He, better than any other person, can watch the minor injuries and can go much further in investigating them than it is practical for the safety man or a committee to do.

Some firms develop trained investigators, specialists in safety investigation. The safety director should be highly competent in this respect, but he may find another, such as an inspector, or safety committee member, or a foreman, whose aptitude and interest give him superior ability. When such a person is found, his abilities should be made use of to the maximum.

A committee of the supervisory staff is commonly used to investigate the more serious cases. For this purpose, it works well if executive interest in safety is keen, but if done merely at the request of the safety man, it is not likely to be effective. Such men dislike dropping whatever they may be doing to undertake something else promptly and thoroughly, unless the executive makes it very clear that he wants "just that."

Committees of workmen are particularly valuable in bringing to light hazardous conditions and practices not readily discoverable by persons not actually doing the work. In every shop, there are older experienced "heads" who know the setup and the work practices so well that they can often "put the pieces together" much more surely than even the most skilled investigator not similarly experienced in the specific operation involved.

How best to get the necessary information in each case cannot be stated in a definite manner, because of the great variety of causative factors, tangible and intangible, which develop as one probes deeper and deeper for the truth.

The first requisite is to start with an open mind. "Someone was injured. What part of him is involved; what was he doing at the time; where was he; who was with him; what did he say happened; what do the findings of the doctor or nurse indicate?" Immediately following an accident is the best time to get this information.

The procedure of making an investigation in order to obtain optimum results requires good judgment and ability to collect the facts, weigh the evidence, arrive at satisfactory conclusions, and select suitable remedies.

Familiarity with the plant equipment used in the various operations will assist in the recognition of hazards that may have been overlooked for some time in the operation. The foreman or supervisor who accompanies the safety man must coöperate, since consultation with him as to possible causes and remedies will help to explore the underlying difficulties. We must remember that, in general, physical hazards as well as unsafe acts play important parts in the great majority of accidents. It is not sufficient merely to recommend a guard and overlook an unsafe act, such as rendering the guard inoperative or placing the hands in the danger zone unnecessarily. It is equally insufficient to limit attention to the unsafe act if a better guard would reduce the likelihood of injury from the unsafe act.

Promptness is essential since conditions may be changed quickly and the details forgotten. Promptness also helps to impress upon the minds of the workers in the immediate vicinity that management attaches great importance to their safety.

Minor injuries and no-injury accidents

The question as to whether all minor injuries should be investigated has been a much discussed point. Theoretically, they should be, but there are serious practical difficulties. Undoubtedly, a serious injury is, in most instances, closely akin to a long series of minor injuries or close calls, all of which are from the same basic causative factors.

The close calls are not easy to detect; the first-aid cases are relatively easy. If a close watch is kept on them (and such of the close calls as can be discovered), forewarning will thereby be had of most of the serious injuries. However, the number of first-aid cases in the average plant of some size is large enough to keep a considerable force of investigators working full time if all were investigated in as great detail as the serious injuries should be. Heinrich arrived at the ratio (for all industry) of 1 lost-time injury to 29 first-aid cases to 300 noninjury-producing accidents (or potential injury occurrences). Other data indicate that Heinrich's ratio is probably conseravtive, but also show wide variations as among the various industries, different establishments within the same industry, and in comparing different occupations. Many factors are involved. A working force that fully understands the infection hazard reports minor injuries for treatment and shows a high ratio. Where reporting is poor or the first-aid treatment is substandard, a low ratio with many infections is commonly found. Point-of-operation machine operation generally shows a high ratio of severe injuries; hand tool work, a very low one. Bad tool maintenance and the unskilled use of tools yield many minor injuries. Bad methods used in the handling of small, sharp, or rough articles bring a similar result.

Under such conditions, one often finds 50 or even 100 minor cases per lost-time injury.

People generally dislike to be investigated in any way. Workmen who will willingly submerge this dislike to coöperate in the investigation of a serious injury will not do so willingly for a "mere scratch." One large organization which undertook the detailed investigation and reporting of every minor injury found its infection rate rising because the workmen got tired of being investigated and let many minor injuries go untreated.

It would be difficult to overemphasize the importance of closely watching the minor injuries. As pointed out above, in most cases, a serious injury is merely one of a long series of close calls. It may be the first of the series, or the hundredth, or any other. In any event, these minor injuries and the close calls constitute warnings of the serious injuries certain to lie ahead if adequate preventive action is not taken.

The safety man (and the foreman as well) should maintain close contact with the first-aid department. Doctors, nurses, and first-aid attendants are in an excellent position to judge which cases should be investigated, and, with the close coöperation of the safety man and the foreman, can detect most of the cases that justify detailed investigation. An obvious example would be a minor injury from a falling object of some size or from a fall from a ladder. On the other hand, a finger nick received by a man at bench work is to be expected occasionally. But much repetition calls for investigation into such factors as the arrangement of the work, the tool housekeeping, the condition of the tools, the aptitude of the worker or workers involved, and the training they have received.

At the time of the accident

When an accident occurs and someone is injured, the first concern should be for the injured individual. He should be placed in the proper hands for treatment. Usually, his condition is such that immediate interrogation should be avoided in order to give the doctor or first-aid man an opportunity to make him comfortable, treat for shock, and take care of the injury. It is a mistake to run the risk of upsetting the victim by pressing him with questions. It is much better to wait until he has had a chance to collect his thoughts and get his nerves under control. Usually, the investigator can go right to the scene and get a fairly complete story from those who were present and from the conditions he finds upon his arrival. In all serious cases and in all other cases where practicable, conditions at the accident scene should remain unaltered pending the investigation.

There are times when the safety engineer should go to the scene of the accident at once to assist the doctor in determining the possible extent of the injury. For example: A man is splashed with a chemical. Was it acid or alkaline? How concentrated was it? What solvent or medium can be used to remove it from the skin? Is it a hazardous or non-hazardous chemical?

The injured man may be confused or ignorant of what he was handling. Many of our trade names and mixtures are unknown to the medical profession, and correct treatment of eyes or skin is contingent upon what the contact was.

When the safety director directs or himself undertakes to investigate an accident, his approach to the foreman and to the injured man should be indicative of trying to help and not in any way of a desire to convict or find fault. This approach helps greatly to bring out the facts, for neither will feel it necessary to conceal anything.

At the scene of the accident, all the conditions should be reconstructed mentally, the occurrence pictured, reenacted if necessary, and only then should definite conclusions be reached. The very human tendency to reach a conclusion early in an investigation and then use only that subsequent information that tends to confirm it must be resisted. Doubtful points should be checked on from as many different angles and as objectively as possible.

The report form

Practice varies, but it is common procedure for the foreman to fill out a standard report form covering his findings. The results of any investigation additional to his are usually made up in descriptive form in such detail as circumstances warrant. The samples herewith of forms in use are fairly typical. Note that the one is merely a descriptive report of accident, a single question as to how to prevent a recurrence. The other is a "Review of Accident" form calling for a detailed analysis of the accident with the assignment of responsibility and also calling for definite preventive action. The safety man will make his own notes on each such case and in addition to his copy of the foreman's report and that of any other investigation will have the medical report. He is thus in a position to weigh all the evidence, investigate further if necessary, advise on and follow up on the corrective action, and see that any information gained that may have a bearing elsewhere is made full use of.

Examples of cases. The following examples of the fruits of accident investigation are illustrative.

Case 1—Carbon tetrachloride. Two men using carbon tetrachloride reported to the dispensary with headaches. The first one had placed a one-gallon can between an electric fan and himself and the fumes were being blown in his face. The simple remedy of placing the can so that the fumes were blown away from him overcame the condition. In addi-

REPORT OF ACCIDENT TO AN EMPLOYEE

INJURED EMPLOYEE: Name .... Number ..... Dept. .....
Address ....
Nationality .... Age ..... Married or Single? .....
Number of children under 18 years .... Number of dependent
adults ...... Occupation when injured .... Was this his/her
regular occupation? .... If not, state regular occupation ....
How long in department? .... Piece or Day Work? ....
Day rate ....

ACCIDENT: Date .... Hour .... Place where accident
occurred ....
Full description of how accident happened. Also name, part, and shop
number of machine or tool appliance concerned in accident ....
....
Was part of machine causing accident properly guarded at time of ac-
cident? .... Hand or mechanical feed? .... Give description
of guards ....
Was employee following Safety Rules? .... Was accident due to
lack of ordinary care by injured person? .... If so, how? .....
....
Was accident due to negligence of any person other than the injured?
.... If so, who and how? ....
How can recurrence of such accident be prevented? ....
....

INJURY: Full description oi injury and part of person injured ......
....
Did injured resume work after receiving medical attention, or was he/she
sent home? ....
If sent home, what time did he/she ring out? .... Is employee
back to work? ...... Name and addresses of witnesses to the accident
....
....

Name of foreman   Name of immediate
in charge of work   supervisor

Where possible, give further description of accident and its cause on
the back of this report, illustrating, if possible, by sketch, drawing, or
photograph.
Report made out by .... whose position in the Company is ....
Date report made out .... Signed ....

INJURY REPORT

WHITE COPY TO DISPENSARY
YELLOW COPY TO SAFETY DEPT.
PINK COPY TO SUPERVISOR

NAME: _____ CLOCK NO. _____ DATE: _____

OCCUPATION: _____ DATE OF INJURY: _____ TIME: _____ A.M. / P.M.

SUPERVISOR: _____ DEPARTMENT: _____

INJURY OCCURRED AT BUILDING # _____

NATURE OF INJURY: _____

CAUSE OF INJURY: _____

Is further treatment required? **Yes/No** To return on: _____

Is outside doctor or hospital treatment required? **Yes/No**

Will injury cause loss of time? **Yes/No**

Notation of subsequent treatment should be made on the reverse side of the Dispensary copy of this report.

NATURE OF INJURY

WOUNDS:	LACERATION	1
	CONTUSION	2
	INFECTION	3
	FOREIGN BODY	4
	PUNCTURE	5
EYES:	FOREIGN BODY	6
	BURN CORROSIVE	7
	" HEAT	8
	" FLASH	9
	WOUND	10
	IRRITATION	11
BURNS:	HEAT	12
	CHEMICAL	13
	FRICTION	14
SKIN:	DERMATITIS	15
	IRRITATION-RASH	16
FRACTURE		17
STRAIN		18
SPRAIN		19
GASES:	NAUSEA	20
	DIZZY	21
	IRRITATION	22
PAINS		23
MISC.		24

Body diagram labels: EYE, HEAD, TEETH, FACE, SHOULDER, NECK, COLLAR BONE, ARM, CHEST, ELBOW, RIBS, FOREARM, BACK, WRIST, ABDOMEN, HIP, HAND, RUPTURE, FINGERS, THIGH, THUMB, KNEE, LEG, ANKLE, SHIN, INSTEP, TOE, FOOT

F-450
REV. 1/50

TREATED BY: _____

tion to this, the investigators found that 25 per cent of the quantity of carbon tetrachloride he had exposed was sufficient for his needs.

The other man was dipping some laminations in a small can of the fluid and was spreading them on his bench to dry. He was inhaling the fumes while these were drying. A change in this procedure so that the dipping operation was done just before he went home overcame the trouble. Both of these jobs were done occasionally, involved only a small quantity of the cleaner, and did not require an exhaust, but they did call for an understanding of the nature of the material and the exercise of

REVIEW OF EMPLOYEE ACCIDENT

Name _____ Pay No. _____ Bldg. _____

Age _____ Service with Co. _____ Occupation _____ Date of injury _____

Nature of injury_____

Cause of injury _____

Probable length of disability _____

ANALYSIS OF CAUSE

INSTRUCTION	UNSAFE PRACTICE	POOR HOUSEKEEPING	IMPROPER PLANNING
( ) None	( ) Taking chances	( ) Improperly piled	( ) Layout of operation
( ) Not enforced	( ) Short cuts	( ) Congestion	( ) Layout of machine
( ) Incomplete	( ) Haste	( ) Material lying about	( ) Unsafe processes
( ) Erroneous		( ) Bad containers	( ) Lack of equipment
	PHYSICALLY UNFIT		( ) Lack of data or rules
INABILITY OF EMPLOYEE	( ) Defective	DEFECTIVE EQUIPMENT	
( ) Inexperienced	( ) Fatigued	( ) Misc. material & equip't.	MENTALLY UNFIT
( ) Unskilled	( ) Weak	( ) Tools	( ) Sluggish - fatigued
( ) Ignorant	( ) Sick	( ) Machines	( ) Violent temper
( ) Poor judgement		( ) Lack of maintenance	( ) Excitability
	IMPROPER WORKING	( ) Poorly made	( ) Sick
LACK OF CONCENTRATION	CONDITIONS	( ) Not apparent	( ) Home troubles
( ) Attention distracted	( ) Ventilation		
( ) Inattention	( ) Sanitation	UNSAFE BLDG. CONDITIONS	IMPROPER DRESS
( ) Thoughtlessness	( ) Light	( ) Fire protection	( ) No goggles, gloves,
	( ) Temperature	( ) Exits	masks
POOR DISCIPLINE		( ) Floors	( ) Unsuitable -
( ) Disobedience of rules	PHYSICAL HAZARDS	( ) Openings	long sleeves
( ) Interference of others	( ) Ineffectively guarded	( ) Miscellaneous	( ) High heels -
( ) Fooling	( ) Unguarded		defective shoes
( ) Disregarded	( ) Guards removed		( ) Failure to wear
instructions	( ) Guards tampered with		safety shoes

( ) Give cause if not covered by any of the above: _____

RESPONSIBILITY: Employee _____ Supervision _____ Divided,E and S _____ Not placed _____

Reason for placing responbility as above _____
_____
_____

What action by supervision might have prevented accident?_____
_____
_____
_____

What action will be taken to prevent recurrence? _____
_____
_____
_____

Date_____ Made out by _____ Signed by _____

                                                Foreman   Supt.

SEND I COPY TO WORKS MANAGER AND I COPY TO SAFETY DEPT.

judgment in using it. These two cases pointed directly toward the need for more careful and adequate instruction and better supervision.

Case 2—Babbitt job. A company had a job on which babbitt was poured to fill a hole in a casting. A plate was placed under this hole to hold the babbitt in place. In order to prevent it from running out through the spaces between the casting and the plate, the operator's practice was to fill in these spaces with wet asbestos. When the molten metal touched the wet spots, a slight spattering would occur. Goggles and special sleeves were worn to prevent burns, but one day a man received face burns from the spatter. The remedy was simple, namely, to substitute whiting mixed with a very heavy oil. More adequate instruction should have prevented this unsafe practice. Job safety analysis should have caught it. So should the foreman and the workmen's safety committee.

Notifying other departments and plants

After the investigation of an accident has been completed and a method of prevention has been decided on, our next step is to find out what other departments or plants may have a similar condition which requires attention.

The information should be broadcast to foremen and all interested safety men in other plants, so that they may profit by the experience of others. This is usually done by a letter giving the particulars and a photograph or sketch, if necessary.

This system is also used when a good guard is designed or a safer method of doing a job is found or some special new safety equipment is placed on the market. In this way men are kept abreast of the times and can take action promptly. Experience has shown that the value of information obtained is dependent on the use which is made of it.

Corrective action——Profit by experience

It must be understood that everything possible should be done in all plants to prevent accidents, because that is the first important step. Second, if an accident occurs, we must profit by it so that there will be no recurrence. The adage, "It's an ill wind that blows no good," applies to acident prevention.

Since the real purpose of an investigation presupposes action, it must be prompt; otherwise, it will be largely wasted. Action should include:

1. Prompt consideration of every recommendation and compliance with it.

2. If recommendations are not to be followed, an explanation of the reasons is required.

3. Delays necessary in order to make changes or obtain other equipment should be explained fully.

4. Consideration should be given in all other departments, to see if the same condition applies, whenever physical hazards or unsafe practices are found.

5. The effectiveness of an investigator is contingent upon the decisions, the distribution of knowledge pertaining thereto, and the action taken.

Summary

Reviewing this matter of investigation of accidents, we have these salient points:

1. Analyze the case carefully and impartially.
2. Have the proper people do this.
3. Don't dismiss it by saying the man was careless.
4. When you get the correct information, take some action to prevent a recurrence.
5. Do not fail to apply preventive measures in all sections where a similar hazard may exist.
6. Avoid looking for excuses and get the causes.
7. Avoid trying to convict someone for negligence, and remember that the worker, the supervisor, and the company are usually at fault to some degree.
8. A knowledge of all circumstances surrounding an accident is essential.
9. Make use of the information obtained.
10. A summation of all these points usually indicates a definite need for more education and training of the worker as well as a closer follow-up by supervisors and management.

Chapter Eleven

Layout and Arrangement; Purchasing for Safety

Layout and arrangement

The layout and arrangement of a plant or any industrial undertaking involving equipment is generally done by engineers with special training. That plant layout should include full provision for the safety of the worker as well as the production requirements is obvious. If the safety engineer has a fair knowledge of the principles the layout engineer applies in planning a plant and its operations, he will be greatly assisted in checking over the plans before actual work has begun, and thus the expense of later changes will be saved. Such knowledge will also help him in detecting hazards due to faulty planning of established plants.

Either the engineers who develop the plant layout should be well trained in safety (rarely the case), or a highly competent safety engineer should be included in the planning staff. An excellent illustration of this need is furnished by a well-accepted definition of good plant layout as (a) placing the right equipment (b) coupled with the right method (c) in the right place (d) to permit the processing of a product unit in the most effective manner (e) through the shortest possible distance (f) in the shortest possible time. Note that in this definition no mention is made of safety. A plant layout including all of these items properly would, incidentally, include many safety provisions, but that is not enough. If one is to get the minimum of hazard (the maximum of safety) into a plant layout, it must be planned in. Therefore, an additional item should be included in the above definition, i.e., (g) with the maximum of safety for those who operate and service the plant.

The detail involved in the full inclusion of safety in the planning stage of even a plant of moderate size is far too great to deal with adequately here. Therefore, this discussion will be limited to basic considerations and to items deemed to be of major importance.

The safety engineer should be in on all of the initial planning because unless he is acquainted with such matters as the products that are to be made, the processes to be used, the size and character and arrangement of the buildings, the kinds of machinery required, and the approximate size of the working force, he cannot foresee some of the hazards that may or will be involved, in time to have provisions for their control included in the layout as the blueprints are drawn. It is axiomatic that changes in a plant in being are expensive, frequently prohibitively so, and that changes while the plant is under construction are less costly and less often prohibitive. Changes in the blueprint stage cost little, though they may delay the start of actual construction somewhat.

Failure to include the safety-engineering viewpoint and "know-how" in the earliest planning stages has been responsible for many disasters. That it is responsible for a great total of injuries and deaths can be attested to by every safety engineer who has had to struggle against hazards needlessly built into plant processes and operations. We know what can be done by what has been done. There are a very large number of modern plants that have been excellently planned and engineered from the safety viewpoint. Unfortunately, there are far too many that have not been and are full of needless hazards as a result. Few plants built before 1920 were planned to include the maximum of safety for those who operated and maintained them. Many still are not so planned, particularly the smaller plants. This is largely because safety information and indoctrination is only now beginning to be included in engineering and architectural curricula.

Even the most experienced planning staff is likely to overlook some hazards. Therefore, as early in the planning stage as practicable, the safety engineer, checking the plans, should start to develop his list of the items to be considered. In such a list, there will be a number of major items, each of which will include many, and in some cases, a multiplicity of lesser items. He should also keep in mind that some even of the major items wil be interdependent and overlapping. For example, the site selected may have an important influence on the provisions required for fire prevention and protection, or process hazards may call for special types of arrangement and spacing of buildings and so on. A list of major items that one experienced engineer has found useful is:

1. Site
2. Transportation facilities (to and from plant)
3. Facilities for the handling and storage of goods and products
4. Personal service facilities
5. Walkway surfaces
6. Lighting, heating and general ventilation
7. Elevators
8. Boilers and pressure vessels

9. Electric wiring
10. Fixed machinery and equipment
11. Portable equipment and tools
12. Provisions for servicing plant and equipment
13. Fire prevention and protection
14. Provisions for health and safety

Early in his professional experience, this engineer began to develop such lists, filling in the details under each major item as his experience grew. Ultimately he found it seldom necessary to consult them, but he still found them useful for reference purposes, and never gave up the practice of developing item lists for new or unfamiliar operations, processes, equipment, or hazards.

Some engineers prefer to use a somewhat different approach, based on type of hazard. They develop a list of the types of accidents that may occur and the hazards that may be involved in the operations, activities, and processes to be carried on in the plant for which the plans are being developed. Then they examine each part of the plan in detail in the light of the hazard possibilities and "plan them out" as far as possible. For a certain rather typical metal working plant the list of major items was:

1. Transportation hazards
   a. Traffic to and from plant
   b. In-plant traffic
2. Falls
   a. On walkways and floors
   b. To a lower level
3. Machinery hazards
4. Process hazards
5. Hazardous substances
6. Environmental factors—Noise, excessive vibration, radiant energy, illumination, excessive temperature, etc.
7. Provisions for employee service—First aid, sanitation, locker and wash rooms, eating facilities, etc.

The advantage urged for this approach as against the other is that since the purpose is hazard elimination, the emphasis should be placed on type of hazard rather than on kind of equipment or type of activity. The answer seems to be that whatever approach the engineer responsible for "built-in" safety finds he can use most effectively will be adequate, provided he has the necessary professional qualifications for this very difficult and exacting service.

Thoroughness is a first requisite. Its importance cannot be over-emphasized, particularly when the process or operation may carry the possibility of disaster. A thorough knowledge of the hazards possibly involved, or lacking that, a careful assembling of the combined knowledge of others, is equally essential. Almost countless instances of catastrophes or serious cases of worker death and injury resulting from failure to comply with one or both of these essentials could be cited. The widely publicized and highly destructive chemical finishing plant explosion in Los Angeles during World War II furnishes a good example. No safety engineer knowing the hazards of this process would approve the location of such a plant in a heavily populated area. Additional safeguards and much more accurate and reliable controls also are necessary. The liquefied natural gas fire in Cleveland, also during the war, and also causing heavy life and property loss, is another outstanding example. Lack of adequate knowledge of the properties (at the extremely low temperature necessary) of the metal of which the tanks containing the liquefied gas were made was the major factor. However, had this installation been away from a populated area, and had the tanks been properly diked as is customary for large oil tanks, the fire would have been contained. The safety engineering approach would also have dictated storage in a bank of small tanks protectively separated, rather than in two huge tanks as was the case in this installation.

Flow Sheets

Process and operation flow sheets are a familiar device in plant and process planning. By making them in sufficient detail to include the hazard points and the in-built provisions for hazard control, they can be similarly useful in planning for safety. The entire plant layout plan should be drawn to show over-all relationships of building and structures, roadways, traffic flow, water and service lines, etc., and particularly the locations for the storage of hazardous substances in bulk, if any. Ground slopes and levels can be very important where combustible liquids are used or stored in quantity.

The over-all layout plan is supplemented by building layouts showing machine and equipment relationships and space allowances. The hazards connected with the various machines and processes can be described on supplemental sheets and keyed to the respective machines, processes, or operations. Since planning engineers have developed definite methods, procedures, and symbols "of the trade," a safety engineer concerned with plant layout safety should study at least one of the number of texts used in accredited courses on the subject. He will, unfortunately, find little mention of safety in them. He will have to fill that in himself, but he will learn about production planning.

Planning in the operating plant

It is emphasized that planning should not be thought of as limited to new construction. In every going plant there are more or less frequent changes in machine and equipment arrangement, in processes, in operations, and in work methods. Also, there are frequent small construction jobs; a new water line, additional piping, a tank installation, a building addition, or some new machinery. All of these should be carefully planned in advance, including careful and thorough analysis of the hazards involved and the thorough working out of adequate control measures. Failure to do this seldom yields disasters, but it frequently brings worker deaths and injuries. Perhaps the most notable example of this was the large number of lead poisoning cases (a number fatal) that resulted from the use of lead in repairing the flaws in the all-metal automobile bodies, when these were introduced. The toxic properties of lead were well known, and adequate control methods had been developed, but they were not known to the production executives involved, and they failed to look up the readily available information until the situation was forced to their attention by the complaints of the workers who sickened from breathing the lead fumes.

Production necessities frequently require that such changes be made quickly. However, the hazards connected with the use and processing of all of the hazardous substances used at all widely or in considerable volume are so well documented that a very limited reference library will, in a few hours at most, yield the information needed for their safe use and handling. Furthermore, in every state having any substantial volume of productive industry, technical advice is readily available from labor departments, health departments, technical schools, or research agencies connected with industry.

When the accident hazards involved in such occasional changes escape correction, it is simply because the executives responsible fail to make sure that someone with basic safety "know-how" is in on the planning. Of course, in a plant having a well-developed and well-directed safety program, such matters are well taken care of. Unfortunately, such establishments are in a very small minority, and since hazards "ride with new or occasional jobs," the resulting injury toll is heavy.

The factors that influence plant layout

It is costly to have products that are being manufactured retrace their steps through the factory building. It is also costly to lift them to upper floors. In other words, holding the handling and transporting of materials to a minimum helps hold costs down. Since the handling of materials and articles is a major source of accidents, keeping handling to a minimum helps to keep accidents down. This is merely another example of the intimate relationship between accidents and costs and is particularly important because of that relationship.

The development of the plans for the modern factory building should include thorough consideration of all processes and operations involved, including the work that will be performed and the prevention of injury to the workmen performing it. Building the plant and then fitting the process to it inevitably involve compromises by which safety (and, as a rule, cost and efficiency as well) suffers. This might seem to be an argument against the use of the standardized type of factory building. However, with proper planning, the benefits of standardized construction can be had without compromise hurtful to safety, particularly if the standardization is related to the needs of a particular industry.

The essentials that must be met in the planning will be influenced by such factors as the type of product to be made, the materials to be worked with, the kind of operation contemplated, and the type of personnel required. A product lending itself to continuous production, as paper or textiles, imposes one set of conditions. A product assembled from manufactured parts, as shoes or automobiles, brings other conditions. Certain specific properties that wood possesses determine the methods of its processing. Metals require different methods. The manufacture of magnesium from sea water involves an entirely different plant and process than that for its manufacture from the ore. The tremendously important and rapidly developing and expanding field of the chemical industry brings a wide variety of new problems and varied techniques.

Provision must be made for ventilation, exhausts, storage, fire hazards involved, toxic and irritating gases, special explosion-proof lighting, motors and switches; loading and unloading facilities for corrosive liquids from tanks and tank cars, proper grounding, dikes at storage areas, relief valves for pressure control, suitable emergency exits, safety showers, drum handling, waste solvent disposal, storage and handling of compressed gases, etc.

A typical flow chart used in the chemical industry shows how liquids or solids are started in the process on the upper floors, are reacted or mixed as the operation requires, and finally are packaged on the lower floor ready for shipment. Very little manual handling is involved since the pumps and gravity do the work. Obviously, a one story building would not be suitable for the efficient operation of this kind of a process.

In general, the importance of the kind of factory building and layout as a primary tool with which to carry on production, and into which all other production tools and mechanisms fit, cannot be overestimated. The building and layout must fit the job to be done, if that job is to be done most effectively.

The relationship between plant layout and process arrangement is so close that health and accident hazards cannot be disassociated from either of them. If the planner or layout man is thoroughly familiar with conditions and applies acident prevention principles, he will not overlook provision for the following:

Adequate space.   Congestion leads to confusion in the area and the probability of accidents. The absence of sufficient room for machine or equipment makes it more difficult to work, and, therefore, the planner must have in mind the size of the equipment and the necessary radius of action required by the worker as well as the area needed for storing work to be done, work completed, and the handling of this work by himself or others. Ample head and elbow room, particularly over and around moving equipment, such as traveling cranes and other apparatus requiring servicing, sometimes is overlooked. Good practice provides for clearance such that a person riding or working on the top of such equipment will not be in danger of getting caught against or striking his head against girders, ceiling, columns, and so on. Inadequate storage space is also responsible for poor housekeeping. It also increases the difficulties of handling and storing incoming materials, those in process, and the finished product.

Safe access.   Failure to provide for safe access to every point to which men must go, such as cranes, and the tops of boilers and machines, is responsible for many falls. In order to realize fully the importance of such provision, the safety planner should "follow the oiler or repair man" with sufficient frequency to keep well informed as to the hazards he faces in his daily work.

Safe maintenance.   This includes particularly the safety of men doing such work as window cleaning and repairs, overhauling of overhead electrical equipment, and work on cranes, machinery in pits, and in tunnels and out-of-the-way places, such as elevator penthouses.

Adequate air and light.   The number of employees who should work in a given number of cubic feet of space varies considerably and is contingent upon the nature of the work and the presence of air contamination. Many factors are involved in good lighting. The intensity of light required depends entirely on what the area is used for, since obviously a toolmaker's area requires considerably more light than does a storage section. Glare, quality of light, location of light source, contrasts in color and brightness, flickering and shadows, all must be considered. The provisions of the "American Standard" should be complied with.*

---

* In 1915 the Illuminating Engineering Society issued its "Code of Lighting Factories, Mills, and Other Work Places." This was approved as American Standard and revised

Services. In the layout, provision is made for the arrangement of machinery and fixed equipment. Provision must also be made in the arrangement for servicing those areas so that traffic will flow in and out without interfering with the various operations. Modern factories provide room for battery trucks, three- or four-wheeled push trucks, various skids, and tote boxes. The widths of aisles, in order to provide for traffic, are of prime importance. If battery or other powered shop trucks are used, the minimum width for two-way traffic requires an allowance of at least three extra feet, after making provision for the width of two trucks.

Pedestrian rush-hour traffic flow to time clocks, lunch rooms, and exit gates makes it necessary to provide extra clearances in order to accommodate the peak loads. Allowances must also be made for handling bulky loads. Marking the aisles, generally with white or yellow paint, and eliminating blind traffic intersections help considerably in keeping traffic lanes open, so as to provide for a steady flow.

Expansion. A far-sighted planner allows for expansion of business in the layout. If this is done properly, the need of rearranging departments or moving from one place to another in order to overcome congestion and expedite manufacture is avoided, or at least minimized.

Management may consider planning and processing from only a cost, quality, and volume standpoint, overlooking the fact that effective control of these will largely reduce accidents. Poor planning is often a major factor in a high accident rate, and the safety man can do much to correct it. The need for changes is indicated by unduly large amounts of materials in process in operating areas, workers interfering with one another, overcrowding of production areas, traffic jams, accumulation of waste and scrap, and processes not following one another in an orderly sequence. Recommendations by the safety man should be given careful thought, since changes involve a considerable expenditure in many instances, and unless the problem, with the remedy, is properly presented, the probability of corrective measures being taken is lessened. A considerable knowledge of industrial management is necessary in order to appreciate the principles involved and to make practical recommendations for correction.

An important duty of the safety man should be that of checking plans and specifications for layout and arrangement of equipment. This is an important function because it affords an opportunity to discover and correct conditions that may otherwise be built into the plant and plant equipment and later result in injuries.

---

from time to time. The latest revision, "Recommended Practice of Industrial Lighting," published by the Illuminating Engineering Society, 51 Madison Avenue, New York City, was approved by American Standards Association in 1952 and issued as "American Recommended Practice of Industrial Lighting."

The proper placing of machines, allowing sufficient aisle space and room for the material that will be placed around them, is of particular importance. The kind of flooring to be used, the safe floor load, the material with which to construct platforms, the placing of sheet metal guards, curtains, or other things to confine the process to a given area are also important. For instance, provision should be made for placing a shield or a curtain around a welding area or section so that the injurious rays do not cause flashes or other injury to those working or walking near by. It is poor practice to locate a chipping operation along an aisle or other space unless a proper shield is installed. Metal shears should be so located that the cut pieces will not drop off or fly into an aisle or other frequented place. A paint spray booth using a volatile solvent should never be located next to a welding area, because of the explosion, as well as the fume and fire, hazard. One does not want a furnace in proximity to the carpenter shop with its wood dust hazard and its considerable stock of inflammable material.

Consideration should be given to the location of the tool cribs so that workers do not have to walk too far to get their tools. Generally, we find the cribs with windows opening onto an aisle. Allowance should be made for space such that a man can stand at the window to get his tools and not be endangered by or interfere with the aisle traffic, which, incidentally, may include loads borne by overhead cranes.

Drinking fountains should not be located near machines which throw off dust and dirt or where fumes from painting processes are created. Drinking fountains are usually installed to suit the convenience of the standard plumbing installation, and therefore the safety and convenience of the persons using the fountains is at times not adequately provided for. At times it is less expensive and may be better to relocate the process or equipment than to move the fountain.

Isolation of hazardous locations

Much too often we find paint-spraying, metal-cleaning processes and dusty work placed on the manufacturing floors without consideration for the health of and annoyance to workers in other sections. Whenever possible, the layout should include isolation by using a separate building or partitioning off the area of these operations. In order to protect the employees within the hazardous areas, allowance should be made for the installation of exhaust equipment with collectors. Sometimes it is sufficient to carry the exhaust well above the roofs. In each instance, the nature of the substance, the possibility of its being carried back into workrooms by natural air motion or creating a neighborhood nuisance, should receive full consideration.

Provision for outlets and other electrical connections as well as for supplying compressed air for portable equipment is often overlooked. An adequate supply of connections would eliminate the need of running hose lines and electrical leads across aisles.

Marking bays so that locations of hazards can be easily identified is of great value. It is common practice to use first the building number, next the bay by using A, B, and C running crosswise of the building, then the floor number, and next the bay number counting lengthwise from one end of the building to the other. For example, "10-B, 403." This would indicate Building No. 10, B Bay, 4th floor, and allowing for the usual twenty-five feet, length and width, the third bay from the starting point, or seventy-five feet from the end.

FLOOR PLAN TO INDICATE
LOCATION BY BAY NUMBERS

10A404	10B404	10C404
10A403	10B403	10C403
10A402	10B402	10C402
10A401	10B401	10C401

10 = Building #10.
A-B-C = Location of bay from side to side.
4 = 4th Floor.
01-02-03-04 = Location of bay from end to end.

Purchasing for safety

The safety man in industry is not an entity unto himself. It is necessary for him to coöperate with the entire organization and also to obtain the coöperation of other departments and men in the organization. This high degree of teamwork is especially important because it relates to the purchasing of equipment and supplies. It is the purchasing agent's responsibility to buy various items of machinery, tools, equipment, and materials used in the establishment. His responsibility should also be to see that these are not only usable on the various jobs but also that they include the maximum of safety for the user. In some companies a safety man is charged with the responsibility of checking all plans and specifications for machinery and equipment. Certain items that are reordered from time to time, such as safety shoes, goggles, respirators, protective equipment, and the like, are included on standard lists that have been prepared after due investigation and approval, and the purchasing department is instructed to select from the types on these approved lists. Maximum and minimum quantities are established for the ordering of supplies.

This is a much more satisfactory arrangement than to have the responsibility for safety equipment rest with the department head where the equipment is used, although he should be in close contact with the individuals who prepare the approved lists. These individuals ordinarily would include a representative of the engineering or methods departments where plans and specifications are prepared as well as the safety and purchasing departments.

This same degree of coöperation should exist in the small plant as in the large. Those responsible for the protection of the workers must see that safety is adequately provided for in the purchasing of supplies and equipment.

A short-sighted purchasing policy would place price above safety, but every fully safety-minded management knows that a policy of careful attention to safety in all purchasing is actually a money-saver.

Purchase of machinery

As a result of the persistent demands of safety men and safety organizations, as well as the adoption of legal requirements that machinery be made safe, great progress has been made by machinery manufacturers in making their products safer to use. Safety is being built into machines more and more through safer design and construction and more complete guarding. However, there is much need for further improvement, particularly of widely used point-of-operation machines, standard models of which are offered in the competitive market. This applies particularly to woodworking and metalworking machines. The usual practice with these machines is to add guards designed and manufactured for attachment to the standard models rather than to design machine and guard together as a functioning whole. While fairly satisfactory guards for these machines are available, many points of hazard can be much more adequately safeguarded by including the full safety of the operator as a basic requirement in the design and construction of the machine.

Further improvement in present practice depends upon the extent to which purchasers will demand fully safeguarded machines. Purchasers who buy on a price basis often fail to take the safety of the operator into account. They "shop around" for the machine, and, if a guard is required, follow a similar practice in buying it. Safety suffers in the process, for such guards vary widely in their effectiveness. They are, in fact, after-thoughts, and they generally show it. Any machine part on whose correct function men's safety depends should be considered the most precious part of the machine, and its appearance should be indicative of such an attitude. Poorly designed, poorly finished guards obviously added as more or less of an after-thought testify eloquently against any professed desire for "safety first."

Purchasing unguarded machines to be guarded later is also not likely to save any money. Often the purchased guard must be altered or added to, or extra cost is involved in installing it. Therefore the final cost of this course may be high.

The purchaser who is so little safety-minded that he purchases on this basis is not likely to be able to judge correctly the relative merits of guards sold competitively or to appraise the sales arguments of the competing salesmen. As a result, guards are often purchased, tried, and discarded, and the machine is operated unguarded until an accident or a specific requirement as to guarding causes another type to be tried and, perhaps, discarded in turn.

Purchase orders should, in all cases, specify that machinery be fully safeguarded and comply fully with state or other applicable safety requirements. Machinery manufacturers will coöperate gladly with purchasers to work out safety problems just as they commonly do all problems of operation, but the need of and desire for such service must be a part of the purchase inquiry if it is to be rendered effectively. Even this procedure does not, however, preclude the need of a safety inspection of new equipment before it is placed in operation, because not only may some things be overlooked in planning and building it, but the installation may be faulty. Then, too, operating plans may have changed by the time the machine has been received.

Protective equipment and supplies

The safety man who keeps himself posted on the new equipment and supplies available, together with their advantages as compared to others, is in a good position to decide what should be used in his establishment because he knows the demands of his organization and the application of the equipment, as well as the outside sources of supply.

The selection of all safety equipment and safety items should definitely come under the jurisdiction of the safety man. All those that are needed in a given plant should be included on a standardized list in order to guide the purchasing department in placing the orders. The following list is suggestive:

1. Acid-handling equipment.
2. Carboy-handling equipment.
3. Electrode holders.
4. Face, head, and eye protection (goggles, helmets, face-masks, hard hats, etc.).
5. Fire-fighting equipment.
6. Foot protection (safety shoes, foot protectors, boots, etc.).
7. Guards for specific purposes.
8. Hair protectors (hair nets, caps, turbans).
9. Hand protection (gloves, hand leathers, finger cots).
10. Ladder feet.
11. Linemen's equipment.
12. Protective clothing (aprons, sleeves, shoulder pads, asbestos garments, knee and shin pads, gauntlets, etc.)
13. Respiratory protective equipment (respirators, gas and hose masks, oxygen apparatus, sand-blast helmets).
14. Safety cans.
15. Safety literature, posters, bulletins, signs, etc.
16. Safety mats.
17. Special safety tools.
18. Stretchers.
19. Testing instruments (CO indicator, speed counter, explosometer, velometer, etc.).
20. Wire rope clamps.

Of course it is not sufficient merely to provide for the coöperation of the purchasing department and the safety engineer in the purchasing of supplies. The proper application of this equipment is of vital importance in order to secure the benefits expected. This application can be made through systematic procedure adequately followed up and maintained. It is essential that each foreman know fully what safety equipment should be used by the men under him, how it should be used, and its limitations. In some plants, foremen's meetings are held for instruction and discussion in this field. In others, it is handled chiefly by direct contact between the safety men and the various supervisors. Finally, close coöperation between the foremen and the safety man is needed to discover the limitations of the safety equipment and also to discover desirable improvements or additions.

Examples of the need of adequate information and correct application would be:

1. A respirator suitable for filtering out dust particles is of little or no value when used in an area containing fumes or gases. An inadequate protective device may be worse than none, for it gives a false sense of security.

2. The hazards involved in emptying the acid out of carboys by hand might be met by substituting a pump, but if this applies too much pressure or suction and thus causes a breakout, one type of hazard has merely been substituted for another.

3. A gas mask suitable for an area in which carbon tetrachloride fumes are present would, in most cases, afford little or no protection against carbon monoxide fumes.

Chapter Twelve

Plant Housekeeping

In factory parlance, we use the term *housekeeping* to signify not only cleanliness, but a place for everything and everything in its place. A condition of this kind cannot be maintained by an occasional grand clean-up and setting things in order. It must be continuous and given proper attention and thought. A place is clean when it is free from unnecessary things. It is in order when those things that are about are in their proper places, properly arranged, and in satisfactory condition. Grease or oil out of place is a frequent cause of floor slipperiness. If articles fall from overhead, they have been out of place. If dirt and litter are about, these are out of place. If material is poorly piled or placed, the material is out of place.

An orderly arrangement is not only conducive to a good accident record, but it is representative of competent management, efficient workmanship, and a better place in which to work.

Typical accidents due to poor housekeeping

1. Tripping over loose objects on floors, stairs, and platforms.
2. Articles dropping from above.
3. Slipping on greasy, wet, or dirty floors.
4. Running against projecting, poorly piled, or misplaced material.
5. Tearing hands or other parts of the body on projecting nails, hooks, or sticks.

Typical items of unsafe housekeeping

1. Excessive material, waste, or chips in working area.
2. Aisles congested.
3. Tools left on machines.
4. Waste containers overloaded.

5. Locker and washrooms unclean and in disorder.
6. Acids in open containers.
7. Broken glass about.
8. Electric leads and air lines across aisle.
9. Poor lighting.
10. Insecure, uneven, or otherwise improper methods.

The following lists are purposely limited. The student of the subject may find it mentally stimulating to develop his own lists, making them as complete as possible.

Housekeeping assistants

Since arrangements that are advantageous to production are also advantageous to housekeeping, consideration must be given to, and provision made for, the following:

1. Planning and layout of plant.
2. Proper layout of work area.
3. Anticipation of waste, scrap, dust, spillage, liquid splashing, and so on, and inclusion of means of control such as:
   a. Receptacles for waste and scrap with orderly means of disposal.
   b. Over-flow pans.
   c. Scrap guards.
   d. Chip screens.
   e. Chip catchers.
   f. Chutes.
   g. Exhaust and collector systems.
   h. Drains for liquid splash.
   i. Provision for storage.
   j. Transportation of the raw material and the finished product.
4. Efficient sequence of operations to avoid "bottle-necks."
5. The cleaning of windows, skylights, overhead equipment, ceilings, walls, roof trusses, and so on.
6. The elimination of ledges and other dirt catchers.
7. Safe and efficient cleaning methods, as vacuum cleaning, wet sweeping, scrubbing, and cleaning tools and equipment, cleaning compounds, and so on.
8. Adequate and safe provision for painting.
9. The marking of aisles and storage areas.
10. Scheduling cleaning to get adequate cleaning without interference with production.
11. Protective equipment for cleaners such as belts, gloves, boots, and goggles.

A large proportion of fires in plants are due to poor housekeeping. Oil-soaked rags and clothing ignite from spontaneous combustion. Dust collectors not properly cleaned similarly cause fires. Inflammable and combustible materials help feed the fires once they start.

In general, orderliness and cleanliness in a plant presuppose that management has supplied or provided:

1. Storage places for materials.
2. Cabinets and holders for tools and portable equipment.
3. Containers for materials in process.
4. Prompt removal of materials and refuse.
5. Clean place for the workers to change clothes and wash.
6. Careful training of the employee.

Often inadequate timing and planning for the handling, storing, and placing of materials causes delay or congestion that upsets the sequence of operations and yields a state of disorder.

Tool housekeeping is very important. The average plant uses a great variety of tools most (or all) of which are furnished by the company. Close control of their issuance and use saves tool cost. Tool maintenance is normally included in tool-room control, but maintenance that is reasonably satisfactory for production needs may not be adequate for safety. For example, one can do good work with a chisel whose head is mushroomed, but failure to prevent mushrooming of "struck" tools is a prolific source of injuries, chiefly to the eyes.

Good tool housekeeping is important both in the tool crib (or tool room) and on the job. Orderly arrangement of tool crib, suitable and adequate racks, pens, and holders, and an orderly routine in checking in and out, inspecting, repairing, and handling are essential.

At each machine and work bench, there should be a suitable holder or place for each tool, jig, or part used. In many plants, at least the heavier of such tools or parts and those subject to damage are kept on special wheeled racks that are returned to the tool room at the end of the shift.

Workmen should be taught to lay out their tools on each job in an orderly fashion. The workman who does this, having a definite place for each tool and keeping each tool in its place when it is not in his hands, will do more and better work and will be less subject to accidents.

Disposal of scrap. If suitable and convenient containers for scrap and waste are provided, and if the workers are trained to use them instead of letting the floor catch all the waste and then spending time and energy to clean it up, expense will be saved, safety will benefit, and the factory will be a better place in which to work. A good foreman or production engineer can estimate the quantity of waste in advance and determine suitable means of collecting and moving it as it is produced.

Marking locations. Areas clearly marked and identified as aisles, storage spaces, receiving and shipping points, assist in keeping things in order. Often the condition of a department is upset not because of lack of space, but because someone has placed a skid or loaded truck in zigzag fashion. The next one is placed the opposite way, and, as a result, there is disorder and a wastage of space through simple failure to place the loads properly. Orderly arrangement also makes it much easier to remove the stored material or equipment.

Preventing spillage. Oily floors are a common accident and fire hazard. The primary effort should be to prevent the spillage by design and construction of equipment and its adequate maintenance. Splash guards should be provided wherever oil (or other coolant) may be thrown, and drip pans wherever drippage may occur. The idea is to keep oil *off* the *floor*. This should receive careful attention in layout and planning.

Housekeeping and increased production. Under a demand for greatly increased production, the tendency is to "let down" on housekeeping including such things as the piling of materials and articles, cleaning of areas, keeping things checked up, and removing scrap and waste. This, of course, is conducive to accidents. If an operator requires a certain amount of space in which to work in ordinary times, surely he requires the same amount, if not more, when working under pressure for maximum production. Some firms find it desirable to have a decentralized system wherein each department has its cleaners, material movers, and others required to maintain good housekeeping and good order. This procedure is satisfactory, provided these men are not taken from their regular work to do something else. They must, of course, be provided with whatever equipment or other aids are needed. Many firms use special clean-up men, who go from department to department in an ordinary routine to carry out their specific duties of cleaning windows and lamps, emptying waste cans, removing scrap, and so on. Both systems have their good points, and sometimes a combination of both is desirable.

Responsibility must be definitely placed as to who is to do the cleaning and what area he is to cover. Otherwise, out-of-the-way places such as roofs, overhead pens, shelves, yards, small buildings and sheds, cellars, basements, and boiler rooms, are overlooked until such time as they get into a deplorable state. It isn't unusual for the sweepers to say, "I was not told to sweep that stairway," and as a result, dirt and rubbish accumulate and remain until an injury or inspector calls attention forcibly to the condition.

Management's responsibility

Management must take a definite part in the housekeeping program, and unless it accepts the responsibility not only of planning but also of enforcing consistently the measures decided on, good conditions will neither be secured nor maintained.

To begin with, the proper consideration must be given to orderliness when laying out the operations and processes.

Next, provision for specific facilities is required. A simple example of this might be the working area in a screw machine section:

1. Unless cabinets or shelves are supplied for storing the miscellaneous parts of the machine, the floor will be used.

2. The nature of the work in process produces chips that must be scrapped. Therefore, suitable containers must be provided.

3. Oil used as a coolant might splash and, therefore, splash guards and oil pans will be needed.

4. Considerable raw stock will be used and provision must be made for storing this.

5. When the parts are machined, tote boxes must be available for them.

Setting up a plan in the executive office without arranging for proper supervision to see that it is followed up and carried out is often the cause of a poor result. It is essential that the foremen and other supervisors follow through and obtain the coöperation of all employees. Sometimes it is necessary to allow a few minutes during the day for cleaning up, but it is best to clean up as required while the job is in progress.

Occasional grand clean-ups when an officer of the company or some other persons are expected do some good, but such spasmodic, hurry-up jobs would be unnecessary if a satisfactory plan where in operation.

Attempts have been made to reward foremen for superior performance with regard to safety and housekeeping by the inclusion of these items in profit-sharing plans. This can be accomplished by setting standards for rating the efficiency of the various departments and periodically appraising them on a point-rating or percentage-of-perfect-rating basis. Properly set up and objectively administered, the idea has considerable merit.

Allowances for costs

Modern management, of course, realizes that suitable working conditions involve a certain amount of expense, which must be included in the cost of the finished product. This expense might include special features in the construction of the buildings and the necessary equipment for the carrying on of a cleaning program. Whether the work is done in part by the operators or by specially designated laborers or cleaners is incidental, the primary purpose being to secure satisfactory results with the most efficient use of time and expense.

Improving housekeeping by competition

We expect to find excellent conditions throughout the shop if the chief executives, supervisors, and foremen are sold on the benefits of orderliness and cleanliness. In addition to this, it is, of course, necessary in order to attain any goal to have a plan which meets the specific essentials. For good housekeeping, the interest and coöperation of the supervisory group are an absolute essential, because it is this group that controls the conditions that they themselves create. The coöperation of the rank and file is also essential, but the supervisory personnel must provide the initiative and the leadership.

Many firms have found that competition of some kind, which stimulates thinking as well as action, goes a long way toward bringing about improvement. In making use of competition, or special drives, committees are appointed to make inspections. These may consist of an executive committee, a rotating committee of supervisors, a combination of supervisors and other employees, or representatives of the safety committee.

Inspection may be made weekly, semi-monthly, or monthly at irregular times so that clean-up squads cannot get busy just before the inspectors arrive and then let down on the job until the next inspection is expected.

Why should we have good housekeeping?

A clean and orderly place makes employees respect the company, plant, and working area. It assists in improving the quality of the products, the efficiency and safety of the worker, his morale and pride. A customer or visitor has more confidence in an organization when he finds things properly taken care of.

Orderliness in the working area is conducive to orderliness in the thinking area of the individual. It is the foundation of good working conditions and goes far toward reducing fatigue. Clean and attractive areas inspire the worker to keep things clean. A dirty, dark area attracts refuse and other material.

The following is typical of the type of form used in rating the various departments. Basic to the fair and effective use of any rating system is a clear understanding by each member of the rating committee of just what is to be regarded as justifying an award of a maximum score and also what deductions are to be made for the various faults found. It is usually best at the start to set the standard not very far above conditions in the best department. Gradually it may be raised as general improvement is secured.

PLANT HOUSEKEEPING INSPECTION CHECK LIST

COMMITTEE .... DATE ....

GROUP .... DEPARTMENT ....

Buildings:
   a. Are walls clean for this department? ....
   b. Are windows clean for this department? ....
   c. Are walls free of unnecessary hangings? ....
   d. Is proper light provided? ....
   e. Are platforms in good condition? ....
   f. Are stairs clean and well lighted; have they standard rails and standard treads? ....

Floors:
   a. Is floor surface good for this department? ....
   b. Is it swept clean, free of loose materials, and is it clean in the corners, back of radiators, along the walls, and around the columns? ....
   c. Is it free of oil, grease, etc.? ....
   d. Are operating floors, or work positions, free of loose stone, scrap, metal or other materials? ....
   e. Is the building free of unnecessary articles? ....
   f. Are receptacles provided for refuse? ....

Aisles:
   a. Are aisles free of obstructions? ....
   b. Is there safe and free passage to fire extinguishers, fire blankets, and stretcher cases? ....
   c. Is there safe and free passage to work positions? ....

Machinery and Equipment:
   a. Is it clean and free of unnecessary material or hangings? ....
   b. Is it free of unnecessary drippings of oil or grease? ....
   c. Is position around it clean and free of rags, paper, etc.? ....
   d. Are lockers and cupboards clean and free of unnecessary material, both on top of them and inside of them? ....
   e. Are benches and seats clean and in good condition? ....
   f. Are drinking fountains clean? ....
   g. Are toilet rooms clean and well ventilated? ....
   h. Are proper guards provided and in good condition? ....

Stock and Material:
   a. Is it properly piled and arranged? ....
   b. Is it loaded safely and orderly in ships, cars, trucks, etc.? ....

Tools:
   a. Are they properly arranged in place? ....
   b. Are they free of oil and grease? ....
   c. Are they in good working condition? ....
   d. Are tool rooms orderly and clean? ....

Grounds: (Fifteen feet from outside wall or to first railroad track)
   a. Is yard outside building free of refuse such as fruit peelings, scrap, wood, iron, etc.? ....
   b. Were winter hazards checked? ....

Chapter Thirteen

Maintenance

The proper maintenance of plant and equipment is essential to continuity of production. Satisfactory operating results are contingent upon having buildings, equipment, machinery, the portable tools, safety devices, and the like, not only in operating condition, but maintained in such manner that they can be relied upon not to delay production or make it necessary to stop work to make repairs.

Good management does not permit the practice of merely good enough maintenance to keep things usable. Instead, its policy is one of anticipating deterioration and setting up overhaul procedure designed to correct defects as early as possible in their development. This obviously requires close integration of maintenance with plant inspection. Preventive maintenance means replacing such worn parts as pipes, valves, etc., before they fail, and establishing a fixed schedule to do this.

Although every management knows that the steady production of goods of requisite quality requires that plant and equipment be kept in good operating condition, many do not appear to realize the worthiness of systematically following a policy of preventive maintenance. Instead, they try merely to keep at least the more essential machinery and equipment in good enough condition to avoid breakdowns, probably in the belief that this course means the minimum of expense. Actually, the weight of evidence is heavily on the side of those who believe that a system of maintenance that keeps all machinery, equipment, and plant in top operating condition at all times is the most economical in the long run. As one prominent operating executive put it, "The cheapest way to operate any machine is to keep it in good-as-new condition until obsolescence justifies its replacement."

A policy of preventive maintenance systematically followed is particularly important in accident prevention. There are several reasons for this. First of all, breakdowns of any sort tend strongly to yield worker injuries directly from the breakdown, and indirectly from the confusions, the interruptions in work sequences, and the hurried changes they cause. The pressure thrown on the maintenance and repair department by the breakdown of key equipment usually means that these men must do hazardous work against time. A management that insists upon full compliance with all applicable safety procedures in all such emergencies proves its safety mindedness thereby.

An especially high standard of maintenance is required for equipment whose failure can be especially serious. Some plants keep extensive records of maintenance inspection and overhaul for all plant and equipment. Others keep such records for "critical" equipment only, such as:

1. Electric hoists and cranes
2. Hooks, chains, eye bolts, slings, and cables
3. Pressures vessels and relief valves
4. Digesters, cookers and the like
5. Temperature control devices
6. Fire detection and extinguishment apparatus and equipment
7. Elevators.

Faultless maintenance of devices and equipment upon which the worker's safety depends is an obvious must. Any management or any worker tempted to temporize with this *must* should remember that safety equipment constitutes "the last thin line of defense" between the person or persons involved and the hazard in question. Failure to maintain safety equipment in as nearly perfect condition as possible is inexcusable.

A preceding chapter discussed safety-inspection methods and procedures at length. Much of this inspection has to do with maintenance, but preventive maintenance frequently goes much further and requires far more detailed taking apart, testing, and reconditioning than does inspection to find hazards and hazard points. The same basic principles and methods are applicable for the most part, however. Perhaps the chief difference is that for highly-specialized or complicated machinery, the inspector must have highly-specialized skill and knowledge. For some purposes, he must use special equipment and procedures, for example, X-rays to discover hidden flaws in castings and welds, radiography to determine the physical condition of the metal of which vital parts are made, and magnaflux to detect minute cracks.

Common accident-producing defects

Detailed analysis of mass accident data from industry in general unfailingly shows that the great majority of injuries are due to hazards that are common to practically all branches of industry. A similar statement applies to maintenance defects. The great majority of injuries attributable in whole or in part to poor maintenance come from what might be termed the ordinary, every-day kinds of defects. The following summary is illustrative:

1. Floor, stair, and walkway maintenance. Roughness, slipperiness, holes, splinters, poor patching, and the like, contribute particularly heavily to handling accidents and to slipping, tripping, and falling. In fact, thorough accident investigation shows them so commonly involved as to justify the dictum that determining the condition of "whatever he was walking, working or standing on" is always a must in investigating accidents.

2. Floor condition is particularly important about machinery and hazardous processes.

3. Men seem to be prone to fail to see defects that develop in commonly-used familiar equipment such as ladders, portable steps, railings, slings, ropes, chains, and hand trucks, yet these are prolific sources of injury.

4. The importance of *tool room control* of all hand tools is emphasized in Chapter 15, but defective tools are important enough in injury causation to justify their mention here.

5. It should be obvious that machine guards should always be maintained in perfect condition. Yet, a substantial proportion of "machinery" injuries in industry in general are attributable in whole or in part to inadequate guard maintenance.

6. Personal protective equipment. Although this is discussed in another chapter in detail it is emphasized here that unless an effective system of inspection and maintenance of all such equipment is set up and maintained, numerous defects will develop and will have a part in causing injuries. Few persons will, of their own volition, watch the condition of such equipment as goggles, respirators, shoes, aprons, and hand-protectors closely enough to catch developing defects soon enough for safety.

Typical recurring examples

The following cases of injury caused by maintenance defects are from accident data covering a large number of establishments representing a diversity of industries, mostly in manufacturing, but also including a number of quarries and construction jobs. These were all recurrent cases, in some instances almost identical in detail:

1. A key part in a single-action safety device on a punch press broke allowing the press to repeat. (An amputation is the usual result in manual feeding.)

2. A worn steel spring used to disengage a clutch failed causing the machine to operate unexpectedly. (Again an amputation is the frequent result.)

3. A loose nut frees a key bolt and allows a part to fall, or allows enough play to throw an excessive strain on some other part or fastening causing a breakdown.

4. Fires from overheated bearings.

5. Abrasive wheel explosions due to excessive play in bearings, incorrect mounting, or worn wheel.

6. Mushroomed heads of struck tools.

7. Failure of scaffold plank.

8. Failure of ladder, usually rung breakage.

9. Electric shock or burn due to insulation failure in electric-powered hand tools or portable equipment.

In chemical plants, commonly recurrent injury-causing accidents due to poor maintenance were acid leaks at pipes and fittings, valve or fitting failures from corrosion, packing gland blowouts, failure of relief valves to function.

Safety in maintenance work

Maintenance men should obviously be experienced mechanics, high in reliability and mechanical ability, but also they should be alert, have good judgment, capacity to "learn" machines and operations new to them and willing to change their work methods to meet changed situations. They must be willing to accept orders, work well with the minimum of supervision, and carry out a job to full completion in all details.

Safety mindedness is particularly important in maintenance work. Although many maintenance jobs are largely routine (for example relining a furnace, replacing a bearing, or changing a heavy motor), new situations are frequent, hazards are numerous and varied, and an emergency may arise at almost any time in many kinds of jobs. This means that safety training for maintenance men should go much further than for men on production work. Since much, at times most, of the work of maintenance and repair is non-repetitive, the emphasis should be placed on imparting a thorough knowledge of the kinds of hazards and hazardous exposures likely to be associated with the various jobs or kinds of work involved, and how to avoid or provide adequate protection against them.

Maintenance men, particularly riggers, those who do overhead work, electricians, and welders, should be well trained in the inspection of the equipment they work with. Even though there is (and there always should be) a well organized inspection procedure, each man should, himself, carefully check each piece of equipment on which his safety depends, before he uses it. Such particularly critical equipment as slings, boatswains' chairs, supplied air respirators, and the like should be checked occasionally on the job.

Planning and analyzing the job

Many of the points made and principles discussed in other chapters apply to maintenance jobs. Also, much of the technique of analyzing the job by breaking it down into its component parts is also applicable, particularly the example given of analyzing and planning the rebabbitting of a large mill bearing. If the indicated procedure is followed properly, the job will have:

1. Careful planning
2. Suitable equipment for the work available
3. Hazards anticipated and provisions made therefor
4. Necessary supervision, if needed
5. The proper selection of the men for the job.

Unfortunately, many accidents occurring during a maintenance job are overlooked because they do not result in injury to the worker. Examples of these follow:

1. Moving machinery; crane cable breaks, dropping machinery. Damage to the equipment but not to person.

2. Heavy loads being transported on factory trucks break through floor and tip over.

3. Ladder placed without being secured or bolted slides down.

4. Load on crane not raised high enough crashes into other equipment.

5. Drain cock in tank breaks off and oil or other liquid flows over the floor.

6. Material, tools, parts drop from above.

7. Dust collector catches fire.

8. Short circuit on wires.

9. Overloaded crane cable breaks.

10. Falling from scaffolding without injury.

11. A passing nausea or dizziness from inhaling fumes or gas.

12. Welders flashing pockets of gas without damage.

Getting protective equipment worn

The personal protective equipment that maintenance men should have and use is often a very troublesome problem both to the responsible executives and to the safety director because much of the work is under conditions that make some of the equipment uncomfortable to wear or a hindrance to free movement. Goggles steam up or get dirty. Mechanics, particularly those who "get around" (sometimes referred to as "boomer" mechanics), riggers, and the like tend to be highly individualistic. If they did not learn safe procedures and the use of suitable protective equipment when they learned their trades (and few of them who got their training before 1940 did), they do not take kindly to much of what good safety performance sets down as necessary. Although much of the content of other chapters bears on this problem, in the last analysis, it must be solved on a man-to-man basis between each maintenance foreman and each man under his direction. The safety director and frequently the personnel director can often help and advise, provided they have the respect of the foreman in question, but the primary responsibility must be exercised by the foreman.

The details of safe practice for maintenance men

It is not practical to include herein the details of safe practice in maintenance work, because they will vary from job to job, plant to plant, and by branch of industry as well. However, it is practical and helpful in any given plant or establishment to develop rules of safe practice that cover at least the more important things. A great many plants have done this and have printed these rules in booklets for maintenance men only.

The clean-up after the job

Although this is a detail, the failure of some maintenance and repair man or crew to restore the machine or apparatus or job to a safe operating condition has so frequently brought worker injury that emphasis here is justified. Since maintenance men generally work in departments other than their own, the tendency is to avoid cleaning up after completing a repair or overhaul job. A maintenance job is never complete until the entire area is restored to order, and particularly until the machine or equipment worked on is back in operating condition with all safeguards in place and in full operating condition. "He left the guard off" is far too often the finding of accident investigation. Holes made in the floor should be repaired, loose material and articles removed, equipment taken away, grease or oil cleaned up, and so on.

Chapter Fourteen

Handling Material

The subject of handling materials is an exceedingly broad one. All raw materials, parts, material in process, finished products, scrap and wastes used or produced in industry must be handled. The means used, therefore, must vary to meet such factors as character of material, size, weight, rate of handling, distances moved, the purpose of moving or handling—to mention a few. The methods and procedures used vary not only as between plants, but also as between departments within a plant, so that, whereas the handling of materials is an important function of over-all planning, the needs and problems of each department also must be studied in detail and suitable methods decided upon.

The reports of the agencies administering workmen's compensation acts show that, on the average, at least 25 per cent of compensable injuries in the manufacturing industries are connected with the handling of materials and objects. Accident experience also shows that the substitution of suitable mechanical means of handling for manual methods reduces accidents greatly. Also, it is faster and more efficient, and, if the relationship between volume of goods moved and the cost of the equipment required is within proper limits, the unit cost of moving will be favorable also. This factor of volume of material to be handled is vital, for even in the most modern, best-planned, and best-equipped plant, much lifting, carrying, and handling must be manual in whole or in part.

Since the subject is so big, this discussion is of necessity limited to certain phases of it that are of major importance to safety.

Methods of handling material

General methods (in addition to hand handling) of moving material commonly used in industrial establishments, both large and small, are briefly by:

1. Hand lift trucks
2. Dragging or sliding on skids or rollers
3. Wheelbarrows
4. Hand trucks, power trucks, and tractors
5. Hoisting apparatus
6. Overhead traveling cranes
7. Conveyors
8. Mechanical shovels
9. Elevators and escalators
10. Chutes (gravity or under pressure)
11. Pumps for liquids.

The basic fact that the unsafe acts of individuals are a factor in the majority of accidents justifies of itself the substitution of mechanical for manual operations wherever practicable. This statement implies, of course, that the mechanical means used must be of safe design and construction, suited to their purpose, thoroughly guarded, properly maintained, and that the personnel selected to operate them be properly qualified and adequately supervised. Typical hazards of the use of such equipment are overloading, poor arrangement of material, operating at excessive speed, lack of adequate space for operation, lack of skill, and improper attitude on the part of the operator.

Safe practices and methods should be applied

Those responsible for, and those who do, the actual work should have a knowledge of safe practices as well as methods. Following are some ways to prevent accidents and injuries:

1. Men should lift with the leg muscles, keeping their backs straight and their knees bent. One man should not attempt to lift an object alone if two men are required for safety.

2. When very heavy or long objects are carried by two or more men, teamwork and motion in unison is essential. One person should be the leader and direct the work. Special tools should be used whenever possible. Sometimes a whistle is used for giving signals for lift, walk, and let down.

3. In handling long material such as pipe, lumber, and ladders, the front end should be held high and the rear end low. This is done so that the front end is above the height of a person when turning blind corners.

4. A very heavy object should not be raised by hand if a crane, hoist, or other method is available. Such objects, especially if odd in shape or bulky, may get out of control and cause an accident.

5. When rolling tanks or other heavy round parts either up or down an incline, the motion should be controlled with ropes or tackle, and men should never stand on the downhill side.

6. Since many handling operations consist of loading and unloading near machines or processes, safe practices are likely to be overlooked because the piling is temporary. Actually, the hazard may be greater in such a location than in a warehouse. Even if the hazard is slight, bad piling establishes a precedent which later leads to injuries. Therefore, piling should always be properly done.

7. Tools and equipment such as shovels, forks, crowbars, wheelbarrows, hand trucks, cant hooks, and other handling gear should be kept in good operating condition.

8. Protecting the hands by gloves, leather pads, and the like, and protecting the feet by safety shoes and foot guards are of value when handling lumber, metal in various forms, boxes, and any other articles heavy enough to injure the feet.

9. Holes and unevenness in floors cause material to be shaken from loaded trucks.

10. Aisles should be clear and wide enough to allow ample space for all traffic they are called upon to carry. Sometimes traffic should be rerouted.

11. The piling of material must include proper tiering and securing, as well as proper provision for its safe and efficient removal. Supervision and training must include safe means of its removal. Material piled for unpiling from the top may become unsafe if removed from one side.

12. When using wheelbarrows, the load should be placed well forward to make it easier to lift and push the barrow. Overloading should be avoided and the runway should be smooth, steady, and strong. Knuckle guards should be provided for passing through narrow doors or between columns.

13. Proper slings should be used and placed correctly when making a lift. Loads should be secured to prevent tipping and sliding.

14. Hand lift trucks are in general use throughout industry. It is important that the proper type of truck be selected for the task and that it be kept in good condition. Care must be exercised to keep the center of gravity of the load as low as possible to prevent tipping, shifting, or falling off of material. Push, rather than pull, should be the rule. Handles should be left in a vertical position when not in use so that no one will trip over them. Counterweights, springs, or hooks may be installed for this purpose. Maintenance is particularly important with the hydraulic hand lift trucks to prevent "dropping" the load. If a brake can be applied to advantage, this should be done.

Industrial trucks

Industrial trucks, usually powered by storage batteries or internal combustion engines, are used extensively in industry for the handling of materials to and from stockpiles, to and from machines, and on through to warehouse or loading platform or car. These trucks are of many types, weights, and capacities. Some weigh several tons and have a capacity of several tons. The power is carried through simple operating controls to the travel motors, which drive the truck and operate the lifting devices at the will of the operator.

The platform type, which is used to carry the load from one place to another, requires either manual or mechanical handling for loading and unloading.

The elevating type of platform truck makes use of a skid or pallet on which the load is placed. The platform is inserted under the skid, elevated to lift it from the floor, and the truck carries it to some other point.

The fork lift truck makes the lift by means of a two-prong fork instead of a platform. It is designed to lift the load up to about ten feet from the floor, permitting high piling to conserve space. Since this involves heavy floor loading, floor strength must be considered when planning for the use of these trucks.

Another type of truck simply acts as a tractor to pull trailer loads of material.

Generally, the supervision of the trucks and operators is centralized in a transportation department, and the operators have specific assignments. The flow material is controlled by job tickets, which indicate where the material is to be placed. In large organizations, it has been found satisfactory to have an incoming and outgoing material bay. This allows for a general delivery point from which the department men convey the material to the specific point. When the work is completed, it is placed in the outgoing bay if it is to be consigned to another department. Thus, the general transportation department operator comes in with a load, deposits it in the incoming bay, checks the job tickets, and takes a load out with him.

The smooth flow of material is so vital a part of production that the careful selection of the operators of these trucks in the interest both of efficiency and safety is an important matter. Some plants find it best to license all truck operators after first giving them special training in the operation of the truck, the routine to be followed, and the rules and regulations to be observed. The method used is similar to the procedure in licensing an automobile driver and includes an operation test, a verbal quiz, and registration. A truck operator's badge must be worn when operating the truck.

Racks for tiering skids

The primary function of fork trucks or other elevating mechanisms is to place skids, drums, bales, or pallets either in racks or on top of each other in order to save storage space. Skid tiering racks aid stability and give greater flexibility. They provide for the placing of two, three, or four skids one on top of another on a rack or track so that the lower skids may be removed without disturbing the upper ones. They are used in stock rooms, accumulation areas, machine shops, fabrication shops, and outdoor storage. By proper planning and layout of floor space, utilizing wherever possible existing aisles and open area ways, more material can be placed in a given area, and each unit load is readily accessible at all times.

Miscellaneous methods of handling material

Far-seeing supervisors will plan to use special tools and fixtures to simplify the handling of materials used in their department. Examples of these are:

1. A tote box handle that is attached to the tote box so that it can be dragged along the floor.

2. A special fixture in which to place compressed gas cylinders so that they can be lifted or hoisted on a crane.

3. Car movers.

4. Rope used for snubbing to act as a brake when unloading heavy drums from trucks.

5. Pike holes for rolling barrels.

6. Tongs and pliers for handling hot metal.

7. Hand hooks for freight handlers.

8. Hooks for rolling logs.

9. Rollers for heavy, bulky material.

10. Special slings.

11. Chain hoists.

12. Traveling, gantry, and wall cranes.

13. Clamps for handling sheet steel, barrels, boxes, and so on.

14. Box car loaders.

15. Special hand trucks for drums, others for carboys.

Conveyors

Special conveyors and Monorail systems are used in many instances to eliminate manual labor, expedite the movement of material, and also to facilitate the processing or assembly. Examples of these are:

1. The automobile assembly line.

2. Conveyor systems on which to hang and move material to be painted so that the spraying operation can be done at the exhausted-spray booth.

3. Roller conveyors at certain points that allow for loading baskets and then passing them through the degreaser, washer, or dryer areas.

Improved methods as they apply to safety

If up-to-date improved methods are used in all cases of handling material, we remove, to a great extent, the human element by using mechanical devices to replace manual labor. This phase of plant operation is often neglected in spite of the fact that much time and money is consumed in the handling of materials. Such weakness decreases the efficiency of the organization and increases the number of accidents. The installation of proper methods, therefore, reduces the hazards as well as the cost. Frequently, allowance is not made for the growth of a plant or the changes in products and processes. Management becomes accustomed to the old methods and accepts their limitations. A competent safety man, in close coöperation with the methods or planning department, will examine with a critical eye the system in use with a view to improving conditions.

Typical indications of out-of-date or faulty methods are:

Lack of orderliness.   Improper sequence of operations and arrangement of machines makes it necessary to move stock back and forth rather than in a direct line to the finished product.

Lost material.   Lost material makes it necessary to provide additional expeditors or searchers to locate material in process that has gone astray.

Manual lifting.   Any excessive amount of hand lifting of heavy objects indicates the need of such mechanical aids as lifting devices or special trucks.

The absence of suitable traffic aisles or storage space.   Inadequate aisle space and insufficient storage space will inevitably create disorderliness. Therefore, provisions for aisles and storage spaces and a place for everything are of prime importance.

Skids, boxes, and containers overloaded or carelessly loaded. This might indicate poor supervision, poor training, or lack of suitable containers.

Equipment in poor repair.   This includes wobbly truck wheels, broken truck bodies, faulty power equipment, floors in poor condition, worn cables and slings, worn or broken tools, which indicate the results of lack of maintenance.

In most of the larger organizations we find that attention has been paid to these things. Establishments that haven't done so would benefit by paying more attention to symptoms of this kind. They would improve both safety and efficiency by applying suitable remedies.

Applying safety measures in handling materials

So many problems are involved in a subject of this kind that no one can deal with all of them. Searching out the obvious hazards and applying the corrective measures is definitely a part of the safety man's duties. Let us take a few examples of hazards and apply the remedy.

Operation, Hazard, or Injury	Preventive Measures
1. *Overhead crane load:* One-eighth inch steel plates, 60" by 90" slip out of crane sling. Man struck on head.	Proper binding of load. Crane load should never be passed over heads of workers. Arrangements made to warn workers, by bell or other signal, to get out of way. Use spreader for lifting this kind of load.
2. *Incoming railroad car:* Material jammed between side of building and car.	Proper clearances between sides, tracks, and fixed objects. Supervision of loading and movement of railroad cars, adequate lighting, reduction of speed, special training.
3. *Handling acid carboys:* Carboy broke, acid splashing on man. Possible injuries: burns, inhalation of toxic fumes, eye injuries.	Use trucks designed especially for acid carboys. Arrange for runway if necessary to get on platform. Assign duties to specific individuals. Provide adequate safety equipment such as goggles, rubber boots, aprons, rubber gloves. Provide shower bath for use in case of accident. Give special training and instructions as well as information regarding the hazards involved.
4. *Piling materials:* Falling materials, strains from lifting, falls, foot and hand injuries.	Special equipment for piling. Methods worked out to suit materials and conditions, training in proper way to lift and to pile materials, adequate storage space, orderliness, lighting.
5. *Handling stock or articles at machines or processes:* Abrasions, cuts, bruises and sprains of hands and arms, slivers in hands and arms, foot injuries, dermatoses, eye injuries from flying particles, burns.	Gloves (not on revolving equipment), wrist and hand leathers, aprons, safety shoes, goggles. Reduce handling by layout of machines and processes and by motion study and special handling methods suited to specific conditions.

OPERATION, HAZARD, OR INJURY	PREVENTIVE MEASURES
6. *Emptying and cleaning tank cars:* Suffocation or poisoning on entering tanks, burns from acid drips, falls from cars, explosion of inflammable gases, electric shock from extension cords.	Testing of air in cars, steaming out, washing out, or ventilation of cars, use of fresh-air masks, use of life line and watcher outside car, training, supervision, proper ladders, platforms, and tools, and equipment, safeguarded extension cords and lights, protective clothing.
7. *Transporting materials and articles through the process:* Struck by trucks, hand pinched, torn or bruised under or between articles, articles falling on feet, falls over loose articles, strains, getting caught by powered conveying machinery.	Planned and routed traffic, clear aisles, trained power vehicle operators, hand truck of proper type, adequate spaces for placing at machines or other stations, housekeeping and order, complete guarding of all hazardous moving parts. Good maintenance of equipment and floors.
8. *Preparing for shipment:* Strains, tool injuries, falls.	Order, training, proper equipment, adequate space, supervision.
9. *Opening baled, crated, or barreled material:* Cuts and abrasions from sharp edges; nail wounds, strains from lifting, tool wounds.	Adequate space for work, proper tools, training, supervision, housekeeping and order, hand, foot, and leg protection, lighting.

Auto trucks and railroad cars also play an important part in the delivery of materials. No mention has been made of details in connection with these important phases of material movement since they should be dealt with as a separate subject. The same is true of pipe line as used for gas and oil.

The engineer's part

Through engineering we have substituted mechanical power for manpower. Mechanical feeding and handling equipment has replaced dangerous manual handling, which in itself is always slower and more costly. Workers thus released are available for more important jobs. Since the substitution of mechanical equipment for human labor reduces the number of men exposed to hazards, we automatically reduce the number of accidents and injuries because of this fact alone. If we continue to develop and train workers efficiently to apply the mechanical devices that have replaced manual labor, we can continue the downward trend of the accident rate. The results are contingent on proper supervision, training, enforcement, application, and maintenance of the various equipment used.

Management has a special interest

If the layout of a plant is designed to provide for an eventual increase in production capacity, it must be flexible enough to accommodate volume fluctuations in all lines. In this way, congestion will be relieved and better operating efficiency will be obtained from manufacturing and storage area and from improved arrangement of machinery and equipment.

Since production is material in motion, low costs can be achieved through an efficient materials-handling system. The basic aim should be to locate the proper equipment, engineered to the correct procedure, at the right shop, to enable the manufacture of the unit in the most efficient manner, in the shortest possible time over a minimum distance.

Because production is material on the move, we must consider the fundamental requirements necessary in a well-planned shop. These must include:

1. Adequate facilities to receive, inspect, and distribute incoming material.

2. Short, direct routes to and from principal raw stores areas and processing areas to provide fast, efficient movement, and storage of material.

3. Proper arrangement of machinery and equipment in each department to provide ample room to place material within easy reach of workers.

4. Free access to machines and assembly benches for quick delivery of material within each department and for fast pick-up of outbound material and waste.

5. Grouping of machines and departments so movement of material between operations is as short as possible, with a minimum of backtracking.

6. Adequate storage facilities for material in process between operations.

7. Stock rooms and tool cages with facilities to receive, store, inventory, and disperse parts and tools with minimum handling and effort.

8. Facilities to pack or crate finished products efficiently and to ship by all classes of carriers.

If these basic requirements are satisfied, the plant will have a materials-handling system that can move and store material efficiently with the least possible effort, greatest safety, and in the shortest possible time consistent with economy.

Naturally each service department employs non-productive labor—labor which adds cost to the product and to the possibility of accidents resulting in injuries. By reducing the number of people exposed, by using suitable equipment, careful planning and supervision, we can show reductions in cost, time, and accidents.

Suggested procedure for management

1. Analysis of past injuries resulting from handling material.

2. Analysis of existing methods with a view to improving them.

3. Improved supervision and training of every worker, bringing to light the hazards involved in material handling.

4. Enforcement of rules and instructions in safe handling practice.

5. Checking up on the maintenance of material-handling equipment.

Following through with this procedure helps us to progress along well-founded practices and effective principles.

Chapter Fifteen

Hand Tools

Hand-tool injuries are relatively numerous in all branches of industry. Since they result from the use of tools that are defective or unsuited to the purpose, or from unsafe methods of use, corrective measures can be carried out within the department. Too often there is failure to appreciate the importance of keeping hand tools in good condition and of eliminating the use of the wrong tool for the purpose. The attitude of the supervisor in a large measure controls the practices and working habits relating to small tools within his department. All tools must be made safe, maintained in good condition, and used properly.

Hand tools are not ordinarily thought of as dangerous agencies likely to produce injuries. Also, it is generally assumed that the injuries they do yield will be minor in nature. Actually, the use of hand tools in the manufacturing industries as a whole and in many individual industries is a major source of injuries.

It is true that the proportion of permanent disability cases from the use of hand tools is low as compared to such cases in many other activities as, for instance, the operation of machinery. However, the total of serious injuries is still large. Flying particles from mushroomed heads, overtempered points, or the material being worked on, destroy many eyes and cause many puncture wounds. Many fatalities result from the use of electric-powered hand tools. Furthermore, the fact that the proportion of minor injuries (non-lost-time cases) is high means that a large total of working time is lost during the treating of these little injuries. Hand-tool injuries can be prevented as definitely as those from any other source, and it is just as profitable to prevent them.

Hand tools of one sort or another are used in every industry, more particularly in the metal-working trades, in maintenance and repair work, construction, logging, and lumbering. Some tools are common to all of these, as well as special tools peculiar to certain occupations.

Control of accidents

We can control accidents directly attributed to defective and improper hand tools, but we have more difficulty in controlling the action of the worker who might strike the tool a glancing blow, thus causing a piece of steel to fly at high velocity and strike his eye. The accident in cases of this kind cannot always be controlled, because of human imperfection, but the injury can be avoided by the use of goggles.

Hammers with corrugated heads help prevent the heads from glancing off nails. If crystallization has taken place in the head of a hammer, or a highly tempered piece of steel is struck, chips are likely to fly because of the brittleness of the material. Blacksmiths must use care in tempering all hand tools, particularly those used for chipping or similar operations, because of the danger of pieces breaking off and flying.

Because of this danger, all heat treating should be done by those skilled in the art, who understand the properties of the metals used and know how to apply the treatment required in each case. This point deserves emphasis, for until the quite recent past, tools and chains were made from a very limited range of carbon steels which any good blacksmith could temper properly. Metallurgical research has brought a multiplicity of steels, which require specialized heat treatment. Also a much greater technical understanding of the crystalline structure of steels has been gained. Heat treatment is a highly specialized art.

Needless to say, material from which hand tools are made should be of good quality and appropriate for the use to which it will be put. A periodic inspection of all tools would include the collection of those that need dressing, repairing, and replacements. This work, of course, should be done only by persons qualified to do it. Tools not in use should be stored safely on racks or shelves designed for them or should be placed in tool boxes.

Use of wrong tool for purpose

At times the supply of suitable tools is not sufficient to meet the demand, and, in other cases, through lack of training or knowledge, a tool in excellent condition is used for a purpose for which it was not designed. For example:

1. Machinist's hammer used for driving nails.

2. Carpenter's hammer used for hammering metal.

3. Drill sharpened for drilling steel used on brass or copper without removing the lip.

4. Screw driver used for a chisel.

5. Use of open-end wrench which is too large for the nut to which it is applied.

6. Knife used as a screw driver.

7. File used as a drift pin to remove the drill from the chuck.

8. Wrench used for a hammer.

9. Pipe used on ordinary wrench for leverage.

Tools must be used correctly and for the purposes for which they are designed. Otherwise, we may expect accidents and injuries.

Incorrect methods of using tools

Let us assume that we have a hand tool in excellent condition and are using it for the right purpose. The way we use it must be correct also to avoid accidents. For example:

Sharpening a pencil. Push the sharp edge of the blade away from the body.

Use of monkey wrench. Place the wrench on the nut in such a position that the pull on the handle tends to force the jaws further onto the nut. This would ordinarily mean that the open jaws are facing you while you are pulling instead of pushing on the wrench.

Chisels. When chiseling wood or metal, do so in such a way that if the chisel should glance from the object it will fly away from your body.

Draw knife. Keep far enough away so that if the knife leaves the wood, it will not cut your body.

Hand saws. Placing the fingers or thumb close to the blade when starting to cut is dangerous.

Hatchets, axes, and adzes. Fingers, toes, and other parts of the body must be well out of line with the swing of the tool so that injury from a glancing blow or a miss may be avoided.

Pliers and wire cutters. Ordinarily these are safe tools, but their use on or about live circuits results in many short circuits, burns, and shocks.

Files. Unless a handle is used to cover the sharp pointed tines, there is danger of receiving a puncture wound in the palm of the hand or at the base of the wrist. Never hit a file with a hammer; pieces of the hardened steel are almost sure to fly. If used to pry with, it may break, causing pieces to fly.

Defective tools

Following is a list of defects that may be found in the more common tools used:

Chisels, punches. Mushroomed or chipped heads, chipped or dull edges or points, overtempered heads and points, too short for hand safety.

Mallets. Uneven, worn heads, poorly secured handles.

Electric-power tools. Worn, deteriorated, or inadequate insulation, split or chipped plugs, worn or bent plug terminals, defective switch, vibration, sparking, wrong drill, projections on chuck, lack of guard (as portable grinder or saw), worn or insecure chuck (or other attachment device), disconnected ground wire or absence of a ground wire.

Files. Handles missing, chipped ends, teeth worn smooth or filled.

Hammers. Loose, split or rough handles, chipped or battered heads, sprung or broken claws (carpenter hammer), poorly secured handles (nails in place of wedge).

Hooks. Dull points, handles improperly shaped, leaving finger-pinching hazards.

Knives. Lack of finger guards, dull or nicked edges, loose or split handles.

Lifting jacks. Worn threads, ill-fitting or sprung safety pawls, inadequate base, sprung, ill-fitting or inadequate operating handle.

Pick axe. Loose or split handles, dull or bent blade, bent shank.

Saws. Improper set, sprung blades, loose or splintered handles, dull.

Screw drivers. Split or battered handles, dull or bent blade, bent shank.

Shovels. Split, rough, or loose handles.

Tongs and pliers. Poorly shaped, worn or chipped jaws, handles improperly shaped, leaving finger-pinching hazard.

Wrenches (pipe, monkey, end, and the like). Worn or sprung jaws, battered heads, rough, broken, or sprung handles, worn mechanism.

Special attention must be given to corrective measures in connection with these and other defective tools.

Tool-room control of tools

A safety-minded tool-crib attendant, properly trained and equipped to inspect and repair defective tools, is in an excellent position to prevent accidents. All tools should be issued from the tool room and returned to it periodically for inspection and repair. If this procedure is supplemented by an occasional inspection of the tools in each department, and if each foreman coöperates in his daily rounds, a good standard of maintenance and correct use of tools can be maintained.

In some plants, the tool room has its own repair shop. In others, tools that need repairs are turned over to the section designated for this work, and, when reconditioned, are returned to the tool room for reissuance.

Purchasing small tools

The coöperation of the purchasing department to insure the ordering of equipment on the basis of efficiency and safety, as well as price, is necessary.

A central tool and planning department from which supplies for the department cribs are forwarded is generally used. This should be supervised by a man who has mechanical ability, a knowledge of tools and their usage, and who can foresee the application of them in the shops. He is charged with the responsibility for ordering suitable tools for the shop and his requests to the purchasing agent should specify the kind of tool to be ordered, and, if necessary, the catalog number.

This system gives greater assurance of the safety of design and construction, as well as of application.

Provisions for safe handling of tools

Annual expenditures for both durable and nondurable tools run into large totals in the average factory. In order to keep tools in good condition, it is necessary that suitable arrangements be made for storage within the tool crib, for transportation or delivery to the workers, and for suitable holders, shelves, or cabinets for them at the benches or machines. Sheaths or guards for edged or pointed tools are required, particularly where they are carried from one place to another by the worker, as in the case of ice picks, knives, and axes.

Mechanically operated portable tools

Up to this point, we have dealt with hand-operated tools. Power-operated portable tools require special consideration, since they present additional hazards. Following is a list of some commonly used power-driven hand tools:

Grinders.	*Riveters.*
Polishers.	*Hoists.*
Drills.	*Portable exhausts.*
Nut and bolt drivers.	*Circular saws.*
Chippers.	*Small internal and external grinders.*

These tools usually are submitted to a considerable amount of abuse as well as improper usage. In many cases, the point of operation can be properly guarded or other safety precautions taken in order to protect the operator. For example:

1. Every portable circular saw should be equipped with a guard that at all times encloses all of the teeth except those in the cut.

2. Grinding wheels should be equipped with a guard enclosing all of the wheel that the work permits and flanges of the proper size over soft washers. Dropping or striking the abrasive wheel is hazardous.

3. Grounding the cases of electric tools by means of a third wire or central grounding through the receptacle is imperative in all cases to prevent shock should the insulation break down.

4. Powered nut and bolt drivers are difficult to control after the nut or bolt is driven home and, therefore, a release or stop should be provided.

5. The fan blades of portable exhausts should be enclosed.

6. Wherever possible, powered tools should be equipped with deadman control so that if the operator loses his hold the machine will stop automatically.

7. Leads and hose lines should be protected from wear, sharp bends, and damage.

8. It isn't unusual for a man operating a portable air-operated grinder to change the governor in order to increase the speed. This, of course, produces overspeeding with the likelihood that the wheel will explode. The speeds of such equipment should be checked periodically.

Some of the special attachments for machines as, for instance, internal and external grinders used on lathes, require special precautions. Speed variations to allow the use of different sizes and types of wheels are secured by combinations of pulleys. Fatalities and major injuries due to bursting of wheels are on record because workers failed to comply with the instructions issued with these machines, indicating the proper pulley combinations for certain kinds and sizes of wheels. Overspeeding of five or more times safe speed is possible in many cases.

Safety men must recognize and become familiar with all portable equipment and arrange for proper periodical inspections to be made.

A worker properly trained in selecting the right kind of tool for the job, who uses it correctly and keeps it in good condition, should, under ordinary conditions, avoid accidents both to himself and to others.

A safety man or supervisor who checks up on the operation of a tool crib and inspects the equipment therein will find in many instances conditions which indicate the need of a more careful inspection, an improved purchasing system, and more intelligent use and application of the tools involved.

Supervisors sometimes overlook the importance of checking up on small tools and making provision for maintenance, safety, and replacement. This not only fits in with keeping costs and accidents down, but also tends toward increasing production and quality.

Chapter Sixteen

Low-voltage Electrical Hazards

The subject of low-voltage electrical hazards is extremely broad. A large number of factors closely related to safety are involved in the transmission and utilization of electricity, such as design, installation, protective devices, inspection, maintenance, and training.

An issue of *Accident Facts* lists causes of occupational accidents connected with electrical equipment in Pennsylvania industries as follows:

Unsafe Act or Cause	Per Cent
Overloading, poor arranging	36
Unnecessary exposure to danger	10
Unsafe or improper use of equipment	31
Nonuse personal protective equipment	5
Working on moving or dangerous equipment	16
Improper starting or stopping	2

Excellent progress has been made in the control of electrical hazards and the good record has been attributed to the coöperation of manufacturers of electric equipment, governmental bodies, insurance companies, and others interested in the safe use of electricity. The National Electrical Code * and the National Electrical Safety Code † also play an important part in accident-prevention work.

Electric shocks due to the use of electrical equipment occur without warning and are usually serious. The average individual thinks of the hazards of electric shock in terms of high voltage and does not always realize that it is primarily the current that kills and not the voltage. Conse-

---

* Developed under the sponsorship of the National Board of Fire Underwriters and approved as "American Standard." This pamphlet is also issued as "NBFU Pamphlet #70."

† Developed under the sponsorship of the National Bureau of Standards and approved as "American Standard" C-2. Also issued as Bureau of Standards Handbooks 31, 32, 33, 34, 35.

quently, persons who work around low-voltage equipment do not always have the same healthy respect for it that they do for high voltage. They do not realize that the governing factor is the relationship between the voltage one is in contact with and the resistance of the circuit of which his body is a part. If this resistance is low, the voltage may be low and still be sufficient to kill. Deaths from the ordinary 110-volt lighting circuit are numerous.

This chapter will deal primarily with voltages ordinarily used with shop lighting and power circuits (110-220-440 volts).

A person receives an electric shock whenever any part of his body becomes part of an electric circuit through which a sufficient current flows to cause discomfort or worse. Current flow slightly above that sufficient to cause discomfort causes involuntary contraction of the muscles, affects or stops the heart, stops breathing, or causes burns.

The course through the body may be local, as, for example, finger to finger, or hand to hand, or through the heart or central nervous system or other parts of the body, depending largely upon which part or parts of the body touch the live conductor and the ground. The shock may come from contact between a live part and ground or between two live parts at different polarity or phase.

The severity of injury from electric shock will be determined by the:

1. Amount of current that flows through the body.
2. Path the current takes through the body.
3. Length of time the victim is in the circuit.
4. Type of electric energy in question.
5. Physical condition of the victim.

The amount of current that flows through the victim's body will depend upon:

1. The voltage of the circuit with which he is in contact.
2. The insulating qualities of the place in which he is located at the instant.
3. The resistance of his skin or clothing or both.
4. The area of contact with the live conductor.
5. The pressure of contact with the live conductor.

The current will take the path of least resistance through the body or over its surface or will be a combination of the two. Wet clothing may furnish a lower resistance path than that through the body, or part of the current may flow through the body and part ocer its surface.

Current of sufficiently high frequency heats but does not shock. This is taken advantage of in diathermy. Direct current is generally considered to carry less shock hazard for a given voltage than alternating current, but since D.C. arcs are more persistent than those from A.C., it is likely to burn more severely.

Whereas physical condition is undoubtedly a factor at times, its importance is probably greatly overrated. Investigations of deaths from low voltages rarely justify the commonly heard comment, "His heart must have been bad."

Causes of injuries from low voltages

The causes of injuries from low voltages may be listed as follows:

1. Touching live parts.
2. Short circuit.
3. Accidental ground.
4. Overload.
5. Breaking connections.

Grounding all machine tools, casings, and structures

The frames or cases of all tools or structures in which electric devices or circuits are present should be substantially grounded.

The ground wire should be of low resistance and large enough to resist mechanical breakage and to carry off the heaviest current flow that might result from any insulation breakdown or other accident.

Particulars regarding such details as conductor sizes and nature of grounds are beyond the scope of this text. Reference should be made to the National Electrical Code governing them.

Artificial respiration

If the victim of electric shock has ceased breathing, it is essential that artificial respiration be applied immediately if his life is to be saved. He must first be removed from the live conductor, but his rescuer must not make the mistake of coming in contact with the live circuit himself.

For details of the proper procedure in rescuing and restoring the victim of electric shock, the reader is referred to the chapter on first aid. The most recent accepted method is the mouth to mouth blowing of air into the victim's lungs.

Portable electric tools

Accidents and injuries resulting from the use of portable electric tools are much too frequent. Many of these result from failure to ground the metal frame of the tool properly. Defective insulation permits the frame to be energized at, or near, line-potential, thus exposing the workmen to shock. Frequently, the injury from shock is minor compared to the injury resulting from a fall from a ladder or scaffold because of the shock.

The use of portable tools and extension lamps on steel structure and piping, in boilers and tanks, and on other jobs where the operator is in good contact with the ground is especially dangerous unless care and suitable equipment are used. To overcome the hazards, many modern plants are using a lower voltage (32 V) for extension lights and portable tools.

Regardless of where these tools are used, it is necessary to ground the frame of the tool by connecting a separate wire between the frame and a good ground.

A three-wire cord provides for carrying the two power wires and a grounding conductor. The grounding conductor may be connected to the ground by means of a clamp, or the three wires of the cord may be connected to a three-prong plug or contactor. The use of a three-prong plug requires a special wiring system and ground, as well as receptacles to accommodate the plugs. In the latter system, it is essential that the responsibility of connecting the wire be given to qualified people, since the ordinary workmen may fail to connect the proper wire to the ground. It is thus possible to reverse the grounding conductor of a three-wire cord whereby a live wire is used as a grounding conductor, with the result that the frame of the appliance becomes energized.

Because of the frequent hard usage and bad handling of portable equipment, frequent insulation-resistance tests may be necessary. The cords should carry Underwriters Laboratories approval. Portable lamp holders and guards should be made of insulating materials.

Simple rules to follow

1. Do not guess about whether a circuit is alive or not. Consider every one alive until proved otherwise.

2. Use proper instruments for testing circuits.

3. Never touch any wire of a circuit unless you know that it is dead.

4. Use safety equipment when necessary, as rubber gloves, rubber mats, fuse tongs, insulated tools, and the like.

5. Lock open main switches and place tags before working on power circuits so that no one else may close them while you are working. Before closing a switch, make certain other workmen are clear of circuits.

6. Use danger signs and rope off dangerous areas.

7. In installing temporary electric wiring or apparatus, make every job safe.

8. Observe strictly the applicable rules of the National Electrical Safety Code.

9. Allow only qualified men to work on electric apparatus.

10. Arrange for proper maintenance of equipment, leads, and wires with careful follow-up to see that insulation is in proper condition.

11. Never bridge a fuse with wire or other metal.

12. Don't allow men to work on live circuits alone.

13. Don't test power lines with lamps to determine whether they are alive. A 110-V test lamp placed across a 440-V line will blow up. Voltage testers are available for testing.

14. Have periodic electrical inspections made by men qualified by experience and training to do such work.

15. Don't use aluminum ladders on electrical jobs.

WHAT THE INSPECTOR SHOULD LOOK FOR

Equipment and Hazard	*Correct Condition*
Sockets on extension cords or drop cords. Brass shells become "live" readily through moisture or conducting dust and dirt, or through wear or hard usage. The mechanism of key sockets may fail. Sufficient moisture or conducting dust may allow a shock to be received from even a key type weatherproof socket.	Use only insulated combination socket and handle with no live parts exposed.
Cords (extension). Insulation fails, metal lamp guards and metal cases become live through lack of insulation, moisture, or dirt, key sockets fail, plugs break or the parts loosen. Those used on portable power tools are subject to harder use and are more often exposed to oil and grease.	Use heavy, live rubber cord, plugs of the moulded, nonbreakable type. Good practice requires that wall receptacles be provided for all extension cord use. Avoid unnecessary wear and abuse.
Electric wiring. Loose or improperly insulated or inadequately spaced wires may cause fires. Contact even with covered wires may result in shocks. Improperly placed wiring may be damaged.	Install all wiring in substantial and permanent manner when run, if possible; "temporary" wiring tends to become permanent. Properly knob, space, insulate, and secure open wiring. Do not run wiring where it may receive mechanical injury. Allow no cords, pendants or other conductors to be wrapped around or be in contact with water pipes, steel columns, or other metal parts. Use only rigid conduit in damp basements or similarly wet locations. Wiring for such incidental services as electric irons, clocks, etc. should not be substandard.

WHAT THE INSPECTOR SHOULD LOOK FOR

Equipment and Hazard	Correct Condition
Fuses. Often bridged to permit overloads. Refillable fuses with extra links to carry starting overload.	Bridging not permissible, mounting in boxes under lock and key sometimes advisable. Bridging usually evidence of overloaded circuit. Fuses should be on load side of switches and of correct rating for load. Limit extra links for refillable fuses to authorized personnel.
Electric welding receptacles. Men attach welding leads to switch box with clips.	Special standard welder's receptacles should be provided for electric welders. The practice of clipping the leads to switch boxes is dangerous. In some cases clips have been found on the power side of the line, which increases the hazard.
Switchboards. Shocks from exposed live parts, flashes from the operation of air-break switches or circuit breakers.	Guard live parts, fence off space back of all boards, provide insulating mats. "Dead front" boards preferable.
Switches. Shocks from accidental contact or burns and shocks from operation under load.	Use only safety type of switches. Mount them so that blades are dead when switch is open.
Resistances, rheostats, controllers, etc. Burns from resistance grids, shocks from live parts.	Enclosure of live parts with operating handle external.
Treatment of victim of shock. Failure to do the right thing may mean death to the victim.	At least key men in every group should be trained to apply suitable resuscitation. All safety inspectors should be so trained and be competent to train others.

Electricity's "safety valves"

Protective devices used on electric circuits, such as fused switches and air-current breaks, are too often neglected in the plant safety program. Serious accidents due to the misapplication and incorrect operation of low-voltage fused switches have directed the attention of manufacturers and safety men to the removal of these hazards.

One of the first items to be considered is that in many cases, the growth in current-generating capacity of the power system feeding the industrial plant has increased the amount of short-circuit current which must be interrupted when faults occur. The capacity of the protective devices, high enough when the system was installed, may be quite inadequate for later needs.

In many instances, fused switches or obsolete circuit breakers which were installed when the factory was built are still in service. Undoubtedly, these were the best available at the time, but, as in everything else, constant improvements have been made during the past few years. The safest protective devices of ten or fifteen years ago may now provide insufficient protection. They may, in many instances, be incapable of safely opening and closing the electric circuits and of interrupting present short-circuit currents. Consideration should be given to replacing them with devices that will give necessary protection for modern industrial loads.

Most persons realize that hazards exist when they see such signs as *Danger—Hands Off; Do Not Operate,* and other warnings. These of course are not substitutes for physical protection, and warnings are often disregarded.

How often do safety men, when making a plant inspection, check up on the switch and circuit breaker boxes to see whether or not the fused switches and circuit breakers have the proper load and interrupting capacity and are kept free from foreign material? Switches that are capable of handling only their normal current capacity are likely to flash over between phases when called on to interrupt currents beyond their capacity. Even the stalled rotor current of a motor may be far in excess of the normal interrupting rating of such a switch.

If the switch is incapable of interrupting the stalled rotor current, an arc will be maintained and may cause phase-to-phase flashover and severe short circuit. When this happens, it may blow open the box cover and the flash may burn the person who has operated the switch. If the operator closes the switch and the motor stalls, the perfectly natural reaction is to open it immediately. If the switch is not capable of breaking the stalled rotor current, the operator may receive electrical burns from the resulting flash.

The following example will illustrate how accidents may occur. A worker repacking an air compressor had opened the contactor in the motor circuit and the motor disconnecting switch before starting to work. After the packing was completed, he closed them both. The motor stalled and he pulled the switch instead of tripping the contactor. The result was a flashover in the switch box. The front of the box was blown open and the man was seriously burned.

Of course, the worker should not have pulled the disconnecting switch, but mechanical equipment should be arranged to lessen the possibility of accidents resulting from such human errors. Incorrect operation may occur in spite of constant training and reminding.

A further hazard arises from the limited current-interrupting capacity of fuses. In many instances, the short-circuit current available is in excess of the interrupting capacity of any National Electrical Code fuse on the market. The dependability of a fuse within its capacity is unquestioned, yet its limitations must be recognized and the fuse applied accordingly.

Specific types of air-circuit breakers also have limitations in interrupting rating, but a very large range of ratings is available in standard types (rated interrupting current from 5,000 to 80,000 amperes). The advantage of the breaker over the fused switch is that the breaker has no limitation as far as breaking stalled rotor current is concerned, or, in fact, any current within its interrupting rating. Once the proper breaker for the circuit is installed, there is no danger of damaging it or injuring the operator, if the operator should trip it under heavy load or short circuit.

In the fused-switch combination, the fuse is the part that must automatically interrupt overloads or short circuits. The switch cannot. It serves mostly to open or close the circuit under normal load conditions. In some cases, it is capable of interrupting stalled rotor current. In the circuit breaker, on the other hand, the interrupting element is self-contained and is always in action when the breaker is opened, either automatically on overcurrent, or by the operator.

The breaker trips free from the operating handle and cannot be held closed when a short circuit or overload exists. It should be enclosed so that the operator is not exposed to live parts.

Thus it would seem necessary to study our electrical installations and, if they are found inadequate for present requirements, to replace the weak links with higher duty devices. Circuit breakers are more efficient than the fused switch, and provide more effective protection against personal injury.

While this discussion is concerned chiefly with low-voltage circuits, it might be well to mention the importance of checking the adequacy of oil-circuit breakers or other breakers installed on the higher voltage circuits. Do they have sufficient interrupting capacity? No doubt, they were of high enough duty when installed, but has increased system capacity since their installation made them incapable of opening possible short currents? Modernization or replacement of old, overstressed oil-circuit breakers may prevent a fatal accident.

Where the higher voltages are used, steel-enclosed equipments for controlling feeders, motors, and transformers are desirable. They contain the circuit breakers and associated equipment which are thus safely removed from accidental contact. The National Electrical Code permits such enclosed equipments up to 15,000 volts to be installed in working areas.

Chapter Seventeen

Fundamentals of Machine Guarding

Prior to the organized safety movement in industry, it was the common practice to operate transmission machinery (gears, belts, pulleys, shafting, and the like) wholly unguarded. Since the countersunk set screw for use on line shafting had not been developed, shafting bristled with projecting set screws. Few, if any, machines were designed with any thought of worker safety, nor were they equipped with anything in the nature of safety devices or safeguards. Little attention was paid to such matters as the safe placing of machines, the provision for emergency stops, or the safe arrangement of machine controls.

First, emphasis was placed on the guarding of transmission machinery. The frequent deaths of workers snatched up by projecting set screws and whirled about the shafting or caught in meshing gears focused attention on these hazards. Many states adopted legislation requiring the safeguarding of dangerous machinery and set up factory-inspection systems to secure compliance. Methods of guarding were worked out, suitable materials were developed for the purpose, means of eliminating projections from shafting and other rotating parts were found. Standards for guarding gradually crystallized out of this effort, and these standards, enlarged and refined over the years, are now embodied in the "American Standard" safety code for the guarding of transmission machinery under the title "Safety Code for Mechanical Power Transmission Apparatus." The function of the American Standards Association in the development of safety codes is discussed in the chapter, "Safety and Health Standards and Rules."

The provisions of the "American Standard" safety code for guarding transmission apparatus have been adopted or followed quite closely by most of the industrial states and have been widely accepted by industry. Plants whose safety performance is representative of good or best practice comply with the provisions of this code as a matter of course, but in establishments whose safety performance in general is less than good, guarding is likely to be substandard also. Full compliance with all applicable provisions of the code should be regarded as the minimum of acceptable performance. Best practice goes much further, i.e., providing complete enclosure of all moving parts with access doors and gates so arranged that they are locked shut when the parts are in motion. This of course necessitates automatic oiling systems but these are usually more than justified by lesser costs of maintenance and labor. Of course, individual motor drives have relegated mechanical power transmission to a minor role, yet whatever is still used should be thoroughly guarded because unless it is it will continue to yield a quota of unnecessary, in fact, inexcusable injuries, many of them amputations.

Injuries caused by machines are usually serious. Many amputations have resulted from injuries due to transmission machinery and metal-working machines, and woodworking machines have been the cause of many missing fingers. The screw conveyor established a particularly bad record until it became generally recognized that complete enclosure is the only acceptable method of guarding this equipment. Each type of machine contributed its quota of injuries to the mounting toll that inspired the nation-wide effort at prevention. This has accomplished much, but has still much more to do.

Progress in guarding most of the commonly used machines has been relatively slow, however, because their guarding has had to await the development of practical safeguards and their widespread acceptance and use. Fairly satisfactory safeguarding standards have been developed and approved as "American Standard" for most machines, but even here there is need for improvement in detail and in the development of definite specifications for the guards themselves. One of the chief needs is for a change in point of view in two vitally important respects. First, the great importance of machinery safeguarding must be much more universally accepted. Second, the present attitude of *afterthought* guarding must be changed to one of *forethought* guarding; that is, the generally prevailing practice of buying a machine and then guarding it after installation must be changed so that safety is designed and built into every machine. Only by this means can really effective safeguarding be achieved for many of our most hazardous machines, particularly those commonly used in wood- and metal-working.

Frequency of machinery injuries

There appears to be a general underappreciation of both the numerical and the actual importance of machinery-produced injuries. The commonly heard statement that "only from 10 to 15 per cent of injuries are due to mechanical hazards" may, on superficial analysis, seem to be borne out by summaries from the records of various state compensation authorities.

However, if the totals for any industrial state are analyzed on an industry basis, a very different picture emerges. This is shown in Table 17-1.

TABLE 17-1

NUMBER AND PER CENT OF COMPENSATED INDUSTRIAL INJURIES CAUSED BY MACHINES BY TYPE OF INDUSTRY, ILLINOIS, 1949 *

Industry	Number of Injuries	Per cent	Injuries Due to Machines	
			Number	Per cent
All industries	48,405	100.	6,138	12.7
Manufacturing	22,600	47.	4,908	21.7
Non-manufacturing	25,313	52.	1,178	4.6
Agriculture, forestry, etc.	492	1.	52	10.6

* Compiled from Table 12, p. 45. Annual Report on Industrial Accidents in Illinois, Part I. Department of Labor, Chicago, Illinois. Analysis of later data showed only fractional changes.

For Illinois as a whole, only 12.7 per cent of compensated injuries are charged to machines, but for the manufacturing industries, the proportion rises to 21.7 per cent. And 47 per cent of the total of compensated injuries in the State occurred in the manufacturing industries. In the manufacturing industries, machines are thus shown to be a major injury-producer on a state-wide basis. And, under the Illinois method of coding, injuries caused by "machines" does not include injuries due to prime movers, power transmission apparatus, and the like. If injuries due to these causes were added, the percentage due to mechanical causes would be even higher.

The analysis of the accident records of the larger manufacturing firms will frequently show a low proportion of machinery-produced injuries, again seemingly bearing out the oft-quoted statement that only 15 per cent of all injuries are caused by machines. But such firms have gone much further in guarding their machinery than has the average plant, and their experience should be quoted as representing good or best practices, not average conditions.

Seriousness of machinery injuries

Table 17-1 shows that the frequency of injuries due to machines is high, particularly in the manufacturing industry. But severity of injuries is also important in assessing the danger of machines or machinery. One measure of severity is the number or percentage of injuries that cause permanent-partial disability, that is, the loss of a member or the loss of use of a member or part of the body. An indication of the severity of injuries caused by machines is obtained by comparing the number of permanent-partial dis-

TABLE 17-2

NUMBER AND DISABILITY DISTRIBUTION OF COMPENSATED INDUSTRIAL INJURIES, BY AGENCY OF INJURY. NEW YORK, 1947 *

Agency	Total Cases	Per Cent	Death and Permanent Total	Per Cent	Kind of Disability Permanent Partial	Per Cent	Temporary	Per Cent
All Agencies	117,826	100.	1,081	0.9	37,348	31.7	79,397	67.4
Machinery	15,529	100.	39	0.2	8,635	55.6	6,885	44.2
Vehicles	10,769	100.	216	2.0	3,093	28.7	7,460	69.3
Hand tools	9,702	100.	21	0.2	3,773	38.9	5,908	60.9
Elevators, Hoisting, Apparatus, etc.	3,503	100.	86	2.4	1,737	49.2	1,707	48.4
Electrical apparatus	319	100.	23	7.2	77	24.1	219	68.7
Boiler and Pressure Vessels	145	100.	10	6.9	53	36.6	82	56.5
Miscellaneous	45,448	100.	195	0.4	12,160	26.8	33,093	72.8
Working surfaces	21,381	100.	246	1.1	5,860	27.4	15,275	71.5
Chemical and other harmful substances	3,984	100.	143	3.6	454	11.4	3,387	85.0
Highly flammable and hot substances	3,014	100.	32	1.1	597	19.8	2,385	79.1
Other agencies	4,005	100.	70	1.7	909	22.7	3,026	75.6

* Compensation Cases closed in 1947, p. 16. Workmen's Compensation Board. Bulletin No. 4—1949. New York, N. Y. Breakdown of later data showed no significant changes in relationships, so these may be accepted as reasonably typical.

abilities resulting from injuries caused by machinery with the number of like injuries from other causes. This is shown by Table 17-2.

This table shows that for all agencies combined, 31.7 per cent result in permanent-partial disability. But for injuries due to mechanical causes, the proportion is much higher. For example, injuries caused by machinery resulted in 55.6 per cent permanent impairment of one kind or another, whereas 49.2 per cent of all injuries due to elevators, hoisting apparatus, etc., were of a permanent-partial nature. In dealing with New York injury statistics it should be borne in mind that only those injuries causing a time loss of 7 days or more are compensable. Thus, the seemingly large percentage of permanent-partial disabilities is accounted for.

Machine-caused injuries are, therefore, important, not only because they represent a large proportion of all injuries, but also because they are more likely to be severe. It should not be necessary to dwell on the seriousness to a wage earner of an amputation or the loss of use of a member. Workmen depend on the continued effectiveness of their hands, feet, eyes, and so on, for their livelihood. The usual result of a permanent disabling injury is to condemn the victim and his dependents to a scale of living so much lower as to sacrifice most of life's advantages and hopes. The compensation payments at best do little more than cushion the blow, and the war has taught us that our workers are a vital asset to our country. Preserving this asset is not only the essence of humaneness, it is a matter of good common sense.

Harm of the 15 per cent to 85 per cent ratio fallacy

Factory inspectors charged with the duty of securing the adequate safeguarding of machinery are almost continuously opposed by the argument that since only 15 per cent of injuries are from mechanical sources, little can be gained by such guarding, and the required expenditure would better be applied to the prevention of the 85 per cent of injuries due to other causes. At times this argument may be merely an excuse to avoid the expenditure of money for guarding, but in most cases it is undoubtedly an honest opinion due to acceptance of the superficial and misleading statement of the 15 to 85 per cent ratio. As already stated, such a ratio should not be taken as a measure of the relative importance of machinery safeguarding. On the contrary, there are many reasons why machine guarding should be the first prerequisite of any well-rounded safety program. Also, as previously indicated, the percentage of permanent-partial disabilities from machines is extremely high. Serious injuries involve high cost and large time losses. Is it not logical, therefore, to try to eliminate those injuries causing high cost and large time losses?

Perhaps the most important reason for doing machine guarding before undertaking other safety activities is the psychological effect on the work-men. Guarding is a positive and visual proof of the sincerity of the management's interest in safety. Guards cost money and their provision is proof that the management is willing to spend money in its safety effort.

Machine guarding foundational

Machine guarding should be considered as the foundation on which all future safety activities are based. Management cannot expect the men in the shop to work safely, to acquire safe habits, and to be interested in the safety of their co-workers unless they are given a safe place in which to work. A safe environment created, partially at least, by adequate safe-guarding of machines is in itself an incentive for a worker to develop safe working habits.

Machine guarding should not only be adequate to protect from the hazard of the machine, it must itself represent a high standard of quality and workmanship. Poorly designed and poorly constructed guards give the lie to any profession of an interest in safety that the management might make. A guard has but one purpose—to protect someone from contact with a point of danger, and any guard that does not do this fails its purpose. In fact, a poor guard may be worse than no guard at all. It sets up a sense of false security and the workman depends upon a guard rather than upon trying to protect himself against a hazard that he knows exists. Guards can be made attractive as well as useful. Many companies have adopted a policy of painting all guards a distinct color, usually green. This is an excellent idea. It not only makes guards attractive, but it indicates instantly which machine parts are guards.

Machine builders making safer machines

Machine builders in general have incorporated into their current models many safeguards that a few years ago were entirely lacking. All modern engine lathes have the back gears built into a permanent housing with the lever for changing speeds as the only exposed part of the gear train. Belts, which are sometimes a part of the machine itself, are often so placed within the fully enclosed frame of the machine as to eliminate the necessity for a separate belt guard. Many machines have been redesigned to eliminate shearing or crushing hazards; for example, the ordinary reciprocating boiler feed pump. Older models lacked finger clearance between the cross head and the packing glands, and incautious attendants often received crushed hands or fingers in wiping or making adjustments. There are other examples of excellent safeguarding by machine manufacturers. Modern laundry machinery furnishes one. Bakery machinery another. The ordinary abrasive wheel stand as manufactured complete is well guarded, but this is often not true of those assembled by jobbers. Modern meat grinders have been designed with feed hoppers of a depth greater than finger length and a throat too small to admit one's hand.

However, comparatively little progress has been made compared to the tremendous possibilities that exist for building user safety into the machines instead of adding it later in the form of guards. Unfortunately, this is chiefly true of the common highly hazardous wood- and metal-working machines. Machine manufacturers have been slow to accept the fact that the guards on the machine are actually a part of the machine, chiefly because of lack of consumer demand for fully guarded machines. Most machine buyers purchase on a price basis. The purchasing agent, trained to buy satisfactory goods at the lowest possible price, and not being a safety engineer, does not specify that the machine be equipped with guards or that guards be built in. The seller of a machine who includes in his selling price the cost of guards is at a disadvantage when competing with a seller who is not interested in providing guards or built-in safety. This is a condition that can be corrected only by management's willingness to pay whatever reasonable extra price may be necessary to secure a well-guarded machine, plus coöperation between the safety department and the purchasing agent.

Purchaser failure to demand and be willing to pay for the maximum in in-built safety, is merely another symptom of that widespread deficiency disease "lack of safety mindedness." It has been the bane of the safety movement from the start. It numbers more victims each year than does any other disease. The promotion of employer safety mindedness is of course a basic purpose of the "consultative approach" briefly described in Chapter two. The expansion of this approach to include the entire citizenry of the state in a statewide safety program should be similarly basic as is also indicated in that chapter.

Both the American Society of Safety Engineers and the International Association of Governmental Labor Officials have, through many years, maintained committees to promote built-in machinery safeguarding and have gotten some results but their facilities have been far too limited to accomplish much. A far more extensive and intensive program will be necessary if really worthwhile results are to be had.

Homemade guards

In the field of homemade guards—that is, guards built in the shop where used, or guards built by a company specializing in guard construction—knowledge and skill are especially important. Each guard is made to order, each must be specially designed, and each individual machine presents its own problem. State codes give the broad, overall requirements for performance or construction, but the effectiveness of the guard is still dependent upon the skill of the designer and the builder to design and construct a guard that is adequate for the purpose, is sturdy enough to withstand hard service, and does not in itself create a hazard.

Primarily, guards are intended to protect the machine operator or the casual passer-by, and this is the aim of the designer. But in guard design, other important features should not be overlooked. For example, guards should be so designed as to offer maximum protection to the repair man and the oiler. Guards are sometimes interlocked with the driving mechanism in such a way that the machine cannot be operated unless the guard is in place. Automatic machines, such as those used in the manufacture of small metal products as metal boxes for typewriter ribbons, lend themselves to interlocking guards. Many of these guards are very ingenious and their designs offer a fertile field for specialized safety work. The principle of interlocking the guard with the machine control to prevent operation unless the guard is in place could and should be widely applied, and it is so applied in certain plants whose managements are highly safety-minded.

Wherever possible (and it is rarely impossible), provision should be made for oiling machines without removing the guard. A simple way to do this is to locate the oil reservoir outside the guard with the oil line leading to the point of lubrication. On machines requiring grease lubrication, pressure fittings are commonly used. Here, too, long tubed fittings can be used with the fitting for the grease gun located away from the moving part and outside the guard.

Provision should be made for cleaning and adjusting machine parts enclosed by guards. Ease of cleaning or adjusting can be achieved by making panels in the guards which can be removed without removing the entire guard. These sections should be hinged so that they can be easily opened, but are not in danger of being misplaced. They should preferably be interlocked with the controls, but if not, they should at least be "in the way" unless closed. Each guard is an individual problem and no set rule will apply to all possible conditions.

Finally, guards are not a makeshift and should not be considered as such. They are designed and built for but one purpose—to protect against a hazard which might cause an injury, and no trouble or expense should be spared in making guards the best that can be made. If the abilities of competent designers are brought to bear on the problems of safeguarding machinery, improvement will be rapid. Anyone who compares the excellence of modern machine design, from the standpoint of effective machine functioning, with that of machine safety, will be impressed by the fact that safety is often treated as though it were of secondary importance. The safety of those who work with our machines must receive more consideration from those who build them, as well as those who buy and install them.

Chapter Eighteen

Guarding Woodworking Machines

The preceding chapter discussed the fundamental principles and importance of guarding power driven machinery. This chapter will deal with the principles of guarding commonly used woodworking machines, and the following chapter will treat the guarding of commonly used metal-working machines. These are the machines commonly used in many industries, and they are such prolific injury producers that a knowledge of their guarding is of vital importance to the cause of accident prevention in industry in general.

The question as to which machines, as a class, are the most hazardous is often asked. There is strong evidence that the answer is *woodworking machines*. If it were desired to ascertain the relative hazards of certain industries, the frequency and severity rates of those industries would probably be the best criteria of measurement of their hazards. These rates are based on man-hours of exposure, but since accident rates on machine-hours of exposure are not available, some other means must be found to measure the hazards of various classes of machines and of the individual machines within each class.

In lieu of machine-hour frequency and severity rates, a fairly satisfactory measure of the hazard of woodworking machines as compared to other classes of widely used machines can be derived from (a) a comparison of man-hour frequency and severity rates of industries using woodworking machines with industries using other machines; (b) a comparison of the severity of injuries, as measured by the relative number of permanent, partial disabilities, that occur in industries using woodworking machines with industries using other machines; and (c) a comparison of the severity of injuries, as measured by the relative number of permanent, partial disabilities, caused by woodworking machines with injuries caused by other machines. In comparing woodworking machine-using industries with industries using other classes of machines, and injuries caused by woodworking machines with injuries caused by other classes of machines, there is strong evidence to support the belief that woodworking machines, as a class, are the most hazardous of all commonly used machines.

Analyses of the year-by-year injury totals * in the manufacturing industries, broken down by branch of industry, show clearly that injury rates for the woods products industries are relatively high. They also show high severity rates, the discrepancy being markedly greater for severity than for frequency. This high severity is the expectable result of amputations and other permanent disabilities characteristic of the manual operation of woodworking machines. Furthermore, detailed breakdowns of data from the individual branches of industry within the furniture and lumber products industry as a whole strongly indicate a direct correlation between the number of woodworking machines in use and the number and severity of the injuries.

TABLE 18-1

EXTENT OF DISABILITY CAUSED BY SPECIFIED WORKING MACHINES;
MASSACHUSETTS, 5-YEAR PERIOD

Type of Working Machine	Total	Fatal and Permanent Total Injuries		Permanent, Partial Injuries		Temporary Total Injuries	
		Num-ber	Per cent	Num-ber	Per cent	Num-ber	Per cent
All working machines	19,908	46	0.2	2,410	12.1	17,452	87.7
Woodworking	2,496	7	.3	462	18.5	2,027	81.2
Chemical products	79	..	..	16	†	63	†
Clay, glass, and stone products	110	..	..	8	7.3	102	92.7
Clothing	650	1	.2	10	1.5	639	98.3
Food products	1,233	1	.1	147	11.9	1,085	88.0
Metalworking	5,637	13	.2	790	14.0	4,834	85.8
Leather products	2,301	1	(1)	170	7.4	2,130	92.6
Leatherworking— tanneries	661	4	.6	51	7.7	606	91.7
Paper products	678	1	.1	71	10.5	606	89.4
Paper-making	536	3	.6	46	8.6	487	90.8
Printing and bookbinding	543	..	..	64	11.8	479	88.2
Textile	4,192	12	.3	450	10.7	3,730	89.0
Rubber, celluloid, composition, pearl, bone, and tortoise shell	765	3	.4	121	15.8	641	83.8
All other machines	27	..	..	4	(1)	23	(1)

† Per cent not shown because the basic number is too small to make the percentage significant.

* Annual reports of injury rates by industry, U. S. Bureau of Labor Statistics, U. S. Dept. of Labor, Washington, D. C.

Table 18-1 presents the findings of a searching detailed analysis of all of the disabling injuries caused by working machines in Massachusetts during the 5-year period 1933-38. Although these data are so old, the evidence produced by recent spot checking does not indicate any important changes in relationships. Incidentally, it throws no light on the extent to which substitution of automatic machinery may have affected injury rates or injury totals because these checking surveys were limited to plants using the conventional types of non-automated machines.

Of the total of all injuries caused by working machines in Massachusetts in the 5-year period 1933-38, 18.5 per cent of those caused by woodworking machines caused permanent disablement of one kind or another, whereas for all working machines combined, only 12.1 per cent of the injuries caused permanent disability. The next most dangerous class of machines on the basis of severity of injury is rubber, celluloid, and so on (15.8 per cent), followed by metal working (14.0 per cent). Other dangerous classes of machines are food products (11.9 per cent) and printing and bookbinding (11.8 per cent).

Table 18-2 shows the relative importance of the various commonly used woodworking machines as injury producers and also furnishes a comparison of severity. Data are from the same source as those presented in Table 18-1.

Saws caused the greatest number of injuries, but since more saws are used than other machines, this would be expected. No data are available on a machine-hour basis and, therefore, no true picture of frequency of injuries by machines is possible. But data on the severity of injuries, as measured by the number of permanent-partial disabilities per thousand accidents, throw considerable light on which machines cause the most severe injuries.

Of each thousand injuries caused by shapers, 281.3 resulted in dismemberment or loss of use of a portion of the body. Tenoners and other surfacing machines yielded injuries resulting in 252.3 permanent, partial disabilities per thousand injuries. For all saws combined, the proportion was 192.7. Circular-saw injuries were found to be more serious than those by band saws or other unclassified saws, with 243.9 injuries of each thousand resulting in permanent disablement, compared to 115.4 for band saws and 163.4 for other saws not classified. Drills and boring machines, along with sanders, show the lowest proportion of permanent disabilities.

It should be obvious that, since woodworking machines are both widely used and highly hazardous, the methods of safeguarding them, including the rules for their safe operation, must be regarded of fundamental importance. Every industrial safety engineer should have at least a good working knowledge of this subject. But since this text is intended to cover

TABLE 18-2

PER CENT DISTRIBUTION OF INDUSTRIAL INJURIES CAUSED BY WOODWORKING
MACHINES, AND DISABILITY DISTRIBUTION PER 1,000 INJURIES, BY TYPE
OF MACHINE; MASSACHUSETTS, 5-YEAR PERIOD

| Type of Woodworking Machine | All Injuries | | Disability Distribution per 1,000 Injuries | | |
	Num-ber	Per cent	Fatal and Per-manent Total	Per-manent Partial	Tem-porary Total
All woodworking machines	2,496	100.0	2.8	185.1	812.1
Lathes	57	2.3	..	105.3	894.7
Saws	1,323	53.0	2.3	192.7	805.0
Band saws	78	3.1	..	115.4	884.6
Circular saws	529	21.2	1.9	243.9	754.2
Saws not elsewhere classified	716	28.7	2.8	163.4	833.8
Drilling and boring machines, including mortisers	100	4.0	..	80.0	920.0
Planers, shapers, molders, and other surfacing machines, including tenoners	615	24.7	4.9	240.6	754.5
Planers and molders	440	17.7	2.3	231.8	765.9
Shapers	64	2.6	..	281.3	718.7
Tenoners and other surfacing machines	111	4.4	18.0	252.3	729.7
Sanding machines	98	3.9	..	81.6	918.4
Presses	57	2.3	17.5	122.8	859.7
Other woodworking machines	228	9.1	..	127.2	872.8

fundamentals only, this chapter will be limited to basic principles and specific points of major importance.*

Every woodworking machine can be adequately safeguarded for each and every type of operation for which the machine is suited. Practically all woodworking machine injuries are preventable. Numerous firms have proved this by reducing such injuries to a point closely approximating elimination. However, to acomplish this the management must take seriously the job of eliminating them. It must see that all of the proper safeguards are provided, maintained, and used. The workmen must be thoroughly instructed and trained in safe operating methods and be properly supervised. The axiom that "time gained at the expense of safety is too expensively bought" must govern.

* For detailed information on guarding of machines and safe operating rules, see the American Standard "Safety Code for Woodworking Plants," also Safe Practice, Pamphlet No. 20, "Woodworking Machinery and Equipment," published by the National Safety Council,

The high speeds used in cutting or shaping wood requires a high standard of maintenance of machines and tools. A large proportion of woodworking machine injuries is due to or contributed to by vibration, dull or improperly ground cutting tools, or insecurely fastened or poorly balanced cutters. Good housekeeping, good lighting, nonslippery floors, and adequate working space about machines are also important. There follows a discussion of guarding and other safety precautions to be observed for various woodworking machines.

Guarding shapers

The shaper is one of the most difficult of all woodworking machines to guard effectively. No single guard is practical for all the various kinds of work that may be done on a shaper, and as a result, much work is done without any guard whatever. However, every shaper job can be adequately safeguarded. There is no more justification for regarding shaper injuries as unpreventable than there is for so regarding injuries from any other machine. Furthermore, the unguarded shaper is so hazardous that it can be stated with assurance that every one will sooner or later claim its quota of fingers. Therefore, whatever money and effort is required to guard each job should be viewed as a proper insurance expense against the amputations that will otherwise eventually occur. A shaper amputation is likely to cost a thousand dollars or more. This sum will pay for the safeguarding of a large number of shaper jobs, and the operator will still have the use of his skilled fingers.

Shaper injuries result mainly from unthinkingly allowing the hands to contact the knives, from the work catching and drawing the hands into the knives, from kickbacks, and from thrown knives. The fundamental principle of prevention is to provide a positive means of keeping the hands away from the knives, supplemented by eliminating the necessity of reaching close to them. This is accomplished by the use of guards to cover the knives, jigs to keep the hands away as far as possible, and the combining of these with guides to give better control of the work.

Each shaper head should be protected by an encircling guard above the knives extending out well beyond the sweep of the longest knife and adjustable to the height of the work. The guard can often be made to serve as a guide as well. Its function is to prevent the hand from coming too close to the knives or from being carried in when a kickback occurs. The guard will prevent or limit the injury in most cases. Its weakness is that it must be removed for work too large to pass under it. These encircling guards are made in a number of forms. One consists of an inverted cup-shaped cage; another, of a collar encircling the spindle; still another of a combination guard and guide which encloses the knives completely except for a section that is cut away to permit the knives to contact the work. Every shaper should be equipped with the full variety of guards suitable for all the varieties of work done on it, and proper guarding must be a fundamental part of the setup of each job.

A leather strap is sometimes attached to the spindle as a warning device. Since the leather is longer than the knives, it will strike the operator's fingers before they reach the knives. This is a poor substitute for a guard and is specifically not recommended. It requires constant maintenance, gives no protection if the work catches, cannot aid in guiding the work, and its use gives evidence of management's willingness to substitute makeshifts for guarding.

All work too small to give a secure handhold at least 12 inches away from the knives should be jigged. Many shops accept 6 inches as adequate, but the record shows that 12 inches is a much safer minimum. Regardless of this difference of opinion, a definite minimum should be adopted in every shop using a shaper, and its application should be rigidly enforced.

In addition to point-of-operation guarding, certain other precautions should be observed in operating a shaper. Adequate provision must be made to keep knives secure in the spindle. The desire to get all possible use out of a knife often results in the use of a knife worn so short that it cannot be clamped securely on the spindle. Shapers operate at such high speeds that thrown knives have been known to penetrate a partition wall. It is particularly important to keep the knives sharp, for the sharper the knife, the safer the machine is to operate. Care must be used in not forcing the cut, and when more than one cut is needed, the material should be lifted away from the cutter for the return, never backed up on the cutter.

Guarding jointers

The jointer is the most dangerous machine in the surfacing-machine group. Effective guards are available for jointers but they are not always used. The bad accident experience on jointers is chiefly due to the prevalent practice of jointing small pieces without the aid of jigs to hold the work and thus keep the hands away from the knives. The most effective jointer guard consists of a metal cover somewhat wider than the opening in the table, the guard covering all of the cutter head in front of the guide. This guard is held in place by springs and is adjustable vertically and laterally. The stock being surfaced passes under the guard, which rises to accommodate its thickness. On an edging cut, the stock pushes the guard away from the guide, the guard continuing to cover all of the cutter head not covered by the work. The so-called "leg-of-mutton" guard is a wood or metal shield, pivoted so that it swings outward from the guide, but covering all of the cutter head in front of the guide. In using this guard, the material being surfaced pushes the guard away from the guide, but the guard continues to cover that portion of the cutter head not covered by the work. The guard is held in place by a spring, sometimes by a counter-weight. The weakness of this guard is that, in surfacing a wide board, it does not cover the work and therefore does not offer as complete protection as the first type of guard.

It is important that the springs that hold the guards in position be kept properly tensioned, otherwise the guards will not return to their position against the guide. The portion of the cutter head at the rear of the guide likewise should be kept covered at all times. This may be accomplished by installing a self-adjusting guard, which will bear against the rear of the guide regardless of its position, or a metal cover secured to the guide and projecting backward from it. A square head should never be used on a jointer. The use of such a head is prohibited by law in many states. The injuries inflicted by square cutting heads are much more severe than those caused by round heads.

Dull knives will cause kickbacks; so will too heavy a cut. As in the case of shapers, it is vital to keep the hands a safe distance away from the knives. This can be done by the use of a jig or pusher stick when jointing short pieces, but these devices are not substitutes for guards, a guard also being required. The material being jointed should be so held that the hand is not at the front of the work at the start of the cut nor at the back of the work at the finish of the cut. In most cases, the jointing of short pieces can be eliminated by surfacing before cutting to size. Many shops follow this practice, even when it involves wasting moderate amounts of stock, rather than accept the increased hazard involved in jointing short pieces.

Guarding planers, moulders, stickers, tenoners, matchers, and panel raisers

These surfacing machines are less hazardous than shapers and jointers because they are mechanically fed and therefore the operator's hands need not come close to the cutting head. The feed rolls should be guarded to keep the operator's hands from being caught between the feed roll and the inrunning stock. The guard over the cutting head may be designed to cover this, or a separate guard may be attached to the feed-roll frame, which will automatically adjust itself to the thickness of the stock being worked. These are production machines intended for volume work. They produce so many chips that an exhaust system is a practical necessity, and the exhaust hood over the cutting head performs the additional function of a guard.

The corrugations of the feed rolls should be kept clean and free from dust, pitch, and so on. They should be kept sharp by filing as needed, otherwise they may not grip the stock tightly enough to prevent kickbacks.

In addition, a row of antikickback dogs should be placed in front of the feed roll to give further protection, as too thick a board, a hard knot, or a nicked knife may cause a kickback that the feed rolls cannot hold.

Guarding circular saws

No type of saw guard yet developed affords entirely satisfactory protection for all operations that may be performed on the ordinary table saw. Quite satisfactory models are available for ordinary ripping and crosscutting, but for dadoing, grooving, and rabbetting, special guards are necessary. It is safer still to provide special machines for these types of work—machines equipped with guards suited to the operations involved.

Manually fed table-type circular saws for ripping and crosscutting are the most commonly used types of saws as well as the most hazardous. Three important features should be incorporated into every table-type rip-saw guard. These are: (a) A hood that will cover the saw at all times at least to the depth of the teeth. This hood should automatically adjust itself to the thickness of the material being cut, it should remain in contact with the material until the cut is completed, and it should afford a clear view of the line of cut. (b) A spreader that is a part of the guard. (c) An antikick-back device, also a part of the guard.

The guard on a manually fed crosscut saw should combine the same feature in the hood as in a ripsaw. A spreader should be provided, although it may be independent of the guard. An antikickback device is not essential on a crosscut saw. Where a saw is used for both ripping and crosscutting, the saw guard should be of the type intended for ripping.

On both crosscut saws and ripsaws the portion of the saw underneath the table should be guarded, preferably by a complete enclosure with only sufficient opening to permit the sawdust to fall freely or to be exhausted, if an exhaust system is provided. The frequency of injuries from cleaning-up and from making adjustments with the saw running abundantly justifies this protection.

Kickbacks occur in ripping because green or twisty lumber will pinch together back of the saw and the teeth will throw it forward with great violence. In crosscutting, kickbacks are likely to occur if the stock twists when being cut or is turned at a slight angle. The function of the spreader is to prevent kickbacks from these causes. The spreader should be of strong steel, slightly thinner than the saw kerf (width of saw cut) but thicker than the saw disc, and wide enough to give adequate strength and stiffness. It should extend about the same distance above the table as does the saw, should be in accurate alignment with the saw and not over one fourth of an inch distant from it, and preferably should be curved to the contour of the saw. The spreader may be included as a part of the saw mounting; it may be permanently attached to each throat piece, or it may be bolted to the table. Regardless of the method used for attaching the spreader, provision should be made for it to retain its relative position to the saw for whatever size saw is used.

Kickbacks are also caused by knots, unequal dryness of the lumber, forcing the work, and dull or improperly set saws. Antikickback devices, in addition to the spreader, should be provided on all ripsaw guards. These usually consist of two or more pointed projections, pivoted from the sides of the guard in such manner that they drag over the surface of the work when cutting, but when a kickback occurs, they dig in and stop the backward motion of the wood being cut.

When the saw is equipped for automatic feeding, the feed rolls perform some of the functions of the guard, particularly in preventing contact with the saw from the front. Even with automatic feeding, it is usually necessary to place a guard over the saw. The feed rolls help prevent kickbacks, but kickbacks can still occur unless the rolls are kept clean and the corrugations sharp. The nip-point between each feed roll and the stock should be guarded in a manner similar to that described for planers.

Swing cut-off saws are commonly used, and while they are not as hazardous as is the ordinary table saw, they should, nevertheless, be properly guarded. A hood guard enclosing all of the saw except the segment required for cutting should be provided. The guard should be so made that it pivots at the rear of the saw and rides the work at all times. To prevent the saw from being pulled forward beyond the table, or to a position such that the saw will ride the work, a limit chain or other limiting device should be provided. The saw should be counterweighted so that it will be returned by gravity to the nonoperating position back of the table when released, but it should not strike the back stop with jarring force. The counterweight should be secured against coming loose and falling.

Types of cut-off saws in which the saw is mounted on a carriage that rolls forward to the work are becoming more common. In all cases, the saw should be protected by an enclosing hood guard as in the case of the swing cut-off saw. The rollers or wheels of the carriage should be guarded, if so located that they present a finger-crushing hazard. In other types of saws the stock is placed on the carriage and rolls forward to the saw. Sometimes several saws are mounted on the same arbor. In all cases the requirements for a protective hood are the same.

In addition to the guarding, the safe operation of circular saws depends to a major extent on the proper selection and maintenance of the saw and on the observance of safe operating rules. Except when using a universal type saw, a saw should be used only on the kind of work for which it is intended. A ripsaw should be used only for ripping and a crosscut saw for cutting across the grain only. Saws should not operate at speeds exceeding that for which their manufacturer designed them. The safe-operating speed should be ascertained from the manufacturer and never exceeded. If this information is not available, the safe-operating speeds for saws of various diameters as recommended by the "American Standard" Safety Code for Woodworking Plants should be followed.

Saws should be kept sharp and properly set. When a saw is dull, it does not cut clean and straight, and its operator tends to force the work, thus causing kickbacks. When a saw is out of round, the work is all done by the longer teeth, thus causing heating and "snaky" cutting. When this occurs, the saw should be "jointed," that is, the long teeth ground so that the saw is perfectly round. Saw maintenance requires highly developed skill and special knowledge and should never be undertaken except by persons qualified to perform this kind of work. The saw should be securely mounted on the arbor and should be entirely free from wobble. No adjustments of saw, guide, or guard, nor any cleaning should ever be attempted while the saw is in motion. If such work requires that the saw be rotated, this should be done by hand.

When feeding a circular saw, the operator should always stand far enough to one side to be safely out of line of a kickback, should one occur. He should have a good knowledge of the properties of wood that influence its cutting. Soft woods can safely be cut faster than hard woods, and dry wood faster than green. The operator should never force the work in an effort to make it cut faster. This is not only an extremely dangerous practice but it results in bad work and will overheat the saw. When sawing narrow stock, a pusher stick should be used. This is particularly true when ripping stock only slightly wider than the distance between the saw and the guide.

There has recently been developed a new type of saw blade that seems to offer considerable advantage from a safety standpoint. Instead of the conventional tooth design of approximately 100 teeth, this saw has but 8 teeth, and each tooth projects only 0.2 of an inch above the saw periphery. The cut of each tooth is therefore limited, regardless of the speed or the pressure placed on the wood. The tooth design is supposed to eliminate kickbacks and to minimize an injury from direct contact with the saw. The refuse is in the form of chips rather than sawdust. This new saw blade is not intended to be operated without a saw guard, but it has some specific advantages from a safety angle.

Guarding band saws

Band saws are not nearly so hazardous as are circular saws. They do not kick back, and the range of work that may be performed on them is much less. However, certain safeguards are necessary. All of the saw except the portion actually used in making the cut should be enclosed. This involves:

(a) complete enclosure below the table including all of the lower wheel; (b) complete enclosure of the upper wheel, the enclosure covering the wheel at its lowest position; (c) a U-shaped guard enclosing the return portion of the saw from the table to the upper wheel enclosure; (d) a U- or channel-shaped guard attached to the saw guide to protect that portion of the saw between the guide and the enclosure of the upper wheel. The wheel enclosures should be heavy enough to contain a broken saw, and equipped with hinged covers to facilitate replacement of the saw.

In operating a band saw, the operator should stand to the right of the cut to lessen the chance of being struck by the blade in case it should break. Breaks are usually caused by forcing the work beyond the capacity of the saw, or by a poor splice.

Some band resaws are equipped with feed rolls, in which case the rolls should be guarded as are other automatic feeds. The guarding required for the saw is similar to that for the ordinary band saw.

Guarding portable saws

Many types of portable-powered circular hand-tool saws have come into use, particularly on construction jobs. The only type of guard reasonably satisfactory consists of a complete enclosure of the blade. The pressure of the stock being cut against a lug on the guard opens the guard to permit the cut to be made, the guard being in contact with the stock throughout the cut. However, sawdust, particularly if it is resinous or pitchy, is likely to clog up the action of this guard, and frequent cleaning and good maintenance are necessary. As in the case of all other electric-powered tools, both a pressure switch ("dead-man control") and a positive ground are important. The hazard of a tool that, when dropped or laid down, is not thereby automatically stopped, is obviously great. And the danger from even the 110-volt circuit under conditions likely to afford a low-resistance path through the operator's body is serious.

Guarding multiple-head machines

Machines combining two or more cutting tools in the same machine frame are used to a considerable extent to enable several types of work to be done on the one piece of equipment. They save floor space and first cost as against the cost of several individual machines to do the same work. However, they are very difficult to guard adequately and, in most cases, more than one operator cannot work on the unit at the same time without interference. For a home basement workshop, the saving in cost and space is important. For the production shop, much of this advantage falls away. Such machines are specifically not recommended unless each point of operation is fully safeguarded and unless, in addition, the drive is so arranged that only one operating head can operate at a time. When designed so that all of the heads may (or in some models must) be operated together, their hazard is excessive.

Guarding drills, borers, morticers, sanders, lathes

Few guards are possible on machines that employ revolving tools such as drills or boring bars. The chuck for holding the tool should be of the safety type, that is, without set screws or other projections. Where counterweights are used, the counterweight should be bolted to the bar, and other means, such as a safety chain, should be provided to prevent the counterweight from falling. A foot-treadle-operated machine should have a stirrup or inverted U-shaped guard over the treadle to prevent unexpected starting due to someone stepping on it or its being struck by a falling object.

Safety in operation of boring bars and similar machines depends to a large extent on the operator. Loose sleeves or neckties and gloves should not be worn when operating them. Work should always be clamped when boring, never held by hand, and the tool should be securely tightened in the chuck.

The feed rolls of drum sanders should be guarded to protect the nip-point between the roll and the stock being fed. All sanders should be provided with an exhaust system. The exhaust hood should cover all of the sanding surface except the operating area. All manually fed sanders should be equipped with work rests, guides, or aprons arranged to give the maximum of secure support for the work being sanded. Pieces too small to allow the hands to be kept a safe distance from the work should be jigged.

Lathes operate at high speed and throw knots and chips. Cutting heads may come loose and be thrown with considerable force. Chip screens should be used, and these should be made strong enough to hold a thrown head. Goggles should be worn when operating a wood-turning lathe.

Chapter Nineteen

Guarding Metal-working Machines

Metal-working machines are the most commonly used of all point-of-operation machines. Their use is not limited to any one industry; they are used in all industries manufacturing articles of metal that range from locomotives to costume jewelry. In the general category of metal-working machines are included machines for working metals hot and those for working them cold, but since hot metal-working machines are in less common usage than cold metal-working machines, this chapter will deal only with the guarding and safe operating practices of cold metal-working machines.

The preceding chapter pointed out that woodworking machines are, as a class, the most hazardous of all point-of-operation machines with respect to the severity of injury as measured by the number of injuries resulting in permanent, partial disabilities (Table 18-2). These data show that metal-working machines also cause a high percentage of permanent disabling injuries, exceeded only by woodworking machines and machines for making rubber, celluloid, and composition materials. Since more metal-working machines are used than any other specific types of working machines, the number of injuries caused by them exceeds the number caused by any other type of machine.

We cannot calculate the frequency rate of injuries caused by metal-working machines, as injury data on a machine-hour basis is not available. Metal-working machines do, however, produce large totals of injuries each year, a large proportion of which are severe, as is attested by the injuries reported to insurance carriers and to the workmen's compensation authorities of the various states. Their importance, therefore, cannot be overlooked when considering the fundamentals of industrial safety in the field of machine guarding.

The question of which metal-working machines or which types of machines are the most hazardous is of importance to the safety engineer in administering a safety program. In attempting to answer this question, it is obviously necessary to group machines according to type. Machines for working metal in the cold state can be grouped into two major categories— machine tools, and cold metal-forming, punching, and shearing machines, although a few machines do not fit well into either classification.

Machine tools are defined by the National Machine Tool Builders' Association as "power-driven complete metal-working machines, not portable by hand, having one or more tool- or work-holding devices, and used for progressively removing metal in the form of chips." They may be classed by function, which are the five basic methods of removing metal, namely, planing, milling, turning, drilling, and grinding. These functions are defined in the discussions of the method of guarding machine tools. Grinding, honing, and lapping machines are included in this classification, although the chips removed can be seen only under the microscope.

Machine tools range in size from small bench machines, such as a jeweler's lathe, to huge machines weighing up to 50 tons or more. Some machine tools are standard machines intended for general use; others perform a specific operation on a particular product. Such special machines are used extensively in mass production, with speed and accuracy built into the machine instead of depending on the operator. Some machine tools, especially those for a particular purpose, perform more than one function. Thus, a special machine tool may be a combination boring, drilling, and milling machine, or it may perform other multiple functions. The special functions which machine tools can be designed to perform are almost unlimited.

Forming, punching, and shearing machines include all metal-working machines, other than machine tools, which change the shape of or cut metal by means of tools such as dies, rolls, or knives mounted on rams, plungers, or other moving parts. Forming, punching, and shearing machines may also be classified by function. These functions are pressing or punching, bending, rolling, hammering, or shearing, which are further defined in the discussion of guarding.

Data are not available on which injury frequency and severity rates can be calculated for the operators of the different types of metal-working machines. Such rates, if available, would be rates based on man-hours of exposure for operators of machines, in effect, a machine-hour basis, and would constitute an accurate gauge of the relative degree of hazard of each individual or type of machine. But such data are lacking. However, two publications of the U. S. Department of Labor throw considerable light on the relative hazards of various metal-working machines as measured by the frequency and severity of injuries they cause, and the following data are from these sources.*

Frequency and severity of metal-working machine injuries

In an effort to determine whether injuries are more frequently caused by machine tools or by forming, punching, or shearing machines, a comparison of the number of injuries caused by each class of machines with the number of installations in each class was made. The number of machine installations, by class, was taken from an inventory of metal-working machines made by the American Machinist Magazine in 1945. The number of injuries from machines was taken from the Workmen's Compensation Reports from three states over a two or three year period. Reduced to percentages, this comparison is as follows:

MACHINES INSTALLED		INJURIES DUE TO METAL-WORKING MACHINES		
Kind of Metal-Working Machine	Percent	Wisconsin Percent	Pennsylvania Percent	New York Percent
All Cold Metal-Working Machines	100.	100.	100.	100.
Machine Tools	84.	75.4	78.7	60.3
Forming, Punching and Shearing	16.	23.9	17.1	39.7
Others	. . . .	0.7	4.2	. . . .

In all three states the percentage of injuries due to machine tools is lower (75.4 in Wisconsin, 78.7 in Pennsylvania, and 60.3 in New York) than the percentage of machine tool installations (84.), and the percentage of injuries due to forming, punching, and shearing machines is higher (23.4 in Wisconsin, 17.1 in Pennsylvania, and 39.7 in New York) than the percentage of installations (16.). The conclusions seems warranted, therefore, that with respect to frequency of injuries, machine tools are less hazardous than forming, punching, and shearing machines.

In an effort to measure severity, the proportion of serious injuries—deaths, permanent-total and permanent, partial injuries—was calculated for two states (Wisconsin and New York), for various kinds of metal-working machines. The following table shows the percentage of serious injury due to various classes of metal-working machines and from all agencies combined in these states.

* "Machine Tools and Their Hazards," Bulletin No. 129 and "Metal Forming, Punching, and Shearing Machines," Bulletin No. 139. Washington, D. C.: U. S. Department of Labor, Bureau of Labor Standards, 1951.

	Wisconsin	New York
All cold metal-working machines	25.6	59.4
Machine tools	19.1	54.3
Forming, punching, and shearing machines	45.3	67.0
All agencies of injury	9.1	30.7

The wide divergence of percentages between Wisconsin and New York are due to the different provisions of their workmen's compensation laws, also to differences in administering the laws. For example, Wisconsin has a 3-day waiting period before compensation is paid; New York has a 7-day waiting period. Percentage between the two states should not, therefore, be compared. The only valid comparisons are the percentages in each state with other percentages in the same state.

The severity of injuries caused by machine tools as a group is greater than the average for all agencies combined, judging from this statistical evidence. In Wisconsin, the percentage of serious injuries was 19.1 for machine tools, and 9.1 for all agencies of injury combined. In New York, the corresponding percentages were 54.3 and 30.7, respectively.

However, the proportion of serious injury due to machine tools (19.1 percent in Wisconsin and 54.3 in New York) is much less than the proportion due to forming, punching, and shearing machines (45.3 percent in Wisconsin and 67.0 in New York), and is also less than the proportion due to all cold-metal-working machines (25.6 and 59.4 percent).

From the standpoint of severity of injury, therefore, it may reasonably be concluded that machine tools, although relatively hazardous in comparison with all agencies of injury combined, seem to be much less hazardous than forming, punching, and shearing machines.

Frequency and severity of machine-tool injuries

In an effort to assess the relative hazards of different types of machine tools, a somewhat similar comparison was made, that is, a comparison of the proportion of injuries due to each type of machine tool with the number of machine tool installation of that type.

This comparison shows that in all three states, the percentage of injuries caused by machines in the grinding group is considerably higher than the percentage of machines in that group. This would lead to the conclusion that grinding-function machines are particularly hazardous with respect to frequency of injuries. In two of the three states, machines performing milling and planing functions show a smaller proportion of injuries than of machine installations, and in the third state these proportions are about the same. This would seem to indicate that the injury-frequency rate of machines with milling and planing functions is slightly less than would be

PERCENTAGE COMPARISON OF MACHINE-TOOL INSTALLATIONS
WITH MACHINE-TOOL INJURIES

Classes of machine tools, by function	Percent of machine-tool installations in the U. S.	Percent of injuries caused by machine tools		
		Wis.	Pa.	N. Y.
All machine tools	100.0	100.0	100.0	100.0
Milling function	13.7	9.9	3.4	13.7
Planing function	7.1	4.5	5.0	7.5
Turning function	24.4	24.8	21.5	25.8
Boring function	23.0	23.7	24.8	20.2
Grinding function	26.2	37.1	45.3	32.8
Other	5.6	. . . .	. . . .	. . . .

expected if all kinds of machine tools were equally hazardous. For machines performing a turning or boring function, the proportion of injuries in all three states is approximately the same as the proportion of machine installations, indicating an injury frequency that is neither exceptionally high nor low, and that is in line with the number of machine installations in the United States.

The proportions of serious injuries caused by machine tools according to the kind of function they perform have also been compiled for Wisconsin and New York and are given below. The machine tools are ranked in descending order of percentage of serious injuries.

WISCONSIN

Function	Percentage of serious injuries
Milling	27.6
Planing	27.3
Turning	20.4
Grinding	16.7
Boring	16.4

NEW YORK

Planing	66.1
Milling	60.5
Grinding	54.9
Turning	50.8
Boring	49.4

The combination of the foregoing data on frequency and severity, and the approximate ranking by frequency and severity of injuries they cause would be as follows:

Class of function	Rank by frequency	Rank by severity
Grinding function	High	Average
Boring function	Average	Low
Turning function	Average	Average
Planing function	Low	High
Milling function	Low	High

Frequency and severity of forming, punching, and sharing machine injuries

Using the same methods for determining the frequency and severity of forming-, punching-, and shearing-machine caused injuries as was used for machine tools caused injuries, considerable information is made available. With respect to frequency, a comparison of machine installations with injuries is as follows:

PERCENTAGE COMPARISON OF FORMING, PUNCHING, AND SHEARING-MACHINE
INSTALLATIONS WITH INJURIES CAUSED BY SUCH MACHINES

Classes of forming, punching, and shearing machines, by functions	Percent of installations in the U. S.	Percent of injuries caused by forming, punching, and shearing machines		
		Wis.	Pa.	N. Y.
All forming, punching, and shearing machines	100.0	100.0	100.0	100.0
Rolling function	3.9	3.4	3.1	7.1
Pressing and punching function	78.3	76.8	64.1	71.3
Bending (Braking) function	5.5	4.3	5.7	*
Hammering function	6.2	.6	16.0	7.7
Shearing function	6.1	14.9	11.1	13.9

* Not available.

Among machines that form, punch, and shear, shearing machines appear to be outstandingly hazardous with respect to frequency of injury. In all three states, the percentages of injuries caused by shearing machines are much higher than the percentage of shearing-machine installations in the nation as a whole. Machines performing pressing and punching functions appear to cause no more than their proportionate share of injuries in any of the three states, although the total number of installations of these machines, as well as of the injuries caused by them, is, of course, very high. For machines performing rolling, bending (braking), or hammering functions, the data for the three states are apparently inconclusive. For one state (New York) no data are available on injuries caused by machines performing a bending function.

A comparison of the percentage of serious injuries caused by different type of forming, punching, and shearing machines in the two states shows:

WISCONSIN

Function:	Percentage of serious injuries
Pressing and punching	48.5
Shearing	36.2
Rolling	*
Bending (braking)	*
Hammering	*

* Percent not computed when base is less than 100.

NEW YORK

Function:	Percentage of serious injuries
Shearing	67.9
Pressing and punching	67.7
Rolling	63.7
Hammering	62.4
Bending (braking)	†

† Not available.

From the foregoing it is apparent that machines that perform shearing as well as those that do pressing and punching are exceptionally hazardous from the standpoint of severity. The data on the other types of machines are inconclusive.

Since both frequency and severity data are inconclusive, or lacking with respect to machines doing rolling, bending, or hammering, it is not possible to rank machines by frequency and severity as was done in the case of machine tools. There is no doubt, however, that shearing and pressing and punching machines rank high in both frequency and severity.

Guarding machine tools

Machine tools as a class cause less serious injuries than do metal-forming machines, but because of their greater use, the number of injuries caused by them is probably greater than from any other class of machines. The fundamental principles involved in their guarding and suggestions for their safe operation is, therefore, included as a part of this text. For discussion purposes, machine tools will be grouped together by the functions they perform.

Milling consists of machining a piece of metal by bringing it into contact with a rotating cutter with multiple cutting edges. The commonest machine of this class is the ordinary milling machine of either the horizontal or vertical type. Also included in the milling-machine group are planer-type milling machines, gear hobbers, and special machines employing one or more milling cutters in conjunction with other types of tools.

One of the features that makes a milling machine potentially dangerous is that not only is the tool rotating, but also the work is in motion. The operator must be on his guard against both movements. Little point-of-operation guarding is possible on a milling machine, but some type of guard should be used over the cutters wherever possible. Such a guard may be of metal, or, where necessary to see the work, it may be made of transparent material. It should fit as close to the periphery of the cutter as possible and, preferably, should be adjustable to cutters of different sizes. The cutter guard performs two functions—it prevents accidental contact with the cutter head, and it acts as a permanent chip guard.

The control mechanism, usually "start" and "stop" buttons or levers, should be located within the reach of the operator from his normal working position. This is necessary for the operator's safety and desirable for efficiency.

Safe practices on the part of the operator are necessary if the milling machine is to be operated safely. Some of the most important safe practices are mentioned briefly as follows: Chips should never be removed with waste; the only safe way is to stop the machine and use a chip brush. The practice of tightening the arbor nut by using the power of the machine has caused many accidents and should never be permitted. The arbor nut should be adjusted by hand, and the cutter should be placed as far back on the arbor as possible. The material being worked on must be clamped securely and no adjustments of either the tool or the work should be made while the machine is operating. When using the automatic feed, the hand wheel on the table should be disengaged so that it does not revolve. And, since the cutting tool employs a rotating motion, it is especially important that loose clothing should not be worn by the operator.

Planing consists of machining a surface by moving the work back and forth under a stationary cutting tool or by holding the work stationary under a reciprocating tool. Machines in this class include planers, shapers, and broachers. Although these machines are not particularly hazardous, several fundamental principles of guarding them should be observed.

The openings in the bed of the planer should be filled in with sheet metal if the bed is not built with a solid web between runways. This procedure will prevent using the space under the table for storage of tools or the like. Many persons have been severely injured when their arms were caught between the frame of the planer bed and the moving table. The opening in the frame housing should also be filled in to prevent the operator from reaching through the housing and being caught between the work and the housing.

The clearance at the end of the table when extended the maximum distance should be not less than 18 inches, preferably 24 inches. If less than this, a guard rail should be provided to prevent the passage of a person between the table and the wall or other object. On large planers, a runway between the uprights is sometimes provided. The runway should be equipped with a guard rail and a toe board. And it is considered good practice to place a shield guard over the reversing dog, so that they cannot be inadvertently displaced and thus strike the operator.

Some of the precautions necessary for safe planer operation include the following: The material to be planed must be securely clamped on the table and the operator must make sure that it will clear the housing before he starts the machine. When changing stop dogs, the machine should be shut down; they should never be changed while the machine is in motion. On some very large planers, it is possible for the operator to ride the table, but this practice should never be permitted.

The other important machine using a planing action is the shaper. Little mechanical guarding is possible or necessary on this machine. Sometimes a permanent chip guard may be used to good advantage, but this is not always practicable. A clearance of from 18 to 24 inches should be maintained at the end of the ram, but when this is not possible, the opening between the ram and the fixed object should be fenced off to prevent passage. It is also considered good practice to turn the machine over by hand for the first few strokes to be sure that the ram clears the table and the work.

Turning consists in shaping a rotating piece by revolving it against a cutting tool, thus generating a cylindrical surface. Machine tools coming under this category include all forms of metal-turning lathes, including automatic screw machines and boring mills.

On large lathes a sheet-iron shield should be placed over the chuck to prevent contact with the revolving parts of the chuck. This can be made in two or more parts so that it can be moved out of the way when putting the stock in the chuck. Safety lathe dogs, that is, dogs without protruding set screws, should always be used. In cutting certain kinds of materials, particularly cast iron, brass, and other nonferrous metals, a serious hazard is created by flying chips. It is often practical to install a permanent chip guard, but this does not, as a rule, eliminate the necessity of the operator's wearing goggles.

Safety in operating a lathe depends to a great extent on safe practices. Loose clothing should not be worn. A brush should be used for removing chips, and the machine should be stopped when calipering. Dermatitis can result from cutting oils, and means should be taken to prevent it. When putting on a face plate, it should be done manually, never by using the power of the machine.

On lathes where the stock extends beyond the machine, such as turrent lathes and automatic screw machines, provision must be made for guarding the stock, to keep it from whipping about, and to prevent contact with it. A section of pipe, properly supported, through which the bar stock is fed makes an excellent guard and one that is much better than an open support.

Since a stream of coolant, usually a cutting oil, is maintained on most automatic machines, a guard should be installed to prevent the coolant from being thrown. Drippage and spillage are caught in suitable pans and drained back into the system. Floor mats, to prevent slipping, may also be necessary.

The boring mill is another machine tool in which the rotating stock is brought in contact with a stationary cutting tool. Safe operation depends more on safe practices than on mechanical guarding, but guarding reduces some of the hazards. A sheet-iron guard is advisable around the table to prevent contact when the mill is in operation. This guard should be hinged so that it can be opened when the work is being placed.

It is advisable to guard the counterweight on the boring mill with a solid complete enclosure. When setting up the job, the work must be securely clamped and all tools removed before the machine is started. The practice of riding on the table should never be permitted except when setting-up a very large mill.

Boring or *drilling* consists of cutting a round hole by means of a rotating cutting tool. Machines in this class are drills, reamers, and honers. The mechanical guarding of these machines is largely confined to the guarding of belts, pulleys, gears, and set-screws discussed in a previous chapter. Mechanical guarding is important, however, particularly on drills. Where women are employed as operators, guarding is particularly important. A telescoping guard is sometimes used over the drill, and where such a guard is practicable it should be used.

Drills, like many other machine tools, depend chiefly upon safe operating practices for their safe operation. The stock being drilled should be clamped rather than held. A chip brush should be used to remove chips; using waste or gloves should never be permitted. Loose, flowing clothing such as neckties or long sleeves are particularly dangerous when worn at work about a revolving tool such as a drill. When a woman operates a drill press, she should wear a cap that completely covers her hair. Goggles should be worn when using a sensitive drill or other type of hand-fed drill that requires the operator to watch the work closely. One of the dangers of drill-press operation is that met when changing drills. The spindle should be lowered close to the table to prevent the chuck and drill from falling, and the drill should never be changed while the machine is in motion.

Grinding consists of shaping metal by bringing it into contact with a rotating abrasive wheel. Grinding may be internal or external, flat or cylindrical. Polishing, buffing, and lapping are also considered as parts of the grinding process. The four principal hazards of grinding are: injury to the eyes from flying particles; inhalation of dust generated by the grinding process; the danger due to bursting of the wheel; and accidental contact with the revolving wheel. All of these hazards can be eliminated or diminished by mechanical guarding or the use of personal protective equipment, or both.

Protection to the eyes is best accomplished by the use of goggles. Lately, plastic faceshields have come into increasing use, but there has not been sufficient experience with them to ascertain their effectiveness for grinding operations, and dependence on them alone is not recommended. A permanent eye shield should be installed on all machines used by anyone in the shop, as, for example, an emery wheel stand used for sharpening tools.

All production grinding wheels should be equipped with an exhaust system to remove the dust at the point of origin. Grinding dust consists not only of particles of the wheel itself but also of minute particles of the metal being ground, and its inhalation represents a definite health hazard. For most grinding-wheel installations, with the possible exception of certain swing grinders used for rough grinding of castings, the protection hood is built as an integral part of the exhaust system.

Protection to the operator in case the abrasive wheel bursts is accomplished in two ways: by protection hoods, and by protection flanges, chucks, or bands. The details as to construction of protection hoods and flanges, chucks or bands, is beyond the scope of this text, but is available from other publications.* Protection hoods, in addition to keeping pieces of the broken wheel from striking the operator, also prevent accidental contact with the wheel and funnel the dust into the exhaust system. Protection flanges, chucks, or bands act to hold the wheel together if it should break in operation and reduce the chance of breakage.

Abrasive wheels may burst from a number of causes, such as overspeeding, improper mounting on the spindle, grinding on the side of the wheel, jamming of the work between the wheel and the work rest, or a combination of these or other causes. Abrasive wheels should be marked by the manufacturer to indicate the maximum speed of operation, and this should never be exceeded. Wheels should be inspected before being used, or after remaining idle for any length of time. One method of testing is the ring test. When struck by a wooden mallet, a vitrified or silicate wheel gives

* American Standard "Safety Code for the Use, Care, and Protection of Abrasive Wheels," also Safe Practices Pamphlet No. 13, "Grinding Wheels," of the National Safety Council.

a clear metallic ring if the wheel is sound. A bursting abrasive wheel can cause great damage and loss of life, and every precaution must be taken to prevent damage that might cause one to burst. It is important that wheels be properly stored, mounted, and used. Fortunately, better-designed and better-made wheels, along with the excellent work of manufacturers in educating the users in the proper care and use of their products, have greatly reduced the frequency of grinding-wheel explosions.

Guarding cold metal-forming, punching, and shearing machines

Pressing or punching, which consists of forming, shaping, cutting, or assembling metal by means of tools or dies attached to plungers or other moving parts. Machines that perform a pressing or punching operation include power presses, punch presses, plate punches, also power-screw, air, or hydraulic presses. They range in size from small punch presses used to blank out a pen point, through larger drawing presses used to convert flat discs of brass into artillery shells, to huge hydraulic presses that form sections of an automobile body at a single operation. Machines performing a pressing or punching operation are often identified by a name that indicates the particular operation performed. They may thus be known as blanking presses, piecing presses, trimming presses, forming presses, drawing presses, stamping presses, embossing presses, coining presses, assembling presses, horning presses, forcing presses, extrusion presses, flanging presses, bending presses, straightening presses, riveting presses, swaging presses, planishing presses, toggle presses, plate punches, bulldozers, and the like.

The wide variety of work done on presses makes adequate guarding difficult. There is no universal guard suitable for all presses and all kinds of work. On the other hand, a press operating wholly on any given kind of work can readily be guarded satisfactorily. Short runs, particularly on job presses, offer the most difficult problems because, while every operation can be guarded, the time and expense necessary to do so may seem prohibitive. This is particularly true if the expense of guarding is charged against the job being done. It would be much better to charge guarding as a general expense spread over the entire shop than to charge it against one particular manufactured article or machine.

Where short runs are the rule and special guarding not practicable, the best solutions seem to be to provide guards suitable for any work that might be done. Their cost can thus be spread over the life of the press. This is the method used in plants that appreciate fully the seriousness of accidents and the money value of eliminating them. The money spent on guards may well become a profitable investment, if it prevents only a single serious injury.

The problem of guarding is influenced largely by the method of feeding, which, in turn, is largely dictated by the length of the run of the particular job being done. The three methods of feeding are: fully automatic, semi-automatic, and manual. Where a fully automatic feed is used, the operator places the material en masse into a hopper, magazine, feed roll, or other device which, in turn, automatically conveys it under the die. Semi-automatic feeding means that the article is placed singly or a few at a time into a chute, slide, sliding die, dial, or other device which, in turn, feeds each piece to the point of operation. In manual feeding, the operator places each piece individually under the die and usually removes it after the operation has been performed.

Any press operation can be made reasonably safe; the more fully automatic the method of feeding, the easier to guard adequately. Effective guarding will increase, not decrease, production. If the operator knows that he cannot reach into the danger zone, he can concentrate on operating the press at its maximum capacity. Mechanical feeding, either fully automatic or semiautomatic, produces steadier operation, and higher press speed is possible. The production increase alone will, in many cases, justify the change-over from manual feeding to mechanical feeding. If the additional safety of the operator is considered, there is a further incentive to eliminate, as far as possible, hand-feeding. Many jobs that are now fed manually because of the short runs could, in all probability, be more economically and safely performed by semiautomatic feeding.

Since a fully automatic feed permits full safeguarding, this method of feeding should be used whenever possible. In some industries, automatic feeds have been developed to a marked degree. This is particularly true of large companies specializing in lightweight metal products such as cans, small tin boxes, metal spools for adhesive tape, and the like. Several of the large can companies have developed automatic feeding to such a degree that many of their products are completely made, from the first blanking-out operation to the assembly of several component parts, without being touched by human hands. The fact that it is not necessary for the machine operator to get near the point of operation would, of itself, make the operation of these machines relatively safe. In addition, a complete enclosure of the danger zone, with the guard interlocked with the driving mechanism so that the machine cannot be operated unless the guard is in place, is used to make these machines almost completely accident proof.

Automatic feeding does not eliminate the necessity for guarding the point of operation, but it makes guarding easier. Since it is unnecessary for the operator to place his hands under the plunger, the danger zone of the press can and should be fully and permanently enclosed. This enclosure of the ram may be permanently bolted into place or a gate guard may be used. When a gate guard is used, it should be interlocked into the driving mechanism so that the machine cannot be operated unless the guard is in place. It is also accepted practice, when it is possible, to limit the ram stroke to ¼ inch so that no guard will be required.

When fully automatic feeding is impracticable, semiautomatic feeding may frequently be used. Great progress has been made in the last few years in developing semiautomatic feeds. Insurance companies who write workmen's compensation insurance for large users of punch presses have been particularly active in this work. Some of them employ expert designers who will design the equipment, including the die, to eliminate hand feeding. As in the case of fully automatic feeds, semiautomatic feeds do not eliminate the necessity for guarding. For maximum safety, access to the danger zone while the press is in motion must also be impossible. Acceptable methods of guarding presses employing semiautomatic feeding are by a complete enclosure of the ram, limitation of the ram stroke, or a gate guard.

Automatic ejection of the material from the press is necessary where automatic or semiautomatic feeding is employed and is desirable when the press is manually fed. Many methods are employed to do this. Sometimes a blast of compressed air is used to blow the finished product out of the press; hollow dies may be used, which allow the work to drop through the die into a container, or a spring ejector may be placed on the lower die which will push the material out of the die and allow it to slide into a receptacle. Most presses are made so that they can be tilted, and tilting the press is often all that is necessary to provide for automatic ejection. Strangely enough, this fact is often overlooked. The finished product is frequently removed from the press by hand whereas gravity would remove it automatically if the press were tilted.

Hand feeding is by far the most hazardous, and this method of feeding should be employed only as a last resort. When manual feeding is done, it is absolutely necessary that the most effective possible method of guarding be used. There are several fairly effective methods: by limiting the stroke of the ram to ¼ inch, by a gate guard that closes off the danger zone before the ram descends, or by a two-handed tripping device. If the latter device is used, it should be so designed that both handles must be actually operated for each stroke of the press. On some two-handed tripping devices, it is possible to tie down one handle, using only the other. This type of guard is not safe and should never be used. When more than one person is required to operate a press, there should be a control for each hand of each operator in reach of the zone of danger. Gate guards are also used; one type falls ahead of the plunger and, if it meets any obstruction, such as the operator's hand, instantly stops the travel of the plunger.

Guards are also available which pull the operator's hands away from the danger zone as the ram descends, being actuated by a series of ropes operating over pulleys. Special hand tools may also be used to insert stock into or remove it from the press, but because their effectiveness depends upon unfailing use, many safety engineers place little confidence in them. Sweep guards are also used. This type of guard consists of a rod, actuated by the plunger, and is so pivoted as to sweep across the opening of the press as the ram descends, thus brushing the operator's hand aside. This type of guard is generally unsatisfactory as it is difficult to adjust it so that the operator cannot reach around it. If the sweep operates fast enough, it can also strike hard enough to cause an injury.

In addition to guarding the point of operation, presses need guarding from other hazards likely to cause injury. Each press must be equipped with a powerful brake, one that will prevent the press from overrunning the stroke and will stop the ram dead when the treadle is released. For many types of press work, particularly where manual feeding is used, a nonrepeat device is necessary. The nonrepeat device is intended to prevent the operator from riding the treadle, that is, operating the press continuously by keeping the treadle depressed. Nonrepeat devices are of several types, operating either by means of a single-stroke clutch or a mechanical arrangement that disconnects the treadle after each stroke of the clutch. A guard should be placed over the treadle to prevent accidental operation of the press should something fall on the treadle or it be accidentally stepped on.

Means should be provided to block up the plunger when changing dies. Dies should be changed only when all power has been disconnected and the press should be turned over by hand for the first few strokes to make sure that the die operates properly.

Presses can be made as safe to operate as any other machines by a combination of practical guarding, the proper design of the die to include such factors as ease of feeding and automatic ejection, and by the proper selection and training of personnel to operate and service them.*

Shearing, which consists of cutting metal by the shearing action of movable knives. Shearing may employ the action of a guillotine knife, the sliding action of scissors, or the rolling action of rotating disks. Machines performing a shearing function include squaring shears, plate shears, guillotine shears, alligator shears, rotary shears, circular shears, disk shears, and rotary slitters.

Alligator shears are frequently used in junk yards and in production shops for cutting light bar stock. Many of them operate continuously even when not in use. Frequently they are installed facing an aisle or a work

---

* For detailed information on methods of guarding and other safe practices to be observed in the operation of power presses, the American Standard "Safety Code for Power Presses and Foot and Hand Presses."

place used by many persons. Many distressing injuries have occurred because someone in passing slipped and, in trying to keep from falling, thrust his hands into the shears. Hard stock is likely to be thrown with great force when cut, or chips may fly from the knife. Shears should be provided with means of shutting off the power when not in use.

The hazards of operating alligator shears can be reduced. The clearance betwen the jaws should be limited, 3 inches being the accepted standard. A heavy U-shaped metal guard should be placed around the moving jaw and, when possible, a method of feeding, preferably automatic, should be developed that will keep the operator well away from the shears.

Squaring shears should be provided with barrier guards at front and rear of the knife, set less than the thickness of a finger above the bed so that it is impossible to reach under the knife, but so arranged that the operator can see the line of cut. A hold-down device, which descends ahead of the knife, should be installed to hold the material in place while it is being cut. When two or more operators are required to handle materials into or out of the shears, the operating mechanisms should require that each operator's hands be on the controls before the shears can be tripped.

Rolling, which consists of forming or shaping, or reducing the thickness of metal by bringing it in contact with revolving power-driven rolls. Rolling is the process used for bending sheet metal into cylindrical form, for straightening, or for otherwise forming or marking, and for reducing the thickness of metal. Machines which perform a rolling function include bending rolls, straightening rolls, corrugating rolls, beading rolls, flanging rolls, and hot or cold rolling mills.

The intake point should be provided with a stationary guard which will prevent the hands or the clothing of the operator from being drawn into the rolls. Unless the size of the material being rolled prevents it, the opening between the guard and the nip-point should not exceed ⅜ inch. The machine control should be placed as near the run-in point as possible, so that the operator can stop the machine if he should be caught in the inrunning rolls. This may be accomplished by placing a bar operating the clutch or starting mechanism across the front of the roll in such a way that it will be displaced by the arm or the body of a person caught in the roll, thus stopping the machine. Rolls usually operate quite slowly and can be stopped quickly when power is removed.

Bending (braking), which consists of bending or forming sheet metal by means of a tool or die usually actuated by a ram. Some brakes operate in a manner similar to a press, others more nearly resemble the action of guillotine shears. Brakes may be known as apron brakes or press brakes. Brakes are further identified by the particular operation they perform such as folders, flangers, corrugators, or crimpers.

Since brakes operate in the same manner as squaring shears, the same method of guarding is used.

Hammering, which consists of forming, shaping, or breaking metal by means of gravity or power-operated plungers, which may or may not be fitted with a die, the metal to be formed resting on an anvil or a die. The plunger of a gravity hammer may be raised by hydraulic, mechanical, steam, or pneumatic power, the plunger dropping free after reaching a predetermined height. The plunger of a power hammer is both raised and forced down by steam or pneumatic power. Gravity drop hammers are further identified by the method of raising the plunger: helve hammer, board drop hammer, steam drop hammer, air drop hammer, or rope drop hammer. Power hammers are further identified as air or steam power hammers. A particular type of hammer used for breaking scrap is known as a scrap breaker.

Cold metal hammers are another type of machine with a bad safety record. Hammers are used extensively in the cold working of nonferrous metal, particularly in the cutlery industry. Hammers are of many types, some operating by gravity, others through applied power; some with dies, others without. A full discussion of the function and method of operation is beyond the scope of this text, but the major hazards and the means of safeguarding them will be discussed briefly.

The most hazardous work connected with cold metal hammer operation is in changing the die. The dies are very bulky and heavy, difficult to change and to adjust. When changing dies, the hammer should be blocked up, a piece of heavy timber such as an 8-by-8-inch block being used, and a safe means of handling the dies should be provided. A table with an adjustable top, so that the die can be slid into place without lifting, has been found to be very helpful. Shield guards of heavy sheet metal should be placed around the anvils of drop hammers to prevent scale or other particles from flying. The scale guard may be hinged or pivoted into place so that it can be swung out of the way when changing dies. When a treadle is used, a stirrup guard should be placed over the treadle to prevent accidental operation.

This chapter is intended only to highlight the guarding of metal-working machines and to point out the basic principles underlying such guarding. In addition to standard models of machine tools employing the five functional methods of removing metal, there are literally thousands of special machine tools, designed and built to do special jobs. Many of these special machines, as well as standard machines used for a special purpose, require individual guarding treatment. Standard guards are not usable, and protection must be provided in the design of the machine or added by the safety engineer in the plant of the user.

Chapter Twenty

The Prevention of Falls

Falls are one of the chief sources of occupational injury. Data from agencies administering workmen's compensation acts usually show that for all types of industry combined injuries from falls are exceeded in number only by those from "handling." * For example, during a typical five-year period in the state of New York, the proportions of total compensated injuries from these two sources were: handling, **29.3** per cent, falls, **21.9** per cent. For Pennsylvania, a typical year showed: handling, **23.8** per cent, falls, **18.1** per cent. However, in the manufacturing industries, mechanical apparatus comes second, with falls third. For New York manufacturing industries during the typical five-year period, the relationship of these sources was: handling, **29.2** per cent, mechanical equipment, **28.3** per cent, falls, **13.1** per cent. In many kinds of industry and in many occupations, falls are the chief injury source. Among occupations responsible for falls are overhead maintenance, overhead construction, rigging, painting, and many types of outdoor work.

In industry as a whole, falls to the same level produce somewhat more injuries than do falls to a lower level. Obviously, the chance of injury in falling to a lower level is high, but the greater frequency of falls to the same level more than makes up for this difference. In certain industries, of course, like building construction, and in occupations involving much overhead work, falls to a lower level predominate.

In theory, falls are wholly preventable. In practice, their elimination is exceedingly difficult, because it involves great detail and the practically faultless performance of everyone concerned (workmen, supervisors, architects, engineers, management, maintenance forces, and so on). Perhaps one reason why the necessary high level of performance in this respect is so

---

* "Handling," as used herein, means the lifting, moving, placing, transporting, or turning of objects where such action is the primary purpose.

difficult to secure and maintain is that we are all used to falls from child-hood on. A child learns to walk through the tumbles he takes. Adults are characteristically careless in their walking and take their tumbles too, but they are far more likely to be injured or even killed thereby than are chil-dren. Their bones are more brittle, they have farther to fall and they hit harder.

Of course everyone knows that falls from some height are likely to in-jure or kill, but few take the hazard of falls at the same level seriously enough and fail to take even the simplest and most obvious precautions to lessen the possibility of falls by themselves or others.

The fact that the injury and death totals from falls at floor level and on stairs is high is so well established that it deserves emphasis here. It is an expectable result of the increase in bone brittleness, the decrease in mus-cular coordination and in reaction speed that are a normal part of the aging process. It stresses the importance of maintaining all floors, stairs and walking surfaces in the safest possible condition at all times, particularly where elderly people live as in apartment houses, private residences and especially in old folks' homes. It applies also to public places they are likely to visit. It behooves the owners or others responsible for the safety of such places to take this seriously into account.

The prevention of falls may be classified under the following broad headings:

1. Safe surfaces on which to walk and work.
2. Safe means of access to overhead points.
3. Safe footwear.
4. Safe practice in walking.
5. Housekeeping and order.

To be reasonably safe for all who use it, a floor surface should be a true plane, free from cracks or holes wide and deep enough to catch a heel in a manner that might cause tripping. For the high type of peg heel that women wear so avidly, a crack or hole of only about a quarter inch in diameter is sufficient to cause a fall. The frequency of falls due to this wholly unnecessary hazard amply attests to it simportance.

The hazard inherent in such floor faults as slipperiness and depressions due to wear was brought out by a series of moving pictures taken by hidden cameras of people making normal use of a much travelled corridor. These pictures showed that in most cases, the heel contacted the floor at angles of from 18 to 23 degrees with the horizontal. The smallest such angle was 12 degrees, the greatest, 32. Since with an unworn hard heel, the area of contact is hardly more than a line, at the rear of the heel, it is obvious that the coefficient of friction between heel and floor must be high else the heel will slip forward. Furthermore, if the rear edge of the heel lands on the downward slope of a depression, the net effect will be to reduce the angle of contact by the angle of slope. Depressions of as little as 1/32nd inch in depth, in some cases showed downward slopes of as much as 12 degrees with the horizontal.

These pictures showed clearly how most falls on floor surfaces occur. If, when one steps forward, the floor surface fails to hold the heel on contact, the foot slips forward and the walker is thrown off balance. Unless he is relatively acrobatic, he goes down in a manner best described by the commonly voiced statement, "My feet flew out from under me." He usually twists slightly toward the foot that slips and lands on that hip. Unless he gets his hand down in time to break his fall a broken hip is likely. But if he gets his hand down so quickly that his weight is taken on his straightened arm, a badly strained or broken wrist is probable, or even an impacted fracture of the ends of the long bones of the lower arm, at the wrist.

Tripping occurs when the downcoming heel is caught unexpectedly and held, if only for a brief fraction of time. The victim usually falls forward full length unless he is able to get his hand down in time to break his fall, but again wrist or arm damage is likely. This highlights the hazard of a floor crack, break or hole that can halt the forward motion of a heel that starts a slip a short distance in front of it. Of course, if the person is agile enough to regain his balance the floor defect might have prevented a fall due to slipperiness but who would care to count on it?

Wear tends strongly to reduce the coefficient of friction of most floorings. So does waxing, though at least some manufacturers of floor waxes have incorporated anti-slip properties into their products and claim good results if their directions for application, particularly as regards buffing, are faithfully followed. Even with such buffing however, the wax layers will be thicker in a depression than on the level surfaces and therefore more slippery.

The inherent coefficient of friction of flooring materials should always be a major consideration in the planning of new buildings but the frequency of the use of marble flooring, particularly in monumental buildings, indicate that architects are, as a class, not at all safety minded. The famous Federal Triangle buildings in Washington D.C. furnish an excellent example. Marble is used in entrance halls and many of the aisles and stairways. A little water makes smooth marble very slippery. Falls among Federal employees coming to work on wet days were so frequent, including many broken bones, hips mostly, that in wet weather full width lengths of non-slip floor coverings are regularly put down over the lovely marble. Also a safety committee appointed to investigate the situation recommended that strips of abrasive material be inserted in grooves cut in the surfaces of the marble stair treads, but permission to do so was refused because it would lessen in some slight degree, the beauty of the stairs. What do broken bones matter when a touch of beauty is at stake?

Sidewalks and outdoor walkway surfaces present the same hazards as do floor surfaces under roof with the icing hazard in addition. At least where icing occurs frequently in winter, sidewalks should be grooved for drainage and preferably, have an abrasive material incorporated into the surface layer. A sloping walk presents a problem. If the slope is less than about one in twenty five, or so, cross grooves spaced about an inch apart will give good results. It is a mistake to insert an occasional low step spaced many feet apart, and perhaps, irregularly. The hazard is twofold; one may fail to notice a very low step, seven inch risers are the recommended minimum, outdoors. The other hazard is that even if the walker notices the first step he is likely to transfer his attention elsewhere before he reaches the second one and trip and fall. A fall on a single such step is far more likely to cause an injury than an upward fall on a stair because the victim not only has farther to fall but is more likely to land full force on a knee. Such widely spaced steps and risers should be painted a distinctive color, red is preferable, the spacing should be uniform and they should have no nosing for it is likely to catch and hold a toe. Nosing of not over one inch is commonly used on indoor stairs to increase tread width and is justified as safer than narrow treads.

Typical defects

The permissible length of this discussion does not allow all-inclusive treatment. However, typical defects of floor surfaces, stairs, ladders, portable steps, and sawhorses are listed in the following pages. In most cases, the means of correction is suggested by the defect. The comments in the right-hand column are indicative.

DEFECTIVE CONDITION	MEANS OF CORRECTION
Floors:	
a. Holes, depressions, unevenness, wear, sag, working overload.	
b. Projections, as edges of gratings, pit covers, pipes, conduits, etc.	Management must cultivate an awareness of floor hazards. Systematic inspection,
c. Uncovered gutters or drains.	provision for prompt repair and correc-
d. Slipperiness due to wear, grease, oil, water, loose particles, as sand or sawdust.	tion of all defects. Forethought for safety in all construction, alterations, additions.
e. Slipperiness due to use of material with low coefficient of friction, as marble or smooth steel.	Provision of safe load values and maintenance of loading within safe limits.
f. Vibration, springiness, slope.	

DEFECTIVE CONDITION	MEANS OF CORRECTION
Stairs. Common defects are: *a*. Treads—slippery, worn, split, broken, deformed, nonuniform in width, sloping, springy, weak, lack of nosing. *b*. Risers—nonuniform in height, not filled in. *c*. Railing—loose, weak, missing, improper height, lack of hand clearance. *d*. Design faults—too steep, too narrow, too wide (between railings), flights too long, landings too narrow, opening directly onto traffic. *e*. Lighting—too little, glare, shadows, light control inconveniently placed.	Protection for construction jobs and restoration of safe condition. Careful housekeeping, prevention of spillage, drippage, and leakage. Provision of antislip surfaces, sections, or treads. Use of antislip finishes or floor coverings. Excellent maintenance. An excellent all-purpose stair will have 7″ risers, 11″ tread, plus 1″ nosing, riser height and tread width uniform within ⅛″, clear width not less than 36″ nor over 88″, both sides railed if 44″ wide or over, railings not less than 30″ nor more than 34″ from upper surface of top rail to surface of tread in line with face of riser at forward edge of tread, antislip tread surfaces.
Fixed ladders: *a*. Rungs—uneven, spacing, bent, loose, missing, worn, greasy, weak, insecure, nonuniform replacement. *b*. Rails—bent, split, improperly repaired, weak. *c*. Location or placing—inadequate toe clearance at back, hand clearance at rail, shoulder clearance at side, lack of hand holds at top, too narrow or too wide, outward slope, too near traffic.	A fixed ladder should have 12″ rung spacing, 18″ minimum rail spacing, clearance at back of ladder not less than 6½″ at any point, rails carried up above platform or roof and goosenecked or otherwise arranged to give handhold 42″ high; on ladder 20′ long or over, there should be cages 26″ wide, 27″ deep starting 7′ from floor or ground level.
Portable straight wood ladder: * *a*. Rungs—Nonuniform spacing, broken, missing, worn, loose, weak, improperly repaired or replaced, insecure, dirty. *b*. Rails—split, yielding, weak, improperly repaired. *c*. Antislip feet—lacking, wrong type for purpose. *d*. Design and construction—lack of batter, unsafe construction, concealing finish, improper material.	Portable straight ladder should have 12″ rung spacing, ¼″ batter per foot, rungs extending through rails and secured to prevent turning, at least two metal cross braces, clear straight-grained material, oil or varnish finish, antislip feet.

* See American Standard "Safety Code for Construction, Care and Use of Ladders," published by American Standards Association, 70 E. 45th St., New York 17, N. Y.

DEFECTIVE CONDITION	MEANS OF CORRECTION
Stepladder: · *a.* Steps—worn, broken, split, missing, loose, weak. *b.* Rails—bad condition, weak. *c.* Spreader—loose, nonlocking. *d.* Design and construction—inadequate batter, weak, too long, unsteady, concealing finish.	Lattice-type stepladders not recommended, positive locking spreaders, treads spaced 12″ on centers, securely fastened.
Portable steps: *a.* Bad condition. *b.* Design and construction—inadequate batter, weak, too high or uneven risers, unsafe assembly, lack of railing.	Portable steps over 4″ high should be railed. Side batter not less than 1″ per foot of height.
Saw horses: End overhang, inadequate batter, inadequate bracing, weak, bad assembly, bad condition.	Legs should be through bolted. End batter should be equal to overhang. Legs should be cross braced and angle should be braced.

Scaffolds

A wide variety of scaffolds are in common use. The outline below is limited to the barest fundamentals of scaffold safety involving the following: *

1. Suitability for work to be done.
2. Soundness of materials used.
3. Design to include at least:
   a. Adequate railing.
   b. Toeboards.
   c. Ample factor of safety.
   d. Secure support or attachment.
   e. Stability.
   f. Safe means of access.
4. Provision for maintenance.
5. Consideration of relationship to other operations and equipment to avoid incidental hazards.
6. Selection of personnel suited to scaffold work.
7. Careful training and supervision.
8. Maintenance of good housekeeping.

---

* For details of scaffold construction see "Manual of Accident Prevention in Construction," Associated General Contractors of America, Washington, D. C.

Overhead work in general

Much of the foregoing applies to overhead work, but the following comments are of general applicability:

1. All overhead equipment of whatever nature must be serviced at short or long intervals, and suitable provision for such service should be provided for or at least planned for when the equipment is installed. The factors to be considered are:
   a. Frequency of servicing required.
   b. Nature of service required.
   c. Number of workers required.
   d. Weight of tools and equipment likely.
   e. Adverse exposures likely.
   f. Incidental hazards that may be involved.
2. Overhead work involves special hazards and requires special abilities. Planning should, therefore, be very careful and thorough, covering at least:
   a. Personnel to be used.
   b. Instructions to be given.
   c. Special safety equipment and safeguards needed.
   d. Clearance with those in charge of other activities or operations.
   e. Possible emergencies or untoward developments.
   f. Adequate supervision.

Footwear

Unsafe footwear contributes to or causes injuries in many ways. Much attention is rightly being given to the wearing of safety shoes of various types, but it appears probable that falls due, in whole or in part, to improper footwear produce more injuries than do the lack of safety shoes.

Loose or worn soles or heels cause tripping, slips, and stumbles. Loose lacings, buckles, and fasteners interfere with one's stride. Run-down heels bring bad balance and resulting strain, turned ankles, and fatigue.

High heels are very bad. They cause falls through bad balance, bad gait, foot discomfort, foot deformation, and tendon strain. The tiny heels catch in gratings and crevices and slight irregularities. Their small bearing surfaces increase slipping. Whether or not anything very effective can be done to discourage the production and wearing of these "instruments of injury" is a question. It will apparently be necessary to bring about a radical change in the sales approach in the shoe trade, as well as in the feminine viewpoint.

It is possible for any industrial establishment to secure a reasonably good degree of conformity with requirements for safe footwear within the plant, however. Three measures are necessary.

1. Provision of the specified footwear at prices no higher than the employee is accustomed to paying.
2. Convenience of supply and correct fit.
3. A system of arousing and maintaining interest in safe footwear coupled with a continual check on performance in a helpful coöperative manner, rather than dictatorially.

Safe practice in walking

Given good walking and working surfaces and safe footwear properly maintained, we will still have falls due to unsafe practices in walking and working. Each person should cultivate safe walking practices. For instance, Indians and woodsmen are traditionally sure-footed, for, if one is to keep his footing at all in the woods, he must pay attention to his walking. It is as feasible, and often as necessary to stimulate and instruct in safe "foot work" as in other phases of safety. A stair furnishes an excellent example. Falls on stairs, despite good stair condition, yield a continuous stream of injuries. Few persons give any thought to safe stair use and consequently few use stairs safely. The formation of safe stair habits is personally important to everyone, though few seem to realize it enough to do anything effective about it.

Floor housekeeping

The subject of housekeeping in general, is dealt with in another Chapter, but the importance of maintaining at all times a high standard of floor housekeeping is so great as to justify its mention here for emphasis. Dirt, oil, grease, water and other spillages, loose materials, dropped tools and the like, are prolific injury producers. For example, in pipe and machine shops, many a luckless mechanic has ridden to injury on a pipe nipple he or a fellow worker had dropped and failed to pick up.

Chapter Twenty-one

Methods of Promoting Safe Practice

The essentials of first-rate safety performance in any establishment have been likened to an equilateral triangle, the sides of which are safe plant and safe practice resting on the solid base of management interest. Or, putting it a little differently, if any management really wants good safety performance, it can get it. It can make its plant safe. It can develop a high standard of safety-mindedness in its working force, and it can maintain a program of preventive effort that, based on these two essentials, will practically eliminate accidents.

Although much in preceding chapters bears on the promotion of employee interest in safety (in other words, employee safe practice), this and the three following chapters are devoted specifically to major phases of this basic element of safety. The means and methods used to develop, improve, and maintain worker safe practice have been dealt with under varying titles by different authors. For the purposes of this discussion, the following classification will suffice:

1. The essentials of safety salesmanship.
2. The organized safety sales program.
3. Appraising employee attitude.
4. Safety organization.
5. Safety education and training.
6. The new employee.

The essentials of safety salesmanship

Getting men to work safely is primarily a sales job. It has to be. Men can be ordered or even compelled to do things, up to a point, but compulsion cannot get really good performance in anything. Only interest—the desire to do good work—can bring superior accomplishment. Enforcement of at least minimal, acceptable safety practice may at times be necessary. When it is, however, it merely means that the sales effort has failed with the person or persons involved and, therefore, it is necessary to use that very poor substitute, enforcement, pending the time when the sale can be made.

The subject of salesmanship has been abundantly dealt with in widely-known and well-accepted texts, which anyone wishing to study selling in detail should consult. However, fundamentals deemed of major importance to the safety man are presented here in brief fashion.

Essentials of a sound rule

Many things are sold that should not be. Others are sold to perform more or better than they actually will—all of this without any actual fraud, perhaps, but no such sale is sound. The first essential, then, is a good product. A product is good only if it yields the purchaser a profit on the transaction, a profit in service or pleasure or satisfaction, or some other value. Surely safety is such a product. It brings the employee freedom from injury and suffering and loss of wages and bereavement and hardship for his family. And it saves money for the employer and brings him more and better production, a more smoothly running organization, and better repute. It saves loss to the community and to the nation. The salesman of safety should be very careful to make no exaggerated claims for his product. The truth is enough.

The next essential is that the salesman must know his product. There is no substitute for hard study, attention to detail, and clear thinking, if one is to acquire a good mastery of any subject. This is perhaps truer of safety than of many other lines, because safety covers so broad a field.

The third vitally important point is that the salesman should always endeavor to watch his sales effort from the point of view of the prospect. Of course, given a good product, any salesman who merely "goes out and talks about it" and exposes himself to enough possible customers will make some sales, but that is not effective salesmanship. It is really advertising, and though advertising has a sound place in any safety program, it cannot take the major role. Too many safety programs consist of little else. Most safety sales must be made on an individual basis by a salesman who studies his prospect carefully, learns all he can about him, gets him to talk, and guides his thinking along the path that will lead to the sale. He seeks to find out what his prospect's wants and desires are, what things look valuable to him, and he presents his product in a way to prove that its possession will minister to the need or desire or want that it fits.

The three steps in a sale

It is well to point out that there are at least three steps to every sale. (Some sales authorities will insist on more, but three are basic.) These three steps are the *preparation,* the *presentation,* and the *close.*

The *preparation* means (very briefly) getting all possibly helpful information about the prospect, matching it up against the values of the product, and deciding which value or values to use in the presentation—what desires or needs to appeal to. For example, a toolmaker who did not want to wear goggles on some grinding work was found to be an amateur biologist. He had built his own microscope and spent most of his evenings over it. The successful appeal then was the fact that even fine pieces from the grinding could easily cause opacity with resultant damage to vision.

The foregoing example is illustrative of what to present, but not of how to present it. The *presentation* might be made as follows: The toolmaker of the example was an elderly man of long experience, who, however, had not had much experience with the type of grinding in question. Further, he greatly valued fine technical skill; and since neither the foreman nor the safety engineer were possessors of such skill, he did not have much respect for their opinions. But the physician whom the company retained to supervise its first-aid setup was a surgeon of great skill whom the toolmaker liked and respected. The physician's help was enlisted by the safety engineer who brought him out to the job and, with the foreman, showed and explained to him in detail the whole operation. After the physician had satisfied himself that there was a hazard, he told the toolmaker just what the fine flying particles could do to his eyesight. The point was won.

Two things are important in the *close,* the timing and the commitment. If a salesman could be a mind reader, he would press for the commitment the moment he read the thought, "I want that," but it isn't as easy as that. The salesman must judge the proper moment from his prospect's speech and manner, but mainly from what he says. Therefore, the salesman who talks too much misses clues, and the salesman who talks too little loses control of the sale.

No sale is complete without a commitment verbally or in writing to someone on something definite. The toolmaker committed himself by saying to the physician, "All right, Doctor, I didn't see it that way. I guess you are right. I can't afford to damage my eyes. I'll wear the goggles." And the safety engineer further clinched the matter by asking the toolmaker, "Would you like to have Dr. Blank (the oculist) fit your goggles? He might want to test your eyes to see if you need prescription lenses in the goggles. I'll make an appointment if you wish." The acceptance of that invitation made a withdrawal practically impossible.

No new selling point should be brought out after the commitment is made. Selling should stop and some form of commendation is in order if only "I'm glad you see it that way, John. The fact that you do will help me get others to protect their eyesight." On the other hand, bringing in some new idea may upset the sale, because it may run counter to some strongly-fixed prejudice the prospect may have.

To whom must safety be sold?

The answer is, safety literally must be sold to everyone in an organization: the management, particularly the top operating executive, because he must furnish the executive leadership without which the safety effort won't get far; the supervisory staff, because its members carry out the will and policies of the management; the workmen, because they do the work that brings them into contact with the hazards.

Selling the management

A major purpose of this book is to furnish information that will help to convince managements that they should be satisfied with nothing less than best possible safety performance. The chapters "Accident Costs" and "Plant Inspection" should be particularly valuable to this end. However, as previously pointed out, if executive interest is lacking, the first and vital problem the safety man must solve is the stimulation of that interest to the point of effective action. He will probably have to convince the executive of three things:

1. That the accident record of the establishment is not good enough.

2. That other managements have found that good safety performance pays.

3. That good safety performance can be had by an effort the management can reasonably make.

The details of how these three points can best be won in each instance must of necessity be developed to suit the characteristics of the executive in question and the facts of the situation.

Selling the supervisory staff

The key to selling the supervisory staff lies in the simple fact that any person who values his job tries hardest to accomplish whatever it is that his boss appears to want most. If the boss is sold on safety and makes it clear that it is really one of his chief wants, his foremen will undertake to get it for him. And they will keep up their effort just as long as he keeps on wanting it. But if he transfers his interest to something else, their major effort will follow the path in which his interest is keenest and safety will suffer. As long as the top executive maintains his interest in production, cost, and quality, his staff keeps on trying to improve them. If he adds safety to this "sacred three," they will, also. So, selling the foreman on safety is primarily the chief's job, but the safety man can help mightily. He can furnish information and ideas and the safety viewpoint for his chief to use. If the boss wants safety, any source from which help may be had will be welcome. If the safety man knows his "stuff," his advice will be heeded and his help will be welcomed. But if the boss doesn't evidence much interest in safety, the safety man has the hardest of all selling jobs in trying to sell the foremen something that their boss quite evidently doesn't think much of.

Selling the workmen

The foreman is the key man here just as he is in production, but the safety man has a vital part, too. He is the technician of safety, the planner, the organizer, the stimulator. He works with and through the foremen, helping each do the safety job in his field of action. He continually watches the safety work of the whole organization, keeps his chief in touch, and directly, or through the chief, applies corrective pressure wherever improvement is needed. The foreman develops safety-mindedness and promotes safe practice in his men by knowing the work and by a process of finding out each man's abilities and habits and characteristics. He endeavors to direct and lead each man along the lines that will best promote his interest in his work and contribute to his pride in going good work, his satisfaction in his work, and his liking for the job. Men do well at work they like, and poorly at work they dislike. They like what they can do well. They soon come to dislike what they have little aptitude for.

The organized safety sales program

The individual personalized work of the foreman in promoting the safe practice of his men should be supplemented by a definite organized safety sales program. This is a primary responsibility of the safety man. It is a combination of advertising, information giving, and the promotion of worker participation in the accident-prevention program. Although, as pointed out, the foreman is the key safety man, he needs all possible help. A soundly-conceived and properly-prosecuted safety program will be of great aid to the foremen in improving safe practice, just as a sound advertising program aids the commercial sales force to get orders, even though it may bring in relatively few orders of itself.

This general program is directed at the major motivating characteristics that men have. Psychologists, in listing these, differ somewhat in the descriptive terms used and in the prominence they give the respective characteristics, traits, desires, or incentives. However, there seems to be rather general agreement that the following can be effectively appealed to through an organized promotional safety program:

1. Instinct of self-preservation.
2. Desire for material gain.
3. Desire for praise, approbation, or distinction.
4. Fear of ridicule or disapproval.
5. Sense of humanity.
6. Sense of responsibility.
7. Sense of loyalty.
8. Competitive instinct.
9. Desire for power or leadership.

Note that the first of these is probably the strongest motivating characteristic in all forms of intelligent life. Civilized man tends to elevate motives he regards as nobler, but since this instinct is so deeply rooted in all of us, it will, if properly appealed to, prove powerfully stimulative of safe practice. Care must be used in shaping the appeal, but the same may be said of appeals aimed at any of the other motivating characteristics. It is, after all, merely another phase of the third essential of salesmanship, namely the appeal must be so fashioned as to be attractive to or otherwise effective with the prospect. The salesman does this by studying each prospect as an individual and shaping his appeal accordingly. The advertising salesman shapes each appeal to reach a characteristic or desire that all or nearly all men have in greater or less degree. He knows that no one appeal will reach all, but by varying the appeals aimed at each such characteristic, and by aiming several appeals at each of them, he expects to "score an occasional effective hit" on every man (or woman) in the entire working force.

For emphasis, a point already made is again presented, namely, that most men are influenced (perhaps *pushed* is a better word) into safety-mindedness by a process of selling on an individual basis; that is, through definite training courses, by the personalized training and supervision the foreman carries on, and by taking part in such safety activities as committee work or accident investigation, under the proper leadership. The organized safety sales program makes few direct sales of safety, but properly set up and maintained, it aids, strengthens, and stimulates the direct sales work greatly.

Infinite ingenuity has been used in reaching the various motivating characteristics, and successful methods have been reported in almost endless detail. A few deserve special mention.

Instinct of self-preservation.   Feature injuries from typical unsafe practices in a manner to emphasize the possibility of death or the consequences of losing an eye, suffering an amputation, or losing the use of a member. Few people realize how good life is until they face the prospect of losing it. They take the life-long possession of all body members and faculties in full working order for granted.

The presentation must fit. There is little value in depicting the danger of losing an eye unless an eye hazard has been shown to exist. Safety shoes have little appeal to anyone unless it can be shown that his foot is likely to be in position to be caught. A man who has operated woodworking machines for many years and has all his fingers is likely to cite that fact as proof that it "won't happen to him." He doesn't realize that one finger is too many to lose in a lifetime and that, unless he always follows safe practice, the law of averages will almost surely "catch up with him" eventually.

Example.   Workman who is lax in wearing goggles. Offer to sell him a glass eye or send him to the nurse to have a patch put over one eye for an hour or two.

Desire for gain.   Offer rewards in pay, bonuses, cash, prizes, objects of value for good safety performance or safety suggestions. The rewards should have a reasonable relationship to the effort involved and be large enough to be attractive. Absolute fairness must be the rule. Favoritism will quickly nullify all value of this method.

Example.   A dollar or two each month for each workman who goes through the month without a lost-time injury. A specific system of cash awards ranging from $5 to $100 for safety ideas.

Desire for praise, approbation, or distinction.   Persons in whom this trait is strong respond to awards of badges, honor dinners, public mention, personal letters of commendation from an outstanding person, such as the president of the company or a respected public official.

Fear of ridicule or disapproval.   Practically every person is sensitive to the disapproval of his fellows, particularly those whom he likes, but great care must be exercised if this fact is to be made use of. Ridicule is a dangerous weapon, for unless it is very skillfully used, it is likely to induce defiant or emotional behavior that will harm rather than help safety. However, safety performance can often be improved by making it evident that continued faulty performance will bring disapproval.

Example.   When departments are striving for the longest no-injury period, a workman discovered violating safe practice will often correct his behavior when his fellows voice their disapproval or even if it is merely pointed out that an injury would bring disapproval.

Sense of humanity.   No one wants to see anyone hurt. All normal people are moved by suffering. So the slogan "Watch Yourself" is the workshop expression of the fact that to some extent and under some circumstances each of us will undertake to be "our brother's keeper." As one man put it, "I figure I owe it to myself to keep him from getting hurt if I see he is in danger." So the wise safety man encourages this attitude in a matter-of-course way and at every opportunity. He does not question that all men are humane, he merely seeks to bring the instinct out and make it more active.

Sense of responsibility.   Every person feels some degree of responsibility for something. Few people will deliberately fail to try if they know that others depend on them to perform in a specified manner. Assigning one the responsibility to do something and then giving generous (but not false) credit for satisfactory performance combines the force of this trait with the desire for praise.

> **Example.** Assigning to a certain mechanic the duty of keeping the abrasive wheels in safe operating condition and noting with favorable comment a particularly good overhaul job he does on one of them. Assigning specific cleaning duties to a janitor, asking him for suggestions as to how to prevent disorder and dirt, and praising his good performance.

Sense of loyalty.   A man is loyal to his country, to a kindly foreman, to his union, his club, his lodge, his friends, his family. The advertising program, therefore, will direct appeals to these loyalties, but each appeal should have some reasonable relationship to the situation. It can be shown that one should be loyal to the standards set by his associates, his leader, or his company.

Competitive instinct.   Most people love competition in some form. Safety contests rest on this trait. To be effective, the "rules of the game" must be clear, the contest must be a reasonable one, and the issue must be decided fairly. Safety contests are discussed later in this chapter, but it is pointed out here that a form of cheating—bringing injured workers back to practically workless jobs that have been created for the purpose—has brought such widespread criticism as largely to nullify the value of such contests.

Desire for power or leadership.   This can frequently be made use of by appointment to safety committees or to office in safety organizations, to lead safety rallies, to preside at safety meetings, or to positions of special distinction, such as safety monitors, minute men, and so on.

Plant advertising media

The following advertising media are commonly used:

1. Posters and pictures.
2. Plant bulletin boards.

3. Plant newspapers.
4. Messages in pay envelopes.
5. Display of interesting objects.
6. Signs and slogans.

Posters.   Promoting safety interest by the use of posters was one of the first projects undertaken by the National Safety Council. The Council offers posters as a membership service in unending variety. They have proved to have a continuing value. Styles in posters change just as styles in clothing and furniture do. Treatment and presentation change also. Posters must keep up with the times, and their messages must be in accord with current conditions, current events, and trends of thought. They must draw the attention of those at whom their messages are directed. They must stimulate their thought processes, impel them toward the desired type of action or form of conduct or behavior.

Pictures speak a universal language. Everyone can read a picture couched in familiar terms. The easiest and quickest avenue of learning is through the eyes. A picture that conveys a clear message transmits an idea in a fraction of the time and more clearly than can be done by writing. However, picturization is obviously limited to simple ideas and impressions and, therefore, can at best be merely one of the several valuable means of stimulating safety interest and safety practice.

Much depends upon the presentation. The idea must be clear. The setup must fit the idea. Color can fascinate or it can repel. Figures can attract by their naturalness or by clever exaggeration or cartooning. Attractiveness is of major importance.

Posters should be used liberally, but not in overabundance. A few at a time, in locations where each will attract attention, with frequent enough changing to avoid staleness, are much more effective than an accumulation. A given idea is driven home better by a series of posters successively displayed than by the same posters displayed at the same time. They are more effective posted on neat bulletin boards than just posted. Bulletin boards should be well-made, attractive, and well-finished and maintained. The material on them should be orderly. There is difference of opinion as to whether or not it is best to have specific boards solely for safety material. There should be no stale material, however, particularly announcements kept past the dates with which they deal. Bulletin board locations should be carefully selected and well kept. Posters should be securely mounted, protected from soiling, and, if outside, from the weather. Lighting should be good. Posters are best seen above eye level, but whatever the location, wording, if any, must be readily readable from a convenient position. One bulletin board or one poster of a kind for 100 employees is a good ratio in general, though it can well vary to accord reasonably with the density of plant population.

The large outside plant bulletin board. To furnish a continuing picture of the accident record and to stimulate rivalry between different plants or departments, many plants set up large boards at the plant gate or other favorable location. It is advantageous to include some feature to draw attention, such as a clock, indicating thermometer, wind gauge, or drinking fountain, and, of course, the injury score up to date.

Plant newspapers. These are a well-established and valuable media for the building of plant morale, provided they are newsy, interesting, and suitably written. Safety can advantageously be given a large part in them. It is essential that the safety messages be timely, pertinent to plant conditions, practical, and carefully written. If the responsible safety head is not the editor, there should be at least very close coöperation between him and the editor. A column featuring safety suggestions from workmen and the action on such suggestions can be a particularly valuable feature, provided the action on the suggestions actually is good.

Messages in pay envelopes. Used in moderation and couched in a spirit of helpfulness rather than one of command, such messages have considerable effectiveness. Information on off-the-job and home safety can well be given in this way. Also, announcements of special bonuses, awards or prizes, plant outings, and so on, are often made in this manner.

Display of interesting objects. Great interest can often be aroused by displaying something that has been a contributing factor in causing or preventing an accident. For instance, a tool with a mushroomed head, broken goggles, a battered safety shoe, may be displayed, each with its descriptive, short but clear story, including the name, or better yet, the picture of the victim or near victim. Samples of defects caught by inspection or someone's vigilance make excellent displays, as a piece of acid-eaten manila rope contrasted with an undamaged piece, a loaded sprinkler head contrasted with a clean one, a worn extension cord, a wrench with sprung jaws, and the like. Also, specific information may be given, as a properly tied square knot contrasted with a granny knot, or the construction of wire cables. Such displays should be kept clean and free from dust; and while they will not get stale as quickly as posters do, they should be changed when they have been up a reasonable length of time.

Signs and slogans. Properly used, these have considerable value both in giving safety information and in promoting safety interest. Signs should be truthful, definite as to meaning, and in correct English. For instance, a sign that says "High Voltage" should be used only for voltages that standard practice considers high. Where a warning as to the location of electrical equipment carrying low voltages is desirable, some such wording as "Danger—Live Voltages" should be used.

All safety signs should be carefully located to be visible to any person approaching the position of hazard. Signs should be neat, well made and finished, durable for the conditions involved, and kept clean and in good condition.

Slogans can be very valuable, but they must express a worthwhile purpose or goal, and they must be timely. Furthermore, the management must, itself, show by its actions that it believes in them and is earnestly trying to live up to them. An outstanding example is the much-used, often abused, and much discussed "Safety First." If the management really means it and shows its belief by convincing action, this slogan should be posted proudly and kept bright. But posting it everywhere in a plant full of hazards within the power of the management to correct makes a travesty of it, and it is better not to use the term at all.

For detailed suggestions as to the construction, lettering, and so on, of signs, see "American Standard" Specifications for Industrial Accident Prevention Signs.

Employee participation

In general, the greater the employee participation in the safety program, the more effective it will be. Therefore, the organized safety program should include as many activities in which workmen can take a part as possible, and further, it should give them the major roles whenever and wherever possible. Such activities include:

1. Safety campaigns and contests.
2. Safety meetings and safety stunts.
3. First-aid training.
4. Plant fire brigades.
5. Plant inspection.
6. Accident investigation.
7. Job safety analyses.
8. Safety suggestion systems.
9. Safety inventories.
10. Safety committees (safety organization).

Most of these activities are dealt with in other chapters. Detailed information on the remainder will be found in current safety literature. However, a few comments are justified here.

Safety campaigns. The value of occasional safety campaigns to accomplish a specific purpose has been much discussed. Such campaigns are of undoubted value if properly timed and properly conducted. They are timely when a special situation arises that calls for a general quickening of safety interest, for example, general laxity in wearing goggles, a general staleness in the safety work, a seeming epidemic of unsafe practices, or a run of accidents. To be effective, a campaign must be more than a rehashing of "old stuff." There must be an element of newness, variation in presentation, new faces in major roles, new assignments of responsibilities, a freshening and intensification of effort. Good planning and good leadership are required, a definite program set up and followed, a definite goal set, and a definite period specified. The major drawback of such a campaign is that, after it is over, there is a letdown. However, every campaign that measurably attains a worth-while goal will have thereby scored some lasting gains, and even the letdown that follows will usually still represent an advance over the conditions that preceded the campaign.

Safety contests. Safety contests are probably the most widely-used of all devices for promoting safety interest and safety effort. They are used to develop a spirit of rivalry in the interest of safety between individuals in a department, departments in a plant, or the plants of a large company; between establishments in a given industry; between establishments classified as to industry and size in a state or region. The development, promotion, and sponsorship of safety contests has long been an important service rendered by state and community safety councils under the inspirational leadership of the National Safety Council. Many trade associations have also found safety contests between their members to be very effective in improving the injury experience of the participants. A very large number of plants use in-plant or company-wide contests with benefit. There is no question but that safety contests in their various forms have had a large share in scoring the gains made through the years. A study of the methods used and the accomplishments appear to justify emphasis on certain points.

Perhaps the most important point is that the contest rules must be clear and definite and fair to all contestants. The basis of classification and scoring must be such as to give all participants as nearly an equal chance to win as possible. Much ingenuity has been used in developing scoring systems to accomplish this, but in general, the simpler, more easily understood the contest basis, the better. Just as in any game, rules that are not easily understood by the participants seriously inhibit enthusiastic wholehearted participation by the contestants. It should be obvious that the success of a safety contest should not be judged mainly by the excellence of the winning performance or the attendance and enthusiasm at the award presentation. Much more important are factors that indicate the benefits accruing to the non-winners. Such factors as the proportion of those eligible in each class who actually entered, the proportion of the entrants who drop out, and the effect on the injury records of the non-winners and "furtherest from" winners are valuable indicators. Perhaps the guiding principle in setting up and prosecuting a safety contest should be "the greatest good for the greatest number."

Unfortunately, considerable discredit has been cast on some contests, and some low-injury rate records through interpretation of the rules in a manner that most persons regard as a form of cheating. Chiefly, this applies to the practice of bringing the injured worker back into the plant on the next day after the injury and giving him "made" work in order to avoid counting the case as a disabling injury. While this practice of "bringing them back in wheel chairs" is probably far more prevalent in the telling than in the doing, it, nevertheless, has gained sufficient belief to discredit seriously many fine safety performances, some of which were not connected with safety contests. However, it does not appear that the actual volume of such cheating has been great enough to make the difference between an excellent safety record and a poor one. It has, however, made some records appear to be better than they actually were.

Safety meetings and safety stunts.   Safety meetings are standard practice in establishments whose safety performance is good or superior. They are routine in production, and adding safety is merely a step in the incorporation of safety into all phases of plant activity. Some managements include safety intimately in routine staff or personnel meetings. Others hold separate meetings. Some have meetings weekly or even oftener. Others have bimonthly or monthly meetings. Some have regular safety meetings for supervisory personnel, but leave it to each foreman to have meetings of his crew when he feels the need. Others schedule such meetings regularly. Almost any such system works well, provided that it has the essential element of executive interest and supervision. Without that, no system will work well.

Extra meetings outside of working time are often helpful if the element of entertainment is sufficiently included, or if they can be merged with some community or group interest or activity such as church, school, athletic club, and so on.

Plant fire brigades.   The responsibility, the distinction, and the chance of excitement make membership on a plant fire-fighting and fire-prevention brigade attractive to most men. Membership can be largely rotational. Much as is the case with first-aid training, such participation is strongly stimulative of safety-mindedness.

Safety suggestion systems.   Every management should realize that the aggregate brain power and resourcefulness of its rank-and-file workmen is a veritable gold mine of ideas if it can be tapped. A properly-designed and administered suggestion system is an effective means of tapping this latent safety knowledge and ingenuity. Essential to its successful operation are:

1. The management must really want suggestions from its workmen.
2. Every suggestion must be taken seriously and, if it is not usable, an explanation must be made to its author as to why it is not.
3. Action in each instance should be prompt, or the reason for any necessary delay explained.

4. Anonymity should be respected if desired by the maker of the suggestion.
5. Rewards should be in reasonable relation to the value of the suggestion.
6. If the plant is organized, the coöperation of the union should be sought.

While by no means all suggestion systems have proved to be of value, the general experience when the foregoing essentials are reasonably complied with appears to have been very favorable indeed.

Safety cartoons. Cartoons showing bad practice and bad conditions are widely used because of their effectiveness in promoting interest in safety. They appeal to the same side of human nature that IQ tests and cross-word puzzles do.

Safety Booklets

As previously pointed out, the first approach to injury prevention was hazard reduction, chiefly by machinery guarding. While that reduced the flow of injuries chiefly due to the hazard factor, it did nothing to correct behavior faults and injury rates continued far too high. The major effort was then turned to the development of safe work practices and the promotion of worker safety mindedness. One device that soon became widely used was the working up of safety rules for employees and issuing a copy of the rules adopted by the management, formally, usually over top management signature, to each employee. Sometimes these were primarily educational in nature and so designated. Usually they were issued as requirements with the threat, direct or implied, that failure to learn and obey them would bring punishment, perhaps dismissal.

The advocates of the use of force failed to take into account the fact that self respecting workmen resent such an approach and it went far to discredit the use of safety rules. Eventually however, safety rule booklets dealing with safe practice fundamentals were found to have a very worthwhile educational value and soon became widely used, particularly when issued to new employees with a little talk about the importance of learning and following them. It is common practice also for the foreman, in due time, to quiz a new employee on his knowledge of the rules.

A device usually used with a safety booklet is some form of safety pledge. A pledge used by the lamp division of the Westinghouse Co. and printed on the back of their "Safety Guide" booklet is "I pledge myself to do nothing unsafe, to be careful about my work, to do all in my power to keep from becoming injured or causing an injury to any other employee, and to continue at all times my interest in the absolute prevention of accidents."

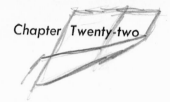

Chapter Twenty-two

Appraising Employee Attitude Towards Safety

It is obvious that means of gauging employee attitude toward safety in general and toward the plant safety program in particular would be very helpful in guiding action to increase the effectiveness of the safety program. If the reaction to each specific measure such as plant safety meetings, safety committee activities, safety bulletins, safety rule books and the like could be readily measured with fair accuracy, it would be very helpful to the prosecution of the safety program. Many serious attempts at such appraisals have been made, and various means have been tried. There have been many disappointments, but enough success has been scored to indicate that it is well worth while to undertake such appraisals. Measures that have proven valuable are:

1. Reports from safety personnel.
   a. Safety inspectors.
   b. Worker-safety committeemen.
   c. Union representatives.
   d. First-aid attendants.
2. Foreman canvass.
3. Sampling by personal contact.
4. Suggestion systems.
5. The safety inventory or questionnaire.

Reports from safety personnel

Inspectors full time on safety can, if stimulated to do so and properly instructed, sound out many fellow employees and report with fair reliability as to their findings. Also, if in their day-by-day inspection work, their attitude is receptive, they will receive many suggestions, hear many "gripes," and be asked many questions. It is best, however, to have them make verbal, rather than written, reports, because such personnel generally dislike "paper work." Also, written reports tend to become routine and to degenerate to meaningless forms. On the other hand, a personal report to a superior on the matter in question can be as complete and meaningful as the condition may justify. The inspector should be told why the information is wanted, how he should ask for it, and in general, whom he should ask. This method should not be over-used, else it will become farcical. Used occasionally through reasonably adept persons, it yields good results.

Safety committees of workmen are, at times and in favorable situations, valuable sources of information on the attitude of their fellow workmen toward safety. Workmen will usually talk freely to their fellows. This can frequently be made a part of their duties, but the amount of time and effort they will be in a position to spend for this purpose will usually not be great. Their services are usually most effective in connection with safety measures in which they have had a part and, therefore, maintain a personal interest.

Alert safety-minded union leaders and safety representatives can frequently furnish valuable information on the attitude of their membership toward the safety program, or specific parts of it. When the relationship between the union leadership and the management is good, and when the union is actively cooperating with the company safety program, the union can be particularly helpful in bringing safety "gripes" to light. Also, it can frequently be helpful in correcting mistaken employee attitudes.

First-aid attendants, particularly the plant nurse, can be especially helpful. A nurse who is understanding, friendly, and intelligent can determine, without too obviously trying to do so, the reaction of most of those who go to first-aid. Her attitude and questioning need not amount to more than a live interest in safety work. In so doing, she will inevitably produce a further profit by promoting interest in safety among many of those to whom she talks.

The foreman canvass

The foremen are in the key position in accident prevention because of their responsibility for, and intimate contact with, both the workmen and the details of the work. They are also in the best possible position to keep in touch with the attitude of those under them toward safety. However, this presupposes not only that the foremen themselves are keenly safety-minded, but that they are also active participants in the safety program. They should have an active part in planning it, and must be kept well-informed on plans, expectations, and results. If these conditions are met, the foreman canvass becomes worth while and reasonably reliable. Very simply, it means the practice of having each foreman undertake in definite systematic fashion, at intervals, usually irregular, to ascertain the attitude toward the safety program, or some specific phase of it, of each workman in his crew. It is best not to keep any records beyond such notes as the foreman may need in order to make his report, and it is usually best not to let the workmen know that even such notes are taken. An exception arises when a workman makes a suggestion for improvement, in which case proper credit should be given as a matter of record. Extensive detailed records are not ordinarily justified, though brief written summaries of the findings on each such canvass will be necessary to give the full picture. Since the purpose of the canvass is primarily to measure the current effectiveness of the safety program, or of some phase of it, there is little point to keeping permanent records of the findings.

Sampling by personal contact

A safety director or safety engineer who is well-liked and "gets around" can sample a cross section of all personnel and reach reasonably reliable conclusions therefrom. He will, however, have to use considerable judgment to avoid being misled by persons unwilling to return an answer he might not like. Also, he must keep his powers of analysis uninfluenced by wishful thinking. Properly done however, his sampling can be a very useful check on, and supplement to, other means of testing employee attitude.

Suggestion systems

The use of suggestion systems to bring to light employee ideas for improvements in processes, methods, or equipment has long been a fairly common practice. They are similarly usable in the interest of safety, and when so used, they can be very helpful in determining employee attitude toward specific safety measures. Suggestions and comments may be invited on means of improving safety meetings or safety contests or the inspection procedure, etc. Criticisms may be asked for, and if answered in the plant newspaper or on the bulletin board, may provoke further suggestions and ideas of value.

Attitude surveys

Employee attitude surveys to find out what the employees think about their company, their supervisors, and their working conditions are rather widely used. Most of them include some questions on safety. A few have been devoted wholly to safety and closely allied working conditions. Out of a great amount of experimentation have come effective techniques that, properly applied under favorable conditons, will bring reasonably reliable results. However, experience indicates that such surveys will be of doubtful validity if undertaken during periods when:

1. There have been mass layoffs or discharges.
2. There are a large number of hirings.
3. Major changes in the company's organizational structure are underway or recent.
4. Employees are restless or dissatisfied.
5. Union organization drives are on, or union negotiations are underway.
6. Major changes in plant or processes are underway.

The majority of such surveys attempt to cover all employees in the given plant or group. In nearly all cases, a written questionnaire is used for this purpose. However, many surveys are made by a sampling process that is more frequently handled by personal interview than by a written questionnaire. Although, in many cases, the survey is made by the staff of the personnel department, the more usual practice is to employ an outside specialist for the purpose, either a professional firm or an university research group. The weight of opinion as expressed by companies who have made use of attitude surveys appears to be heavily on the side of using an outside agency,* partly because of the specialized experience and skills obtainable thereby, and partly because of the greater assurance this gives that the approach will be unbiased and objective. This course also gives greater assurance of complete anonymity, where that is desired. There is nearly unanimous agreement that anonymity is necessary in attitude surveys dealing with controversial matters (particularly how the employee is treated by his supervisor), but since safety is not, or at least should not be, a controversial matter, many feel that anonymity is not necessary. Certainly, if an employee raises a safety point on which he is misinformed, or if his comment indicates a wrong attitude, it is helpful if the matter can be "thrashed out" with him face to face. However, through discussions at safety meetings, announcements on bulletin boards, or articles in the plant newspaper, such anonymous comments and complaints can usually be taken care of just as is common practice with unsigned suggestions received through a suggestion system.

The survey conducted annually for a number of years by the Springfield, Mass. plant of the Westinghouse Co. shows that if properly handled in a plant where management and employee relations are good, valuable results *can* be had even though the employees are urged to sign the questionnaires. Since these are handed out to each worker individually by the foreman, few failed to sign. As would be expected, it eventually became largely a

---

* *Studies in Personnel Policy* #115, published by the Conference Board, 247 Park Avenue, New York 17, New York.

1938 Safety Inventory

Westinghouse Electric & Mfg. Co.   East Springfield Works

Please-read the inventory instructions carefully before filling in this card

JD **4**
65
4   THORMEYER F

017 01 8677

Division .... Department............................... Group .... Occupation ....

1 Equipment used by you .... Machine No. ....

2 Is the equipment properly guarded? .... 3 Kind of safety device used ....   (Brass tag only)

4 What safety improvements do you recommend? ....

5 Where is the nearest fire alarm box ? .... Box No. .... 6 Where is the nearest stretcher? ....

7 Check off the personal safety equipment that you use Aprons (Rubber or Asbestos) .... Gauntlets .... Gloves ....

Goggles .... Leggings .... Respirators .... Tweezers .... Welding Masks ....

8 Do you use Protex (hand cream) to protect your hands or arms? ....

9 What additional personal safety equipment should be used on your job? ....

10 Men—Do you wear safety shoes at work? .... If not, why not? ....

Women—Do you wear Low or Cuban type heel shoes at work? .... If not, why not? ....

11 When working, do you wear Finger rings? .... Arm bracelets? .... Long sleeves? ....

12 Does your work make you nervous or over-fatigued? ....

Continued on other side

238

13 Are there any physical ill effects from your work? ....

14 Does your job require you to Stand? .... Sit? .... Walk around? ....

15 Do you know the company safety rules? .... 16 Do you believe the safety rules should be enforced? ....

17 Are the company safety rules for your benefit? .... for the company's benefit? .... or for the benefit of both? ....

18 What can be done to improve your working conditions in regard to health and safety? ....

19 Have you ever completed a course in First Aid? .... When? ....

20 Would you be interested in attending classes in First Aid, this winter? ....

21 Would you be interested in attending classes in Home, Highway and Industrial Safety, this winter? ....

22 Have you any other suggestions for the advancement of safety in this Plant? ....

....

....

Signed ....

      Employee   Group Leader   Safety Representative   Foreman

HEALTH & SAFETY INVENTORY

WESTINGHOUSE FORM 21780

*Please read the inventory instructions carefully before
filling in this card*

Dept.................................... Group.................... Occupation....................

1. Do you operate a machine?............ Is it properly guarded?........ Recommendations..............

2. What personal safety equipment do you use on your job?................................

   ....

3. What additional personal safety equipment do you require?............................

4. Do you wear safety shoes at work?........ If not, why?...........................

5. Have you completed a course in First Aid?........ When?........ With whom?..........

6. Would you be interested in attending First Aid classes this winter?...................

7. Would you be interested in attending classes in Home, Highway, and Industrial Safety this winter?....

8. Did you use salt tablets this summer?........ Please comment on them.................

9. How much time did you lose this year because of sickness?............ Home accidents?.........

   Automobile accidents?........ Other accidents (explain).............................

10. When were you last examined by a doctor?............ Do you want a physical examination?......

11. Have you any additional recommendations for the advancement of safety and health among our employees?....

.... SIGNED........................
                                                        Name

....   Date

USE OTHER SIDE FOR ADDITIONAL COMMENTS

240

rehashing of answers previously made and was discontinued. It did indicate, however, that safety is so infrequently controversial, that anonymity is less important than being able to discuss each answer with the employee who gave it. The two following paragraphs are quoted from a talk given by a plant executive.

The Westinghouse safety inventory

"In order to promote full employee cooperation, the inventory is well-publicized in the plant in advance and is carried out following the annual year-end stock inventory. This emphasizes the inventory idea and the use of the findings in planning the safety program for the ensuing year. When the working force returns after the inventory shut-down, each foreman or other supervisor hands a card and an instruction sheet to each member of his force with the earnest request that he take stock of his job and surroundings with regard to safety, fill the card out fully, sign it, and turn it in. Salaried workers are included in this distribution. The degree of employee compliance secured is indicated by the fact that, in a typical year, out of 2025 cards distributed, 1904 were returned completely filled out.* The answers to many of the questions furnished valuable clues to needed action. In many cases, the answers revealed the need of more and better guarding, or of more personal protective equipment. Obviously, each guard lack discovered by this means reflects on the inspection service or upon the foreman, or both. Each protective equipment lack reflects on the safety engineer or the foreman, or both. Many such cases brought to light through any one inventory calls for a tightening up of inspection, as well as more attention to safety by at least the foremen involved. If many of the hazards pointed out were previously known, it indicates a need for prompter corrective action.

"Answers to the question, 'Do you wear safety shoes?' brought out the fact that many who should have been wearing them were not doing so, also that this was at least partly due to poor fitting and lack of knowledge of the protection they afford. This indicated the need of more attention to fitting, and also called for a better sales job. The safety engineer would have discovered this condition had he carried out a foot hazard survey either by itself, or as part of a survey covering all types of personal protective equipment. It is good practice to include such items in the job standards. If no job standards have been established, the need should be determined by the safety engineer in consultation with the foreman or department superintendent. If there is no safety engineer, this responsibility should be placed

---

* A copy of the card used in 1962 (chosen as typical) is shown on preceding pages.

on the foreman or department head, in consultation with the safety committee, if there is one."

Questions designed to direct employee attention to specific key facts also
proved to be valuable. For example, the two questions, "Where is the
nearest fire alarm box?" and "Where is the nearest stretcher?" aroused a
great deal of interest, much hunting them out and much pacing off the
distances.

The question, "What improvements do you recommend?" brought many
valuable suggestions, covering a wide range. The need of an improvement
in certain safety equipment was indicated by 18 out of 96 suggestions from
the 1938 inventory. There were many recommendations for better lighting
and better ventilation. These were accepted as indicative of a need for
better application of recognized standards of good practice in these two
important items.

The wisdom of asking such questions as, "Does your work make you
nervous or over-fatigued?" may be questioned. Older workers whose
powers are failing may fear to admit such adverse effects lest it lead to
shifting to a lower paid job or a lay-off. Also, such a question is an invitation to the hypochondriac. Finally, it is often difficult to distinguish between such conditions caused by the work and by off-the-job activities and
tensions. Somewhat similar comments apply to the question, "Do you
experience any physical ill effects from your work?" However, despite these
limitations on the value of these questions, 75 affirmative answers were
received to the first, and 84 to the second. Investigations of the conditions
involved in the complaints showed that a substantial proportion were justified and suitable corrective action was taken.

Many would question the validity of the question, "Do you know the
company's safety rules?" because a moment's reflection would lead the
employee to realize that a negative answer would almost certainly result in
his being bothered or pushed into learning them. The "wise" ones would
answer "yes." The effective way to find out who knows the rules is to quiz
the employees on the rules themselves. The result, 1409 affirmative, 74
negative, bears this out. The question, "Do you believe that the safety rules
should be enforced?" is also subject to a large factor of uncertainty, because
workers would tend to give what they believe to be the desired answer.
The fact that, in this instance, there were only 70 negatives, together with
the fact that more answered this question than answered the preceding one,
supports this opinion.

A modification of the safety inventory idea has been used early in the
safety program by limiting it to safety committee members, or other key
men. In one plant, after its workmen's safety committees had been functioning for about a year, each committeeman was asked to "inventory"
safety conditions in the area he represented. Each used a standard list of

common hazards, supplemented by the hazards peculiar to his area. The results of these inventories were discussed in safety committee meetings and advisable corrective action was decided upon.

The Revere safety test

Revere Copper and Brass, Inc., in cooperation with Syracuse University, has developed a very interesting method of testing worker-safety knowledge. This test makes use of a pamphlet containing 54 sets of pictures, each depicting good and bad practices based on rules in the rule book, a personal copy of which is given to each employee when he is hired, and which he is expected to master.

Each testee is given a copy of the picture pamphlet and an answer sheet having 54 sets of small squares numbered to correspond to the sets of pictures. He is directed to mark an "x" in each square corresponding to a picture in which a safety rule is violated.

Revere started the use of this test in 1945. An official reports that it has proved to be valuable in testing both employees who have lost-time accidents and applicants for employment. He does not recommend for hiring those applicants scoring less than a certain level. He divides scores above that minimum into five levels, which indicate the extent of safety instruction needed. He considers the use of this test to have been "a large contributing factor" in halving the company injury rate during the years 1945 to 1951 inclusive.

Safety surveys for job applicants

The survey idea may be used to determine the attitude of job applicants toward safety as well as toward other matters. Summarization of the returns from over 500 applicants who filled out questionnaire cards at a plant in New England showed in part:

1. 42 per cent considered safe working conditions of first importance, 49 per cent put wages first. The remaining 9 per cent were scattered or indefinite. (The question excluded length of working hours by specifying a 40-hour week.)

2. 34 per cent believed each plant should have safety rules that each employee should know and obey.

3. 63 per cent believed that the employees should have a part in developing the safety rules (if there were to be such rules).

4. 24 per cent liked the idea of suggestion boxes and rewards for safety ideas, whereas 21 per cent considered them a nuisance or a subterfuge.

5. 30 per cent thought safety was almost wholly up to the workmen themselves. 14 per cent didn't think that employers cared whether their workmen were hurt or not, and 48 per cent hadn't thought much about safety.

6. 54 per cent reported that they had never been given any safety instruction. 27 per cent said "a little," and only 14 per cent said they had received careful safety training.

The B & O Railroad Company safety quiz

The B & O Railroad Company safety quiz is an excellent example of an employee-safety survey so handled that response is wholly voluntary. It is started off by a personal letter from the president to each of the approximately fifty thousand employees. The letter emphasizes the company's strong concern for the safety of its employees, solicits their full cooperation in protecting their own safety and that of fellow employees, and specifically asks that the questionnaire to follow be filled out and returned in the stamped, addressed envelope that accompanied it. Some of the questions were designed as thought provokers, others to check on the safety program.

The question, "Would you speak to a fellow employee you saw violating a safety rule?" is of the first type. More than nine out of ten who answered said they would. A sound approach to safety was indicated by the heavy majority for (1) in the question, "Which of these statements is most true?"

1. Accidents are bound to happen.
2. Accidents can be prevented.

There are, in all, 20 questions of the multiple-choice or best-answer type. Each employee is requested to check his answers without fear or favor and "not to sign his name unless he wants to." No space is provided for a signature.

Survey specialists report that for so far flung an organization so scattered geographically, the 16% response obtained is very good for a purely voluntary, mailed questionnaire of this sort. Although more pressure would have brought a greater response, the close contact and follow up used in the East Springfield survey would be unduly expensive on a great railroad system.

Value of safety surveys

The East Springfield officials value the safety inventory highly. Their experience appears to justify the conclusion that, properly set up and handled, such inventories should be valuable in checking on the effectiveness of any well-established and reasonably well-functioning safety program. Good employee cooperation is obviously basic to success. This cooperation could not be expected in a plant in which at least reasonably good attention had not been given to the elimination of physical hazards. In other words, the inventory is, as its name implies, a means of finding flaws, weaknesses, defects, and lacks in performance that is already good.

The use of the safety inventory early in a safety program in order to get the employees' viewpoint and foster their interest is, at best, highly questionable. It would obviously be more difficult to get good employee cooperation, but, if it were gotten, a flood of recommendations too great to be taken care of with reasonable promptness would probably result. It would seem to be much sounder to reserve this device for use chiefly as a check up. Most unsafe conditions and hazardous practices are discoverable by plant inspection, job analysis, accident investigation, and cause analysis. Safety committee activities play a large part in this picture. Suggestion systems, properly set up and maintained, bring in additional valuable ideas and foster further employee cooperation. The safety inventory then supplements all of these things.

The B & O management also finds its safety quiz valuable in bringing out ideas and viewpoints of at least those employees who take the trouble to fill out the questionnaire and return it. Obviously, these are, in general, the more safety-minded employees and, therefore, their ideas should be of real value. That this is actually the case is shown by the numerous points made that the management quickly acted upon. These points included the conduct and coverage of safety meetings, action on safety matters, the effectiveness of various elements of the safety program, and the validity of various safety rules. There was so much of value, that a careful analysis of the returns was made and a detailed report thereon was transmitted to all top supervisors throughout the system.

With regard to the use of the Revere test, the careful appraiser is naturally cautious in questioning the soundness of a conclusion based on such experience and accomplishment. However, the validity of such a test in determining the employability of applicants is at least questionable. Its value in showing the need of safety instruction is obvious. The fact that a number of other employers have tried this method and found it helpful gives further evidence of its value. Nevertheless, the weight of experience emphasizes the limited reliability of any single type of test such as this for determining employability. Its chief value would seem to be to promote the study of the safety rules and as an interest-arouser.

Safety Organization

The effective production executive knows the value of organization. He realizes fully that no objective can be attained, whether it be for production, inspection, training, selling, or accident prevention without organization, and that an objective of accident prevention or elimination does not come about unless all levels of the organization are "tuned in" toward that objective.

Objective organization goes beyond merely the drawing of lines. It attempts to create, first, the lines of authority, and second, the means that will bring about the objective to be attained. With these principles in mind, we can well appreciate that a reduction in accidents cannot be attained without organization, and that organization itself is without effect unless it has the complete support and interest of "top management."

More and more far-sighted executives are becoming convinced that they must maintain organized effort for the prevention of accidents. They increasingly realize that accident prevention is also a good, sound business policy.

A few *musts* should be considered before we discuss specific plans for safety organization:

1. Safety *must* have top management approval, sanction, and support.
2. Responsibility for safety *must* rest with the supervisory personnel.
3. Safety *must* be given equally important consideration with other factors for production.
4. Provision *must* be made for prompt action in the elimination of mechanical and personal hazards.

A definite program should be developed to interest and educate all employees in safety and to secure their active cooperation in the effort to eliminate accidents. Such a program must be based on the full assumption of its responsibilities by the management. The program must supply leadership and executive drive. Safety must be included in all phases of planning, purchasing, supervision, and operation. Once these fundamentals are understood by management, and it fully assumes the responsibilities that are involved, the appropriate type of organization can be evolved. But it is well to remember that whatever form the organization takes, it will function effectively only if it is backed by executive interest and drive. Proof of this is furnished by the fact that each type of safety organization is to be found among firms that have attained and continue to maintain a standard of first-rate performance in eliminating work injuries.

Whatever the size of the firm, the principles and the purpose are identical: *"To create within everyone, at all levels of the organization, a safety mindedness."*

This atmosphere of safety reaching and influencing the minds and actions of those within the organization might well be portrayed as follows:

AREA OF
RESPOSIBILITY FOR
ORGANIZATION

POLICY MAKERS
Top management, giving leadership and executive drive.
EXECUTIVE
The execution of the policy in the establishment of the type of organization, executive meetings, etc. by superintendents and staff heads.
SUPERVISORY
Carrying out in practice—inspection training, education, mechanical safeguarding, etc. by foremen, supervisors, and other staff personnel.
EMPLOYEES
Those affected by policy, procedure and practice.

From the foregoing, it is evident that the major part of safety work and education must be done by the regular organization. We may (making allowances for variations in detail) classify safety organizations in three general types, namely:

A. Those in which the safety work is carried on wholly through the line organization.

B. Those in which the safety work is directed by a safety director reporting to a major executive.

C. Those in which safety work is carried on primarily by committees set up for the purpose.

Type A organization—line organization

Obviously, if no full-time safety personnel—safety technicians—are used, the production executives must become expert in their knowledge of the safety problems involved in their establishment or type of business. The chief executive also must give a larger share of his personal attention to safety than would be the case if he had a highly competent safety technician on his staff. This fact has led some chief executives using this type of safety organization to employ a safety specialist. Such a specialist functions as a technical assistant to the chief executive. Should he possess strong qualities of leadership, he may take over increasing responsibilities for the safety work and bring about a progressive change of the organization into the Type B form.

The strength of the Type A setup lies chiefly in the fact that it centers entire responsibility for all safety effort within each operating unit on the head of that unit. It is his duty to incorporate safety into each and every part of the day-by-day activities of his unit. Just as he plans and supervises the work of each of his men for adequate production and satisfactory quality, so he plans for and supervises safety. He must become the best-informed and most safety-minded person in his unit. The weakness of this type of organization is that supervisory personnel occupied with other production problems find it difficult to acquire the special knowledge needed to reach a high standard of safety performance. This means that too much of the knowledge of how to prevent accidents is gained from the accidents that occur. In other words, it is largely "after-thought" prevention, and, therefore, progress is likely to be slow.

Although some large firms use the Type A setup, it is most commonly found among firms too small to justify the employment of a full-time safety engineer. If, in a small plant, the chief executive will really give, and continue to give, a proper share of his executive attention to safety, steady improvement invariably results, leading ultimately to excellent performance.

Type B organization—safety director

The form of organization used by most large firms is of this type. Its effectiveness depends upon two things—the attitude of the top management, and, after that, the competency and ability of the safety director. Although keen interest in safety by top management is essential to first-rate safety performance in any case, a large share of responsibility for the safety work can be delegated to a strong and competent safety director.

A safety director's job is not easy. He should function both as the special assistant and adviser on safety to the major executive, and as the adviser and stimulator on safety for the whole organization. He cannot interfere with or usurp any of the functions of any member of the supervisory force, but he must work closely with all of them. Since no man can function properly under two bosses, the safety director cannot give orders except to personnel under him, yet he must often secure prompt correction of unsafe conditions or practices. His effectiveness, therefore, will be in direct proportion to:

1. His ability to secure the confidence and respect of every foreman or other executive.
2. The amount of responsibility given him by his "boss."

The safety man must realize that his is a "service" job and that he must not encroach upon the authority of the various members of the supervisory force. His standing with the "boss" will be good if he gets the confidence of the supervisory personnel and if, in addition, he keeps his chief fully informed on the progress of the safety work. To be effective, the actual means of doing this must suit the personal preferences of the chief. Reports should be brief, definite, and factual.

In brief summation, the safety director must first think of the help he can give each supervisor or other staff man. Second, he must try to determine the viewpoint of each so that his help will be well accepted. Third, he must be sure of his facts and careful in drawing conclusions. Fourth, he must keep the "boss" informed.

There has been much controversy over the position that the safety engineer should occupy in the organization. Probably the prevailing practice is to place him under the personnel director, who, in turn, reports to the chief operating executive, usually a vice-president or general manager. Each large plant of a corporation will also have a plant safety director or safety engineer whose position in the plant set-up will usually correspond to that of the safety director in the head office.

In many cases, the safety director reports directly to the chief operating executive, together with the personnel director and the executive heads of the various departments. In a few cases, he reports to the medical director or the chief engineer.

A study of the organizational set-ups in companies that have achieved and continue to maintain extremely low injury rates does not indicate the essential superiority of any one of these or other organizational set-ups. Whatever the position the safety director occupies on the organization chart, it is vitally important that the channel between himself and the executive head be so open and direct that safety matters receive full and prompt consideration, with appropriate action. When this is not the situation, safety performance is, at best, less than of first rank.

The safety director is the center and source of safety information for the establishment. He should have the technical know-how that his professional status implies, and he should keep himself fully-informed concerning the status of the safety performance of his company. This requires the compiling, analyzing, and keeping of the records necessary to this end. Of vital importance is the manner in which he presents this information to management so that it may take suitable action as needed, to supervisors to aid their understanding and efforts, and to the rank and file to promote their interest and participation in the safety program.

Finally, the safety director must be "in on" the affairs of management, at least insofar as they have to do with safety. Since safety must be an intimate part of all plant activity, this means that he should attend all staff meetings having to do with plant operations and should have a voice in all matters that may affect employee safety.

Type C organization—safety committees

Safety work governed by committees is usually found in establishments too small to justify a full-time safety director or where, by preference, the management wishes the work to be directed jointly by the members of his staff. It has the weakness of any setup governed by a committee instead of by an executive.

A committee is, at best, weak in execution. It has the advantage of bringing together the viewpoints of the group and its joint judgment is normally better than that of any individual in the group. But prompt, effective, and orderly execution depends upon the placing of authority and responsibility in the hands of one person and the faithful discharge by him of that responsibility, including both the giving of the orders and the "follow-through" necessary to their proper execution. Therefore, the committee-type of organization functions best when the chief executive himself is chairman and makes use of the committee to:

1. Strengthen his judgment.
2. Keep chosen staff members fully in touch and informed.
3. Promote the interest and cooperation of the committee members.

When made use of in this manner, the Type C organization merges into the Type A setup.

Failure to appreciate the limitations of the committee method is responsible for frequent examples of establishments having, on paper, excellent committee setups whose safety performance is disappointing. Too often the safety committee idea is borrowed from an establishment making successful use of it and is installed in a more or less perfunctory manner. The chief executive, in such a case, presumably views the method as a means of shouldering off most of the responsibility, or agrees to the move upon the urging of an enthusiastic "safety salesman" (insurance or factory inspector, safety council member, or the like), who fails to make clear the fundamentals necessary to secure satisfactory results.

Safety committees in general

Although the advisable committee setup will depend chiefly on the size of the establishment, other factors have a bearing, such as the progress that has been made in safeguarding the plant when committee work is started, the size and relationship of the various departments or plant-units, the type of business (manufacture, construction, transportation, public utilities, and the like). However, the following fundamentals at least should be met in forming the committee or committees decided upon:

1. Each committee should be so made up as to have standing appropriate to its field of work. For instance, a main or governing committee should include such key executives as master mechanic and production manager. A workers' committee should be made up of members well-known to and having the respect of their fellow workmen.

2. The committee membership should encompass the maximum in knowledge of the methods, practices, and conditions in the plant, undertaking, or group represented.

3. The committee should be as small as is consistent with the above requirements. A committee of three functions more effectively than does one of five. The larger the committee, the more the debate and the less the action.

When a committee is formed, certain matters of policy and procedure should be definitely set forth in writing. Written instructions should cover at least:

1. Scope of committee activity.
2. Extent of committee authority.
3. Procedure as to:
   a. Time and place of meetings.
   b. Frequency of meetings.
   c. Order of business.
   d. Records to be kept.
   e. Attendance requirements.

A committee will take its work seriously in proportion to management's attitude toward it. A management that sets up a committee to accomplish a specific purpose, makes it clear that it wants results, and gives effective executive supervision to its activities, will get satisfactory results. Effective committee conduct of safety work in the absence of executive leadership is possible only when committee members have unusual initiative and determination to advance the cause of safety. In such instances they often convert the nonsafety-minded management. Sometimes the "salesman" of safety, failing to arouse adequate management interest, can accomplish his purpose by getting a safety committee organized and aiding it to plan a program that will interest the top management, at the same time that he gets the job started.

Although, as was pointed out, scope of activity, extent of authority and the procedure to be followed should be put in writing and records of activities kept, this should not be carried too far. Too little system leads to confusion, waste motion, duplication of effort, and indirection. Too much system yields "red tape" and the needless expenditure of valuable time and effort. In other words, as is true of any other committee activity, safety committee work requires planning and orderly procedure under executive leadership.

In summation it can be said that the major advantages of committees are:

1. They bring together varying viewpoints and generally yield sounder decisions than does the individual viewpoint.
2. They widen interest by giving active participation to a number of persons in conducting the work.

Major weaknesses of committees are:

1. Group action requires deliberation and is, therefore, slow.
2. The meetings necessarily consume much time of many persons.

Commonly used types of safety committees are:

1. Main governing or executive committee.
2. Workmen's committee.
3. Technical committee.
4. Special-purpose committee.

A large plant may make use of all these types of committees. A small plant may use only one. The point is that once a definite decision is made as to the scope of the work to be handled by committee action, the type of committee needed and the number of committees required are readily determined.

The main or governing committee. The chief function of the main or governing committee is to determine the policy and set the standard or plane at which the safety work is to be conducted. The chief operating head of the plant or undertaking in question should be chairman. This makes it possible for the chair to issue definite orders to the various members as committee decisions are reached, and thus avoids both the delay and the possibility of overruling involved where committee decisions must be referred to a chief executive. It might appear that since the chief operating head can give orders at any time, the use of committees is of little value. If, however, he has an honest desire to strengthen his judgment from the opinions of the committee members and promote the interest of and full participation in the safety effort by every member of the commitee, he will find the safety committee a very useful tool for the furtherance of safety.

Matters for determination by the main committee normally include:

1. Planning for the control of physical hazards concerning:
   a. Purchase of safe and properly guarded equipment, tools, supplies, etc.
   b. Relationships between various departments.
   c. Standards to be followed in guarding machinery, the design of equipment layout of process, etc.
2. Planning and arranging for the promotion of:
   a. Safe operating practices and procedures.
   b. Adequate inspection.
3. Planning and supervising programs of:
   a. Arousing and maintaining worker interest in safety.
   b. Safety training.
4. Disciplinary procedures.
5. Decision as to the disposal of specific problems.
6. Investigation of accidents.
7. Passing on specific recommendations.
8. Study of accidents and accident records.

It should be noted here that, ordinarily, the full committee will participate in the decision on policies and plans, but that action decided upon will be assigned to individuals or small sub-committees. Often such sub-committees consist of a member of the main committee as chairman with the other members not drawn from the main committee. This allows the use of technicians or other personnel as may be justified for specific purposes.

The workmen's committee. This type of committee, which is composed entirely of workmen or of workmen under the chairmanship of a foreman, can have great value, particularly in:

1. Bringing into the safety program the viewpoint and practical knowledge of the workmen.
2. Stimulating worker interest in safety.
3. Investigating accidents.

Fundamental to the effective functioning of a workmen's safety committee is the sincere desire of the management to enlist the help of the workers and obtain their faithful adherence to a course that will promote mutual confidence and respect. Workmen's committees should not be set up unless at least the following essentials have been provided for:

1. The work and place of the committee in the scheme of things is accepted as important.

2. All recommendations and suggestions made by the committee receive prompt consideration. If accepted, the action called for should be prompt. If rejected or modified by the chief executive or a higher committee, the reason for such rejection or modification should be clearly explained.

3. If a foreman or other supervisor is chairman, he should function as the chairman of a committee of equals, never as the "boss."

Firms using workmen's safety committees usually report their chief value to be that of promoting worker safety-mindedness. Until at least the more evident physical hazards are safeguarded, it is of little use to attempt to get worker coöperation to prevent accidents. Every workman knows that safeguards cost money, and efforts to get him to improve his work practices before obviously justified expenditures are made for safeguards will be taken as evidence of management's desire for safety "if it doesn't cost anything." This means that workmen's committees should not be started until at least a reasonably good standard has been reached in the safeguarding of physical hazards.

Technical committees. As the name implies, technical committees are useful on specific problems or activities for which specialized knowledge is needed, as, for example, engineering revision, guard design, and special process problems. Some firms maintain standing technical committees under the chairmanship of the chief engineer, the safety engineer (if there is one), master mechanic, chief chemist, or other technician.

Special-purpose committees. Special committees may be set up for specific jobs, and these are normally dismissed when their purpose is accomplished. Such jobs or purposes include contests, safety celebrations or award occasions, check-up accident investigations, rehabilitation or relief problems, special investigation of specific problems of worker behavior, off-the-job safety, and so on.

In some cases, particularly in small plants, it may be advisable to have a single committee including both supervisors and workmen. Such a committee to be effective must be conducted as a committee of equals. The workmen members of the committee may, in fact, be the most important part of it because, in many situations, their influence in promoting the safety-mindedness of their fellow workers may be greater than that of the supervisors.

Justification for full-time safety personnel

There have been many attempts to devise a standard formula to determine how large an establishment must be to justify the employment of a full-time safety engineer, director, or supervisor, and at what added increment of size he should be given a full-time assistant or assistants. Elaborate charts have been drawn to indicate the number of engineers, inspectors, office personnel, and first-aid attendants justified for various sizes of plants, usually in steps of 1000 employees. Actually, practice varies widely. Size in terms of number of employees is not a satisfactory basis of determination because the range of variation in degree of hazard and complexity of the safety problems and activities is very great between the various branches of industry. High-hazard work such as a heavy construction job, a magnesium foundry, or a logging operation employing 200 men might gain more from the full-time services of a safety engineer than would a low-hazard type of manufacture such as tobacco or hoisery employing ten times as many persons.

Probably the best approach is that of cost as against the savings in direct and indirect costs possible, plus the probable intangible benefits such as better employee morale and the improvements in work methods that the services of a competent safety engineer can bring. The cost will, of course, be the engineer's salary, whatever clerical and stenographic service he may need, office space, and a small charge for whatever insurance, pension, or other benefits the company provides for its staff personnel. Such costs can be estimated reliably in advance.

The savings practicably obtainable must be taken largely on faith. However, if the injury rate is not good, if the chief operating executive really wants to bring it down and is willing to give it a reasonable share of his executive attention, he will be reasonably safe in estimating at least a 25% cut in injury frequency rate during the first year's operation of a well-planned, vigorously prosecuted safety program, with somewhat smaller annual gains thereafter until top rate performance is achieved. If this estimate of possible savings is applied to an estimate of accident costs made along the lines discussed in the chapter on that subject, the decision as to whether or not to employ a full-time safety engineer will be made easier. If the decision is a close one, the intangible benefits certain to accrue if the selection is a wise one should make the venture a profitable one.

In large establishments, the size of the safety staff will be largely dependent upon company policy. When maximum emphasis is placed on the inclusion of safety as an intimate component of operation, safety activities are a line and staff function and are carried on as a part of their day-by-day duties. Safety engineers, in such cases, are what the term implies; engineers who have specialized in the engineering phases of safety and who function as members of the engineering staff. Other companies go to the opposite extreme and have all safety activities that can be set up as such—inspection, accident investigation, job safety analysis, the development of safety rules, the scheduling and handling of safety meetings, safety education and training—handled by the safety department.

Safety representatives

Many managements have found it very helpful to assign specific safety responsibilities other than those connected with their own daily work to selected individual workmen, thus, in effect, making them a part of the formal safety organization. The kinds of activities thus assigned vary widely but may include: cautioning fellow employees seen committing unsafe acts or violating a safety rule; aiding the foreman to develop safe work methods; keeping watch for and reporting hazards; with the approval of his foreman aiding in developing safety interest and safe behavior among others in his crew or department; upon assignment by his foreman investigating minor accidents; in general acting as a safety assisant to his foreman. Attempts have been made to have these men report concerning their safety duties to the safety engineer, but this rarely works well because it divides responsibility. The foreman is the key to the safety performance of his crew just as he is to its work performance. Anything that lessens his responsibilities for the functioning of those under his charge is not good.

Union participation

Whether or not management should invite or even willingly permit the union (if the plant is organized, or partly so) to participate in the safety program through representatives of its own choosing has long been subject to controversy, frequently very heated. However, a substantial number of such joint labor management safety programs have been set up. Some have worked well, others have not, but their number is increasing. Although an adequate and entirely objective appraisal of their value would be very difficult, available reasonably reliable analysis appears to justify the following essentials for their maximum functioning:

1. Both the management and the union leadership must be sincere in their desire to cooperate in the cause of safety.

2. The scope of the agreement and the activities carried on under it must be limited to safety. No extraneous issues can be allowed to enter either by subterfuge or otherwise.

3. The employer must accept and fully discharge his responsibility to make and keep his plant, equipment, and processes as safe as is practicably possible. He must furnish the safety leadership.

4. The union must select its safety representatives solely from the standpoint of their effective functioning in such a joint program. They should:

(a) Be entirely divorced from controversial union activities such as bargaining, grievances, and the like. Safety is not a proper subject for bargaining, nor does it thrive in an atmosphere of controversy.

(b) Be cooperative-minded, sincerely interested in the cause. Their judgment and knowledge of work methods should be good.

(c) Have at least sufficient knowledge of safety methods and techniques to enable them to function effectively with the management safety representatives.

5. The union must recognize management's right to leadership in the joint safety program. Management has to spend the money, and the final decision as to how to spend it and how much is to be spent must be a management decision. However, any management that really accepts and wishes to meet its responsibility "to provide safe plant equipment and processes" will not quibble over any reasonable expenditures that can be shown to be advisable for safety's sake.

Joint labor management safety programs that meet all of the above essentials are getting excellent results in terms of injury reduction. Perhaps an even larger dividend is the effect they have in improving mutual understanding and cooperation between the management and the union.

Some unions have attempted to force management to accept joint programs. No worse mistake could be made. Cooperation in any activity such as safety that requires the whole-hearted participation of everyone concerned can never be brought about by force. Therefore, unless (in any specific case) the union leadership can convince the management that the union can make a worthwhile contribution to safety through being included in a joint program, it had better concentrate on developing the safety competence and "knowhow" of at least selected individuals in such a way as ultimately to be able to prove its case.

Some managements consider safety wholly a management prerogative and refuse to "let labor in on any part of it." Presumably, this attitude is, at times, prompted by fear that the union might attempt to "take safety over." Any attempt by the union to dominate the safety program would doom the whole program to failure, and constructive union leadership realizes this. On the other hand, it should be obvious that if the strength of the union and the loyalty its membership has for it can be drawn effectively into the fight against accidents, much is to be gained thereby. This has been proved through experience. Union participation in the safety program (on the proper basis) greatly improves member interest, and participation in safety activities improves the observance of safe practices and helps to bring out the firing line "job know-how" of those who actually do the work.

Progress to date appears to justify the prediction that union participation in safety will grow and that organized labor will make an increasingly valuable contribution to the cause of safety, particularly in small establishments. If unions will, as a general practice, develop technically competent safety personnel among their membership, they should be effective in carrying the "know-how and practice" of safety to all small business whose employees are union members.

Chapter Twenty-four

Safety Education and Training

It is important to distinguish between safety education and safety training. Education deals primarily with developing the mind, broadening one's knowledge and understanding. Education in a specific subject means, therefore, the acquisition of information relating to that subject. One can be properly said to have an education in a specific field only if his knowledge of that field is reasonably broad and thorough. Training, on the other hand, deals primarily with the development of skill in performance. In industry it refers particularly to the skilled trades as applied to safety. The following definitions are brief but meaningful:

1. Safety education. To develop safety mindedness—a vivid awareness of the importance of eliminating accidents and a mental alertness in recognizing and correcting conditions and practices that might lead to injury.

2. Safety training. Developing the worker's skill in the use of safe work techniques and practices.

Although basically true, these definitions are oversimplifications. Most people do apply some of the additional knowledge they gain through education to their day-by-day activities. Items or bits of knowledge that appeal to them as particularly pertinent, or that can ease their work in some way or give them some advantage or distinction over their fellows are likely to be applied. Few persons will systematically apply new knowledge to their day-by-day activities, however. Safety education applied to the general working force is chiefly valuable in promoting interest, understanding, and active participation in specific safety activities. As applied to supervisory personnel and others who plan and direct, it improves the quality of their planning, makes their supervision more effective and adequate, and stimulates their thinking.

Although the term "training" should not be applied to instructional

259

programs or courses designed primarily for the purpose of increasing knowledge, skills cannot be developed without the acquisition of at least some additional knowledge. So in the last analysis, education and training are not completely separable, each partakes to some extent of the nature of the other. However, the absolute essential for really good success with either is good student motivation. The student must want to learn. He must find the new information interesting or his mind will not receive or retain much of it. Similarly, the trainee must want to acquire the desired skill. Regardless of the reason that motivates him, he must try and keep on trying, otherwise his performance will be indifferent.

Safety education of the employees of any given establishment is carried on mainly by the methods and devices discussed in Chapter Twenty-four. In fact, the title of that chapter might almost as aptly be Safety Promotion and Safety Education. However, even though safety educational activities, in general, use the devices and procedures discussed, the variations in detail are so many that a volume would be required for their adequate description.

Safety courses

One method of safety education was not mentioned in that chapter, namely, the organized safety course. The ESMWT safety courses were touched on in Chapter Two, but these were set up for the war emergency only. A few very limited attempts to establish such courses had previously been made by some of the educational institutions, but student acceptance had been discouraging and little success was attained. That the ESMWT courses greatly stimulated the interest of both the colleges and their students in safety has become evident. In similar fashion, the interest of management has also grown so that some large employers are conducting organized safety courses for their employees. Others prefer to cooperate with educational institutions offering safety courses in the extension curricula. Again, however, as pointed out in Chapter Two, since safety must be an intimate part of all work activities, it should be taught primarily through a process of integration; intimately interwoven in the college and school shop curricula and made an essential ingredient of all training for specific tasks, jobs, occupations, or professions. Every textbook dealing with a subject in which safety can properly have a place should include whatever safety material is pertinent to that subject. For example, chemistry texts should include information on the health and accident hazards involved and the methods of prevention. Electrical texts should deal with life and fire hazards incident to the use and maintenance of electrical equipment. Applied machine design should deal extensively with the hazards attending the operation and maintenance of specific types of machines, for example, woodworking machines, and power presses. Particular emphasis should be given to the elimination of hazards to the maximum practicable degree as a part of design. Guards should be included as an essential of machine design. Finally, shop and laboratory equipment, practices, and procedures in every and all types of schools should be representative of best safety standards and performance as it is found in leading industrial establishments.

To some extent, community safety councils and other social-minded organizations sponsor or organize safety courses intended primarily for key personnel in small establishments. A few state labor departments do this also. These courses vary widely in approach and content. Some use or closely follow the ESMDT courses. Others use the round table conference approach. Usually, however, in order to accommodate large groups of up to several hundred per meeting, the lecture or panel discussion is used with audience participation through question and answer procedures. This method sacrifices thoroughness in order to reach a larger number of persons. It is educative and stimulative, but it accomplishes far less instruction for each participant than do the courses primarily designed for classroom instruction using conventional teaching procedures.

Safety training

Safety training can be described as a detailed extension of the educational safety program applied to specific occupations, processes, jobs, or activities. Various methods of training in safety have been tried, and many of these have achieved considerable success as measured in terms of accident reduction. In general, their success appears to be reasonably proportional to the degree in which, and the thoroughness with which, they apply the principle that skill is achieved only by doing. A highly successful safety training procedure developed out of the wartime training program involves the following elements:

1. A safe method of performing each job operation or sequence of operations is developed and described in simple but adequate detail.

2. The various hazard points are brought to light and clearly described, together with the relationship between these and the various steps in the safe method.

3. The teaching is systematic and thorough. In the somewhat idiomatic English of one successful teacher it is:

    a. Tell him.

    b. Show him.

    c. Have him do it.

    d. Correct him until he has it.

    e. Supervise him to see that he keeps it.

4. The reason for requiring the wearing of personal protective equipment needed, if any, as goggles, safety shoes, hand protectors, and the like is explained and its proper use and care taught in full detail.

5. Specific safeguards needed for the protection of the worker or his fellows are similarly explained and their correct usage taught. For example, point-of-operation-guards on machines, steel mesh gloves in meat cutting, slip-on guards for the blades of axes, rubber gloves and other insulating devices on electrical work, screens and shields to catch flying chips, etc.

Job safety analysis will furnish the basic information needed for the above training procedure. It develops the safe method, brings the hazard points to light, points the way to the precautions that should be taken, and indicates the specific safeguards that should be thrown about each operation. It also aids in the proper placement of job applicants by determining the physical limitations that should be avoided on specific jobs as well as those qualifications that an applicant should possess in superior degree. In theory this would also apply to psychological factors, but in practice the appraisal of these with superior accuracy is so difficult, expensive, and time-consuming that it is not practical as a general procedure. The experience-guided judgment of competent supervisors is sufficient to detect most of the psychological misfits during the training period.

In the chapter on Job Safety Analysis, samples of typical job breakdowns resulting from such analysis are presented. As pointed out in that connection, the job breakdown approach is particularly effective in training the new employee, provided the safety material is properly included and the key safety points effectively presented and thoroughly learned and understood.

The above training procedure is an adaptation and extension of methods whose development started with Taylor and are best exemplified by the Training Within Industry Program that was so highly successful in meeting the war-created need for large numbers of workers with special skills. Its effect in reducing injuries was substantial because, in general, the work methods that are best for production are at least reasonably safe also. However, the TWI procedure failed to give adequate attention to the hazard points, the precautions that should be taken to avoid them, and specific safeguards that should be provided. Nor is teaching merely the safe procedure sufficient for safety. The whys and the hows must also be taught.

It should be obvious from the above that a very considerable amount of detail and careful preparation is essential. The importance of thoroughness in the analytical and preparatory steps cannot be overemphasized. However, all of this makes for simplicity and exactness in the actual teaching process. The teacher must, of course, have a full mastery of the method and its application to each operation or procedure he teaches. This brings us to the chief problem; that of training supervisors to do an adequate job of training the worker. Large firms can profitably set up vestibule schools in which the work methods are taught and whose graduates need little more than average supervision for a while when placed on the production job. But the smaller firms (who, together, employ the large majority of our workers) cannot do this. Therefore, all of the training in most plants must be given by the foreman or other supervisors in charge of the work. Greater attention to foreman training is a vital need in the safety field just as it is in other phases of production.

One of the most serious offenses against safety is the failure to pay adequate attention to safety in our apprenticeship systems. Few of our older experienced workmen have had any serious training in safety. Most of them received little safety instruction in learning their trades. There are few who do not have some unsafe habits, and few consistently follow safe procedures. The apprentice naturally acquires the habits, good and bad, of his instructor and, unless adequately instructed and supervised is likely to add some unsafe habits of his own. The situation is improving, however. More attention is being given to safety training, but the big job lies ahead. Successful and adequate safety training facilities are exceptional as yet. Thus, it is obvious that every school offering courses intended to prepare or improve people for industrial work of any type whatever should include the subject of accident prevention in as thorough and adequate a fashion as the nature of the specific subject permits.

The new employee

A change of jobs, whether it be to a different gang or to a different employer, means an adjustment for the individual. He must become accustomed to a new foreman, fit in with a new crew, and learn the details of a new job. If it is his first job, or his first in industry, he must become adjusted to a wholly new kind of environment. He has probably heard of bad injuries in industry, or perhaps he knows someone who was poisoned or lost his health in a plant. He is apt to be nervous, apprehensive, or even scared. This applies particularly to women in their first industrial employment. In addition, they are likely to find plants and plant work noisy, rough, and dirty until they get used to it. The above emphasizes the importance of careful, systematic induction to give the new employee sound and helpful information about his new work, environment, and job therein. The importance of including pertinent safety information, and particularly the company policy toward safety, can hardly be overemphasized. Since, normally, the new employee wants to make good, he is usually far more receptive to safety information and safety ideas than he will be after he has become reasonably at home in his job.

The experienced new employee, particularly in the skilled trades, is apt to present a different kind of problem. Instead of being timid or nervous, he is apt to very sure of himself and to feel that since he has been around, he knows how to take care of himself most anywhere. In actual fact, he may be more injury-liable than the green new employee because of his overconfidence. Also, unless he has had good safety education and training, which relatively few have had, he is likely to have unsafe habits of which he may not even be aware. In this connection, it is emphasized that the effective way to break a bad habit is to substitute a good habit for the bad one. Habits of action are acquired only through repetition and, hence, the proper procedure in dealing with the bad habit is to repeat the performance of the new method until it becomes thoroughly established and erases the old habit.

Safety training for women differs only in detail from the methods that are effective with men. More attention should be given to safeguarding the hair. Clothing should be provided that combines attractiveness with the comfort and safety necessary for the conditions involved. Special attention must be given to the hazard offered by finger rings and bracelets. Suitable footwear and protection of the skin and hands from irritating substances should be provided. Experience abundantly proves that in work for which women's lesser strength is not a handicap, they are at least as safe workers as men if they have been properly inducted and trained for the specific jobs to which they are assigned.

Specific media in safety education and training

There would be little value in discussing herein the use of the traditional media of the classroom and school shop in safety instruction because, in adapting these to such use, only changes in detail are involved. However, the increasing use of motion pictures, film strips, and slides in the broad field of education is being extended to the safety field. These are being used in traffic safety, home safety, and industrial safety, but since our concern herein is with the latter field, we will limit our discussion to it. The value of these media in safety education and safety training has been abundantly proved, but most of their development for these purposes lies in the future.

The choice of the particular medium for a specific purpose should be made with great care, for if the medium chosen is not well suited to the purpose in question, only indifferent results can be expected. If the treatment is not of a high order, the product may actually be harmful to the cause of accident prevention.

Safety movies and film strips (with or without sound) are available in substantial number and variety. Many of these are excellent both photographically and in their correct portrayal of safety performance and safety techniques. However, some have important errors or omissions in safety detail. A few are so far short of representing first-rate safety performance as to make it evident that the persons who controlled their production had little knowledge of the subject and failed to secure the guidance of anyone who did. Certainly no safety film or film strip should be produced except under the technical control (as to safety) of competent technicians.

The considerations of chief importance in selecting the medium to be used in any given instance are the following:

1. The moving picture is valuable chiefly to present the general idea of safety, to show motion sequences and relationships, and to furnish atmosphere. Its value in giving detailed or exact instruction is very limited because few people retain any considerable part of the details that move across the screen. They get the general idea, the flavor and purpose of the story shown, but their grasp or understanding of detail is helped but little. Furthermore, no one can retain more than a moderate part of what is shown and one is likely not only to miss vital points but even to get them wrong. People get general impressions chiefly by seeing, they acquire abstract facts chiefly by a process of repetitive cerebration, and they acquire skill by repeated doing and striving to do better.

2. The film strip, which can be stopped for detailed showing and discussion of any picture (frame), can be run in place of a movie or as a medium of detailed instruction. It does not show motion sequences and it cannot furnish atmosphere as well as the movies can. But individual frames can include any desired amount of detail for instruction and discussion. The film strip can include the canned lecture or it can be made an adjunct to the lecturer or discussion leader.

3. Slides, of course, are simply a limited form of their offspring, the film strip.

The movies is by far the most expensive to produce of these media and this fact, coupled with its effectiveness in presenting the broad idea of safety, means that its chief value is in promoting safety mindedness in large groups. It can be very useful in developing public or group interest in community-wide or plant-wide safety programs. Since, however, few persons will, of their own initiative, apply ideas they receive in this manner to their own daily actions and practices, safety movies probably have little direct effect in promoting individual safe practice.

The film strip is chiefly of value in classroom or group instruction. With adequate discussion and explanation of detail supplemented by actual practice in the procedures and techniques shown, it is an extremely valuable training aid. For example, correct lifting methods may be shown and the "whys and wherefores" adequately discussed through the use of a film strip. But unless each member of the class is actually drilled in the lifting operation itself until he can perform it correctly and comfortably, he is very likely to continue to lift in whatever way he did previously despite the telling and the showing.

Chapter Twenty-five

Safety and Health Standards and Rules

Standards are essential to an industrial civilization. Each branch of science, each field of industrial activity must, as it grows, develop standards on which to base, measure, and compare its achievements and performance.

Standards may be said to develop by a process of crystallization from industrial progress. A new method or process is found. When proved and sufficiently applied, it yields certain standards which, properly used and observed, can be depended upon to bring dependable results.

Industrial safety is a new and rapidly developing field. It has developed many standards, but many more are needed. Also, many of the existing standards need further refinement. Safety standards may be classified in two groups, namely:

1. *Voluntary, self-applied standards.* The various interests, groups, and individuals engaged in the work of accident prevention have developed standards representative of good practice. Since the purpose is to prevent accidents, the standards amount to a crystallization of experience and are accepted and observed only by virtue of their practical value as aids to prevention.

2. *Regulatory standards.* Laws or rules, having the force and effect of law, have been adopted by governments for the purpose of securing the correction of specific hazardous conditions and of setting forth certain requirements deemed necessary to safety.

The development of voluntary, self-applied standards

The value of uniform detailed standards of industry-wide acceptance for manufactured products was highlighted by the production failures of the first world war. The multiplicity of conflicting standards then in use by the various manufacturers proved so serious a hindrance to the large scale production of military material that by the time volume production was attained the war was over. In fact, some critical articles never did get into production.

The lesson was a hard one but much good came of it, for it led to the setting-up of machinery for the development of standards of national acceptance. The initiative toward this end was taken in 1918 by five leading engineering societies who joined forces to form a national organization for the purpose. They were: The American Society of Mechanical Engineers; The American Institute of Electrical Engineers; The American Society of Civil Engineers; The American Society of Mining and Metallurgical Engineers; The American Society for Testing Materials.

These five together with three departments of the feredal government, Commerce, War and Navy, formed the American Engineering Standards Committee. In 1928 the scope of the work was broadened and the name changed to American Standards Association (ASA). In 1948 ASA was incorporated under the laws of the State of New York.

From its modest beginning in 1918, ASA has grown into a nationwide federation of more than 120 technical societies and trade associations who are either member bodies or associate members. In addition, ASA has some 2,200 company members.

ASA has approved more than 2000 standards as American Standard. Some 425 projects are currently active under the participation of some 10,000 engineers, government officials and representatives of the various cooperating groups and organizations.

American Standards Association

Briefly, the make-up and functions of the ASA are as follows:

Board of Directors.   The executive, financial, and general administrative functions of the association are in the hands of a board of directors.

Standards Council.   The standards council has general supervision over the development of standards. It is composed of representatives of all of the member-bodies of the association. It approves the initiation of projects, the scope of the undertakings, and the personnel of committees. Finally, it sets the approval of the association on the resulting document as an *american standard* or as an *american recommended practice*. Approval of a standard is based on:

1. Regularity of procedure in the development of the standard.
2. Adequacy of representation of the committee responsible for the development of the standard.

3. The degree of unanimity reached in the committee.

4. The status of the proposed standard.

Standards Boards. When standardization activities in a major industrial field are sufficiently extensive to warrant it, standard boards aid the standards council. They coordinate ASA work in their respective fields, and through them standards are passed on to the standard council for final approval. Twelve such boards had been set up by 1960.

Library and standards information. The association provides a general information service for the use of its members and committees. This service includes a library of approximately 20,000 American and foreign standards and related material.

ASA headquarters. The routine work of the ASA is carried on by a technical staff, who follow the various standardization projects and assist in their orderly development. The headquarters of the association are located at 70 East 45th Street, New York 17, N. Y.

The work on safety codes is under the advisory direction of the Safety Standards Board. Its functions include:

1. Investigating the need for particular standards.

2. Defining and limiting the scope of standards.

3. Considering the interrelation of standards.

4. Passing upon the personnel of technical committees.

5. Following up the work on standards.

6. Acting as a general clearing house on safety standards.

It is just as necessary, if a standard is to become of real practical value, for its provisions to represent a consensus of those interested as well as the need for it to be generally appreciated. A sectional committee for a safety standard, therefore, is approved by the American Standards Association on recommendation of the Safety Standards Board only when it includes a balanced representation of those concerned. This representation covers manufacturers, employers, employees, governmental bodies, qualified specialists, and insurance representatives.

When a code has been formulated, it is recommended by the sponsor for approval by the ASA. In order to secure adequate advice, the question of approval is referred to the Safety Standards Board for recommendation on whether the procedure has been followed, and whether the vote of the technical committee shows a sufficient consensus. Upon favorable report, the code is approved by the ASA and, as an American Standard, it is brought to the attention of government officials, insurance companies, and industries concerned. The technical committee is continued to provide for revisions and to interpret the provisions.

Some of the standards approved by ASA have been developed by other groups and then submitted for ASA consideration and approval as American Standard. Notable among these standards is the Building Exits Code, developed under the leadership of the National Fire Protection Association. In similar fashion, the Associated General Contractors of America prepared a volume of safety practice in construction under the title *Manual of Accident Prevention in Construction*. It was approved as American Recommended Practice. Meanwhile, the development of a construction safety code is being carried on by a sectional committee.

The ASA procedure has won a remarkable degree of acceptance and cooperation from the various technical groups and organizations. However, some standards antedate ASA and some well-established standards have not been submitted to it for approval. Outstanding among these are the Power Boiler Code and the Unfired Pressure Vessel Code developed by the American Society of Mechanical Engineers. These codes are fruits of a vast amount of experience and constitute the standards for judging the safety of the types of pressure vessels covered.

Various other technical or industrial groups have developed safety (or health, or both) standards. Such groups include the Portland Cement Association, the American Petroleum Institute, the Manufacturing Chemists Association, the American Society of Heating and Ventilating Engineers, and the Illuminating Engineers Society—to name only a few. Any person wishing to obtain information as to such standards and standardized safety procedures in a particular industry or profession should inquire of the organization representing the group in question.

Regulatory standards

The effort to eliminate hazardous working conditions by legislative enactments has, through a long process of trial and error, finally developed a method that, properly applied, combines quite effectively the force of law with the educative and stimulative methods through which National Safety Council and allied agencies have made great gains in reducing injuries.

The first legislative attack on injuries was simply one of the prohibition of specific hazards. This method necessitates detailed legislation, which involves the following difficulties:

1. Legislative enactments are difficult to modify and thus their detail cannot be kept in accord with the changing needs of our developing industry.

2. Occupational hazards are so numerous and varied that detailed legislation cannot cover them even reasonably well without becoming impossibly complex.

3. Such detailed legislation cannot be enforced without causing hardship in so many instances that it will largely defeat its purpose.

4. Securing reasonable uniformity in such detailed enactments by the legislatures of the various states and the Federal Congress is a practical impossibility.

These difficulties are being increasingly met by the enactment of legislation that in simple, direct language:

1. Requires employers to provide safe work places and safe conditions of work for their employees and to do everything reasonably necessary to prevent their injury while at work.

2. Delegates to a specific agency the duty of drafting rules (and standards) necessary to carry out the intent of the law and of revising and modifying these as conditions require.

3. Describes the procedure required to avoid abridgement of constitutional rights and liberties. Such legislation has been sufficiently reviewed by the courts and the proper procedure is clear. Its advantages have been definitely proved and the states are turning to it increasingly. By 1951, about half the states had adopted legislation of this nature and several other legislatures had it under consideration. Several states have built up extensive systems of safety codes under such laws. Among these are California, Massachusetts, New York, Pennsylvania, Ohio, and Wisconsin.

The procedure in drafting these codes should be substantially as follows:

1. All groups having a legitimate interest in the standard to be drafted are invited to take part in its drafting.

2. The inspection service agency having the duty of administering the standards usually prepares tentative drafts and submits identical copies to a committee representing all interested groups.

3. These tentative standards with changes or additions as approved by this committee then go to the approval authority for its consideration and action as required under the law.

The process of working out safety standards by this method involves the interchange of ideas among individuals and groups who may not and often do not have any other opportunity for such exchanges. This results almost invariably in fostering cooperative effort in the interest of safety. Furthermore, those who aid in the development of such standards almost invariably become advocates of their use, and thus their acceptance grows.

Safety standards, to be worth the effort that is required to develop them, must not only be practical, but they must secure a good degree of acceptance. If they are developed through the combined efforts of all interested parties, they will be practical. But they must be known about and talked about, that is, advertised, if they are to secure acceptance. Safety men everywhere should take an active interest in developing and promoting the use of suitable safety standards. So should manufacturers, technicians, and organized labor. The safety man is in a favorable position to promote the interest of all these groups in safety standards.

In drafting state safety requirements, it is very advantageous to adopt directly, or at least to follow closely, the provisions of applicable American Standards for the following reasons:

1. The method of their development insures that they represent good practice.

2. The method of their development and the degree of voluntary acceptance they thereby receive gives practical assurance that their provisions are, in fact, sound and reasonably necessary for safety, and that the courts will usually so hold.

3. This course will prevent conflicts between the requirements of the various states.

The aim of every state should be to construct by means of mandatory requirements a floor for safety and health at a level representing the minimum conditions that may be permitted in work places.

Performance about this level (incidentally most of the job of accident elimination must be done above this floor of minimum acceptable performance) should be encouraged by advisory rules or recommendations.

States vary in their methods of presenting rules and recommendations. The usual method is to present the legal requirements and advisory material in separate documents. However, several states have experimented with a single booklet in which preventive methods are discussed subject by subject and, at the end of each such subject, the pertinent mandatory rules are set forth in bold type. The *Basic Safety Manual,* published by the Department of Industrial Relations of Alabama, is an excellent example. A similar method has been used in the American Standard Safety Code on Power Presses and Foot and Hand Presses, which presents information on safe operation in a column parallel to one presenting the rules.

When drafting standards dealing with machinery, such as elevators, for which the expense of safeguarding existing installations in accordance with the applicable American Standard would be unduly heavy, some states adopt the American Standard for installations to be made after a specified date and relax its requirements reasonably for existing installations.

Since a large proportion of injuries come from equipment or machinery common to practically all industries, most states find it advantageous to deal with these hazards through standards covering the equipment rather than the industry. Standards on transmission-machinery guarding, portable ladders, stairways, or powered hand tools fall in this class. In addition to standards of this nature, hazards peculiar to a given industry, such as foundries, dry cleaning, or quarrying, require special standards. But a foundry, for instance, would be aided by standards on ladders, stairs, transmission-machinery guarding, powered hand tools, and so on, as well as one dealing with hazards ordinarily found only in foundries. (This principle is followed in developing American Standards.)

It is important to avoid conflicts with the codes and standards of other states. The effective way to avoid such conflicts is to conform as closely with the American Safety Standards as local conditions will permit, for there are practically no other safety standards of national acceptance. The seriousness of conflicts lies in the following situations:

1. Where conflicts exist among state requirements for guarding machinery, manufacturers of the machines involved cannot design and guard their products for maximum safety. Guarding in such cases must be by or on order of the purchaser—in other words, "afterthought" guarding, which is rarely as effective as designed-in and built-in safeguarding. An outstanding instance of this fact is the ordinary circular table saw, undoubtedly the greatest producer of human injury among industrial machines. Since there are no clear and definite requirements on the guarding of such saws, and since state requirements vary widely, none of them is fully guarded by their manufacturers. No fully satisfactory guard has been developed for application to standard models of table saws, but all models could be adequately guarded if the guarding were included in the design.

2. Many firms operate plants in several states. They suffer hardship in meeting different sets of requirements.

3. Workers meeting with different degrees of protection through safety standards in different states become resentful or suspicious and tend to withhold the whole-hearted cooperation so needed in preventive work.

A few states furnish material supplementary to such formally-drafted safety standards in the form of a handbook for the guidance of the state safety inspectors. The handbook covers procedure for inspection service, together with information helpful to the safety inspector in his daily work. Such a handbook is exceedingly important. Without carefully worked-out and well-maintained means of training and instructing its safety inspectors, no state can hope to render a safety service that will reasonably measure up to the need or opportunity. If a force of safety inspectors is to pass on performance under even the most complete and well-ordered structure of safety standards, there must be a good degree of uniformity in the information each gives and the advice each tenders to meet similar hazards.

Plant standards and rules

As already pointed out, each plant must have certain production standards, even though in small, loosely managed and relatively unorganized establishments these may exist mostly in the know-how of the supervisors and their experienced workmen. At the other extreme is the modern, highly-developed plant devoted to the quantity production of a complicated machine that requires not only a great number of drawings, but also performance standards in almost endless detail. For instance, the weight of drawings required to put the B-52 bomber into mass production are said to exceed greatly the maximum load capacity of one of these air giants.

Safety benefits from all this exactitude of detail, for exactitude spells control, and adequate control of any activity yields safety. But as already pointed out in the discussion of job analysis, the planning and control necessary for mass production is rarely extended to activities not in direct production unless done in the interest of safety. But it is increasingly being so extended that, in establishments representative of top safety performance, we find a very considerable mass of safety standards developed to cover specific activities and conditions within the establishment not adequately dealt with by production standards. In addition to job safety standards, these include standards for safeguarding and safety equipment, inspection standards, safe practices, and safety rules.

This is a very important field, justifying much further development in the great majority of industrial establishments. Also the technique of its development, particularly as regards safe practice standards and safety rules, should be given much more attention. Making a physical plant safe and keeping it so is a relatively simple matter. Nor is it difficult to work out safe procedures or to arrive at the wording of rules that are expressive of such procedure. But to get all of the working force to follow safe practices faithfully and consistently is much more difficult. Success in doing so will be determined almost wholly by the extent to which the workmen come to believe in the value of following such rules of safe practice. This means, then, that in developing such rules it is essential that:

1. Every rule be practical from the viewpoint of those to whom it applies.
2. Each hazard or condition dealt with by a rule be definitely demonstrable as unsafe.
3. Rules be limited to safety matters. Extraneous matters, regardless of their importance, should not be dealt with in safety rules.
4. The workmen affected must have a full part in developing the rules.

The last item is the most important of all, so important, in fact, that it is probably true that really satisfactory observance of safety rules is not obtainable otherwise. If a plant is organized, the union can contribute importantly to the safety of its members by taking a position of leadership in working out rules of safe practice and in promoting their acceptance.

Many establishments have developed safety rule books containing rules of general applicability. It is quite common practice to issue a copy to each employee (particularly each new one) and require from him, in due course, a signed statement that he has read, understands, and will observe the rules therein. This course is of little practical value unless the rules and the justification for each rule are really understood by the employee. A rule that a workman had a part in developing will be understood by him. If he knows that his fellows developed the rules, he will be strongly inclined to believe in them. He will accept them gladly from a foreman he likes and respects. In all cases, whatever instruction and explanation is required to enable him to realize the value of the rule and the reasons why he should observe it is necessary if a good degree of observance is to be had.

Chapter Twenty-six

Accident Records and Reports

Since all permanent records must be based on accurate information, it is necessary that forms on which original reports of accidents are to be made be designed carefully. These reports must furnish all essential data in such a manner that the accident-prevention engineer and management can interpret and record the information with a view to accomplishing the purposes of the safety program.

What the report should include

In designing report forms, consideration must be given to the following factors:

1. The report should carry information that is necessary to insurance companies carrying the compensation risk and also to government bodies such as industrial commissions and the Department of Labor.

2. The report should require information that will assist the safety engineer to determine the cause of the accident.

3. The report must be sufficiently complete to permit classification of the accident by location and type.

4. The report must present the type of information that will permit a complete analysis of the accident and circumstances surrounding it so that proper measures may be taken to prevent similar occurrences in the future.

Virtually all state industrial commissions require detailed reports covering any injury through which the worker becomes entitled to compensation under the Workmen's Compensation Act. Laws of different states set the waiting period or the period during which no compensation is payable at from three days to one week. In all cases where the disability extends beyond this waiting period, the general requirement calls for the reporting of the injury on forms approved by the commission within a certain length of time. In general, Workmen's Compensation Insurance carriers require the same original information on this type of injury as is supplied to the Industrial Commission. These insurance carriers likewise require additional reports involving medical expenses, even though the injury may be non-disabling. Some insurance companies also require the reporting of all injuries, even though there was no medical expense or loss of time.

It is apparent, then, that in any case of injury where medical expense is incurred or where a disability is caused, it is incumbent upon the employer to secure sufficient information on the accident so that he can prepare a complete report. These reports, as indicated in Figure 1, carry information relating to the occupation, hours of work, weekly earnings, date of accident, location of accident, accident type, names of witnesses, description of injury, and so on. Within the past few years considerable progress has been made in the standardization of these reports, so that today virtually all information required by the safety engineer for his purposes is made available through the data which must be secured for the insurance carrier or the Industrial Commission. Certain types of accidents will, of course, occur about which the safety engineer will desire additional information, and provision should be made for supplementary reports in order to complete the record.

Reporting minor injuries

There is considerable disagreement among safety engineers as to the necessity of reporting or recording injuries of a minor nature that cause no disability and require no professional medical attention. When one views this type of injury from the standpoint of cause and the possibility of securing clues as to its prevention, it becomes apparent that even though the accident involved little cost it cannot be ignored in analyzing the possible steps that will lead to prevention in the future. The accident that results in a minor injury today, may cause the death of a worker tomorrow. A sharp tool dropped from an elevated platform may, in one case, cause no injury whatever because no employee is struck by the tool. In another case it might only slightly injure an employee working below. But in still another case it might cause fatal injuries. Because of this, the safety program makes necessary the recording and study of as many accidents as possible, even though some accidents result in only minor injury, or possibly no injury at all.

Although it is important that information be secured on as many minor injury cases as possible in order to discover possibilities of more serious occurrences as well as to establish a record in case of future complications arising from a present slight injury, it is likewise true that employees will not make such minor injury reports if a great mass of

INDUSTRIAL COMMISSION OF WISCONSIN
MADISON, WIS.

COMPLETE this form promptly after injury
occurs and send in duplicate to

EMPLOYERS MUTUAL LIABILITY INSURANCE CO.
1200 Empire Building, Milwaukee, Wisconsin

Employer's No._____Accident No._____
       (Do not fill in)   (Do not fill in)

EMPLOYER'S FIRST REPORT OF INJURY OR DISEASE

IMPORTANT: Copy of this report must be sent by employer **himself** directly to Industrial Commission, State Office Bldg., Madison, Wisconsin, on the fourth day after employe leaves work if disability still continues. In death cases, report must be made within twenty-four hours.

(1) Date of report_____Made out by_____ Position_____

(2) Employer's name _____Employer is { Individual_____
                                                  Partnership _____
                                                  Corporation _____

(3) Address _____Telephone No._____
              (Street No.)   (City or Town)

(4) Principal products or business_____
                          (Goods produced, work done or kind of trade or transportation)

(5) Name of your insurance company_____ Policy No._____
                          (If "self-insurer" by commission's order, so state)

(6) Where did injury or disease occur?_____ in_____County
                       (Check) city ☐ village ☐ township ☐

(7) Injured Employe _____
              (Name)   (Home Address)   (Street number)   (City)   (State)

(8) Age _____ Sex_____Married?_____Permit on file?_____
      (Give date of birth if injured under 19)

(9) Occupation _____ Length of time worked for you_____

(10) Previous physical defects: Eye, Ear, Hernia or otherwise_____
                                            (describe)

(11) Under which classification of your policy were his wages carried? _____

(12) Date of injury_____ Time _____o'clock_____M.
             (month)   (day)   (year)

     Last day worked_____Engaged in what work when injured? _____

(13) Wage rate of employe at time of injury. Per hour $_____Per day $_____Per week $_____
     Per month $_____Hours per day_____Days per week_____Piece or time worker_____
            (If paid by month)
     If piece worker, state his average hourly earnings at time of injury $_____

(14) Normal full time employment for injured's class of work. Hours per day_____Days per week_____

(15) Employe's earnings in your employ. (a) Calendar weeks worked in past 52 in same kind of work as at time of injury_____
     (b) Total earnings during such weeks $_____(c) Bonus or premium earned in addition to "total earnings" $_____

(16) In addition to above cash wage, did employe receive board?_____ Room?_____ Tips?_____

(17) Is injured an officer, a partner, or a manager?_____If so, state his position_____

(18) Are his wages carried on your regular pay roll upon which your policy premium is based?_____Or is he in the
     employ of a jobber or contractor? (Give Name)_____

(19) Did injury occur in the course of his regular employment?_____

(20) Describe fully how accident or disease occurred. (Note machine or part, tool, object, substance or thing most directly con-
     tributing to the accident or disease, giving special attention to unsafe acts and to the kind of accident as "struck by",
     "caught in", "burning", "fall", etc.)_____
_____
_____

(21) Did injury occur because of (a) Intoxication?_____(b) Failure to use safety devices?_____(c) To obey rules_____

(22) Nature and extent of injury. (State exactly the part of the body affected, and the character of the injury or disease)_____
_____
_____

(23) If employe has returned to work, state date_____If not, how long will he be away from work?
_____ Did death result?_____

(24) Give name of doctor or hospital_____
                    (Street)   (Post Office)   (State)

(25) If employe was killed, give the following information as to his dependents, using other side of sheet if necessary:_____
_____
     (Name)   (Relationship)   (Age)   (Address)

(26) Names of witnesses:_____

FIG. 1.

detailed information is required or if reprimands or penalties are likely to be inflicted as a result of such reports. In more serious cases, the employee realizes the need of a complete report in order to protect his own rights and to guarantee him benefits under compensation laws, which include the payment of his medical bills and the payment of workmen's compensation. No such selfish incentive, however, is apparent to the employee who receives only a minor injury, such as a skin abrasion, or a slight burn, or a particle in the eye.

In order to encourage reports on this type of injury, it is suggested that a short form be used such as is indicated in Figure 2. These reports should not be ignored by the safety engineer. They should be studied, and where information which they carry indicates conditions or practices that might result in a serious injury on some other occasion, proper preventive measures should be instituted. In some instances it will be necessary for the safety engineer to request additional information before he can be certain that he has the complete history on this type of accident.

REPORT OF MINOR INJURY

DATE_____19_____

1. NAME OF EMPLOYEE_____LOCATION_____

2. OCCUPATION_____DEPARTMENT_____

3. DATE OF INJURY_____19_____TIME_____M.

4. DESCRIBE HOW INJURY WAS RECEIVED _____

_____

5. NATURE OF INJURY _____

6. NAMES OF WITNESSES _____

7. FIRST AID RENDERED BY_____DATE_____19_____TIME_____M.

8. MEDICAL ATTENTION BY DR._____ADDRESS_____

9. DATE OF MEDICAL ATTENTION_____19_____TIME_____M.

CLASSIFICATION No._____SIGNED_____

FOREMAN

FIG. 2.

The matter of accident investigation is discussed elsewhere, but it is suggested, in considering the types of reports that should be secured on each accident, that a special report form covering investigation of serious accidents or accidents that might prove serious, be designed. This form should be of such a nature that it will direct the investigating committee's attention to those points which the safety engineer will want to have definitely established. It is imperative that all available information be secured on every serious accident and on every accident involving the violation of safe practice or safety rules. The analysis of these types of accidents will lead to specific conclusions as to the elimination of both hazards and unsafe practices.

Who should report accidents *

The responsibility for the reporting of accidents should rest on the foreman or the department head. As is true of every operation, the cooperation of the individual making the report should be secured by proving to him that the careful reporting of the facts in each accident case will be beneficial to his operation. Unless the supervisor can see where he will gain some benefit from a careful study and reporting of each accident case, he is likely, in the rush of production, to slight this activity. It is likewise important that the need of such reports be conveyed to all employees through safety meetings, payroll enclosures, posters on the bulletin board, and every other possible means. The requirement that the foreman report all accidents in his department affords an additional opportunity to create a safety-consciousness, both among the foremen and the men. The follow-up of accidents by the safety department and requests to the foreman or the individual for opinions on how the accident could have been prevented, or on how future accidents could be prevented, force the participation in the safety program of supervisors and men. This practice will go far toward correcting the idea that is often prevalent that the safety department in itself is responsible for all accidents, as well as for their prevention.

The routine covering the reporting of accidents will vary depending on the size of the plant and its organization. In some instances, these reports will clear through the medical department or the first-aid room. If a full-time industrial nurse is employed, it may well be that the responsibility of handling accident reports is placed with her. In other plants, especially smaller ones, the reports may be routed through the plant organization in the same order that production reports are routed. These reports should eventually reach the desk of the full-time or part-time safety engineer, and the records covering the reports should be maintained by him.

Building up the record

The preceding discussion has concerned itself primarily with the original report of the accident or injury. It is again emphasized that in developing

---

* The term "accident" is used here to include no-injury accidents as well as those that cause injuries.

this information care must be taken to get all of the detail and to be sure that it is correct. The next step is to place it so that it may be used in the future prevention of accidents.

It is desirable that the safety engineer have available at all times a bird's-eye view of any single accident. His record should be so established that at any given time he can immediately obtain from it such information as days lost to date, compensation payments made, cost of medical and hospital expense, and any other information pertaining to this particular case. In order to consolidate this information, it is suggested that each accident report, together with all other matter pertaining to the injury, such as doctor's reports, compensation payment receipts, and the like, be attached to an accident report backing sheet similar to the one shown in Figure 3. This sheet, when the injury case is closed, will provide all essential information for the establishment of the annual record in the department. It will indicate the total time lost, the date of the injury, the date the man returned to work, which doctors were consulted, the number of compensation payments, the cost of compensation payments, and the total cost of the accident.

Whereas, of course, the purpose of original reports and records similar to the above is to maintain an accurate picture of each individual case, in order that there may be no error in the handling of the case or in the accumulation of costs, the ultimate purpose of maintaining such records goes far beyond the current need. The value of any report depends on the use that is made of the information it contains. Every report should be analyzed in this light. If any information is being called for which is not relevant or which has no particular use, the requirement for furnishing this information should be eliminated. On the other hand, all information that will lead to a determination of causes or to conclusions that will assist in the prevention of future similar accidents should be included with the reports. This information should be of such a nature that it can be used, when combined with other reports, to show trends of frequency and severity rates, types and locations of injuries, by departments or plants, causes of injuries, and accident costs. These cumulative records should, likewise, have a definite purpose and should make possible:

1. The study of causes and location of hazards in order to develop corrective measures.

2. The trend of accidents in each department and the plant as a whole and comparisons of plants and departments.

3. The preparation of concise reports for management in order that it may be aware of the conditions pertaining to safety.

4. The stimulation of added interest among workers.

5. The development of safety rules; the preparation of bulletins, posters, and material for safety meetings.

SUMMARY OF ACCIDENT

_____ COMPANY　DATE ____ ____ 19 ____

TYPE OF ACCIDENT _____ NAME OF ⎰ EMPLOYEE _____

DIVISION _____ INDIVIDUAL ⎱ PUBLIC _____

DEPARTMENT _____ FILE NUMBER　OUR _____ OTHER _____

REMARKS _____

ACCIDENT COSTS

DATE	DESCRIPTION	AMOUNT	DATE	DESCRIPTION	AMOUNT
					TOTAL	

EMPLOYEE ACCIDENT COMPENSATION COSTS

DATE	DESCRIPTION	AMOUNT	DATE	DESCRIPTION	AMOUNT
					TOTAL	

DAYS LOST- FROM _____ TO _____ NUMBER OF DAYS _____

FIG. 3.

With this in mind, consideration can be directed toward several types of records and the purpose that may be served by each.

The second type of record that should be established consists of a summary of all accidents. On this record will be entered information pertaining to each accident in sufficient detail so that the record will present an overall picture of the accident situation at any given time. The National Safety Council has designed a form suitable for this purpose, particularly in medium-sized plants. This form, Figure 3, is National Safety Council Analysis Sheet for Industrial Injuries, Form IS-2. Larger plants often use tabulating machines or other means of accumulating accident data from the original

LOST-TIME ACCIDENTS							
Date	Employee	Div. & Dept.	Injury	Cause	Days Lost	Comp.	Med.

Courtesy National Safety Council.

FIG. 4.

reports. In small plants, a simplified form such as that shown above may be used. It is essential, however, that some type of accident summary that shows each accident that has occurred within a fixed period be kept.

In describing or comparing a plant's safety record, the only cases that are generally used are those involving loss of time from work, that is, accidents and exposures causing disabling injuries. Under the American Standard,* this type of injury is the only one that is so tabulated. The reasons for this standard of comparison are obvious. Any requirement to include minor first-aid cases or medical cases involving the loss of time in comparative records would be likely to create, on the part of employees within a department or a plant, an inclination not to report minor injuries. The development of this attitude would defeat the purpose of the comparison. The same situation would, without question, prevail so far as foremen or supervisors were concerned.

---

* Method of Compiling Industrial Injury Rates.

The continuing accident summary previously mentioned, from which comparative records will be made, should, therefore, carry information on disabling or lost-time injuries only.

Each disabling injury should be recorded at the time of its occurrence and the remaining data called for on the summary report should be supplied during the course of the case or when the case is closed. With such a record, the safety engineer is in a position to determine at a glance the number of injuries sustained during the year or during the month to date, the prevailing type of accident that is occurring, the total time lost from injury, and the costs of these injuries, at least to the extent of medical and compensation expense.

In many plants a similar record is kept for medical cases only, excluding those involving loss of time. Although no non-lost-time cases are used in computing the plant's frequency rate, a record of them is desirable from the standpoint of accumulating all costs.

Basic records of injuries are obviously important in any organization, although too often the value of these records is not realized and they are not utilized in developing the accident prevention program. While the records, in themselves, contain data that must be available for reference in any unusual compensable injury case or wherever information as to the nature of the injury, the amount of time lost, or the compensation paid becomes necessary, other uses are of even greater importance.

From the standpoint of the accident-prevention engineer, the most essential purpose of his records is to make available an overall picture of the accident situation in his plant, in order that he may know where to apply corrective measures and which corrective measures to apply. The record serves the same purpose as does the case record of a doctor. From X-ray, cardiographs, blood tests, blood pressure, and similar data, the doctor determines the type of treatment required by the patient. From a study of accident frequency, location of accidents, types of accidents, types of injuries, and accident causes, the safety engineer determines his program for treatment. It becomes apparent that the records which he keeps must then be of such a nature as to give this information and in such a manner as will permit its use for the jobs for which the engineer desires it.

Recording the causes

Every safety man should establish a routine method of accumulating and tabulating data which, when summarized, can be of much value. The American Standard Cause Code is designed to organize the essential information pertaining to causes in such manner as to enable coding it for statistical analysis. While coding is obviously worth while only when the mass of accident data is quite large, the selection of accident factors used in the Cause Code will be of value to every safety man. See Chapter Five.

Although in the Code the complete practice is developed to a fine degree, it is so arranged that it can be adapted to small companies as well as large organizations. There are definite advantages in using the Standard practice for compiling accident causes. It has been difficult during past years to secure exact information from industries throughout the country as to accident causes and factors. This difficulty has been aggravated by the fact that no two companies used the same means of classifying accidental injuries under the American Standards Association plan. Eventually, most organizations will use the standard classification, which will permit more exact analysis and sounder conclusions than in the past.

For smaller companies, the National Safety Council has designed a form called Standard Industrial Injury Report Form, which permits the tabulation of twenty-five injuries on a single sheet with all pertinent data relating to those injuries. The form is designed to follow quite closely the American Standard Cause Code. Experience has proved that the accumulation of this information, either on this particular form or some other simplified form, has been extremely helpful in discovering causes, locations, and types of accidents in the individual plant, and has led to improved methods in the prevention of those accidents. Regardless of the means used, a realization as to the value of analytical data concerning all accidents within a given plant is of prime necessity. If a logical and successful program is to be instituted and continued, this information must be available.

Reports prepared from records

Although constant contact with and study of accidents and their causes will convince the safety engineer of the need of certain protective devices, guards, changes in construction or operating practices, or use of protective clothing, it must be kept in mind that other individuals in the organization whose contact with and knowledge of injuries and accidents and their causes is limited may not recognize the need of the expenditure of money to reduce the frequency of occurrences of injuries.

It is likewise fundamental that the safety engineer keep management informed of the progress of his efforts, the trend of accidents, the costs of these accidents, and the need of additional expenditures to prevent their recurrence.

For these reasons, the information contained in the records must be compiled for presentation to management including superintendents and foremen, as well as to the men themselves. Engineers do not always have the proper concept of the need of this presentation, nor do they generally have the imagination necessary to present the data in a manner that will serve the purpose for which they are intended. In many cases these short-comings on the part of the safety engineer can be corrected by securing the assistance of the advertising department or the personnel department of the company in preparing and releasing reports. The presentation made in reports to management or to men should not, in any case, be purely statistical. It should be descriptive, with pictures, charts, and graphs so that it will present a view of the situation that will sell management or men the idea that the safety engineer has in mind.

Management participation *

In examining the records of companies where the accident frequency is extremely low, it is invariably discovered that top management of those companies is not only interested in safety but expresses that interest in an active participation in the program. This participation includes at-tendance at safety meetings, commendatory letters to supervisors who have had a good record, messages to employees through the company magazine or on bulletin boards, and other means. The top executives in these companies place accident prevention on the same level as sales, customer relations, production, costs, advertising, and profits. Supervisors in these companies support management's position with the result that the entire organization becomes safety conscious.

The complaint of some safety engineers that the top men in their com-pany do not do these things is a weak excuse for a poor record. It is the safety engineer's responsibility to keep management interested in the safety program and solicit and promote their participation. The safety engineer who does not make a constant effort to secure the participation of top management is failing to use one of the most important influences at his command.

Reports to management

Reports on the accident-prevention program should be made to man-agement monthly. These reports should not be too lengthy, but they should definitely cover certain items relative to the safety program. Among these "necessaries" are:

1. Frequency.
2. Severity.
3. Total time lost.
4. Costs of accidents.

---

* From a talk given by C. B. Boulet before the American Society of Safety Engineers at the National Safety Congress, October, 1950.

APRIL IS THIRD SUCCESSIVE MONTH
WITHOUT A LOST-TIME INJURY

April 30, 1961

Division	Month of Apr. 1961	Month of Apr. 1960	To Date from January 1 1961	To Date from January 1 1960	Last May	Total for 1960
Acctg. & General	0	0	1	0	0	0
Green Bay	0	0	0	1	0	1
Menominee-Marinette	0	0	0	0	0	0
N B & Merchandise	0	0	0	0	0	0
Oshkosh	0	0	0	0	0	1
Power	0	0	0	0	0	1
Sheboygan	0	0	0	0	0	1
Lake Shore	0	0	0	0	0	0
Wisconsin Valley	0	1	0	1	0	4
TOTAL	0	1	1	2	0	8

TOTAL CALENDAR DAYS AND CALENDAR MAN DAYS
SINCE LAST LOST-TIME INJURY

	DAYS	MAN DAYS		DAYS	MAN DAYS
Electric			*Power*		
Green Bay	2590	131 203	Hydro Plants	2809	203 956
Rhinelander	7115	103 993	Washington St. Sub	9940	84 108
Antigo	6325	82 792	Stevens Point Sub	11873	58 053
Manitowoc	3549	61 151	W. Tr. Const. & Maint.	4745	57 065
Oconto, Wa & Wau	1390	42 598	Rhinelander Sub	9811	50 435
Oshkosh	843	25 530	Manitowoc Plant	1897	42 807
Wausau	567	23 569	E. Tr. Const. & Maint.	2428	38 227
Minocqua	204	20 133	Wells St. Sub	9246	37 044
Menominee-Marinette	809	19 550	E. El Const. & Maint.	2093	35 874
Waupaca	1713	12 445	Oshkosh	1367	31 097
Peninsular	471	10 242	W. El Const. & Maint.	3458	23 033
Tomahawk	622	7 553	Pulliam	178	20 234
Merrill	535	7 320	Pulliam Const.	1357	15 524
Stevens Point	295	3 951	West Hydro Maint.	1963	10 494
Chilton-Brillion	223	2 874	Relay Test. & Pole Insp.	659	3 174
Automotive & Transportation			*Gas Distribution*		
Eastern Garages	1011	36 626	Green Bay	630	33 210
Valley Garages	1585	33 622	M & M	1175	29 615
			Two Rivers	5575	27 875
Green Bay	975	68 380	Sheboygan	269	17 154
Accounting & General			Stevens Point	1325	10 720
All Divisions	111	63 359	Oshkosh	210	7 770
			Merchandise & New Business		
			All Divisions	6560	299 161

FIG. 5.

These figures should be given not only for the company as a whole, but also for each individual plant or department. The use of comparative records has an immense psychological value and acts as an incentive to the departments making the poorer record. Such presentations would often convince the foreman or superintendent of the desirability of devoting his attention more actively to the prevention of accidents than he has in the past. The records should likewise show not only comparisons between the departments, but also comparisons between this month and last month, this year and last year.

Although top management will generally understand the meaning of frequency and severity and other statistical data included in the report, in presenting similar reports to foremen or to the men, care should be taken to translate these statistics into language or figures that will be understandable. For instance, instead of showing frequency by departments, it is often advisable simply to show the number of man-days worked by the department since the last lost-time accident. (A sample type of report of this nature is shown in Figure 5.)

It has been found of considerable advantage by many safety engineers to include also in this report a brief description of serious accidents that have occurred during the past month, as well as recommendations made for the correction of the causes of these accidents.

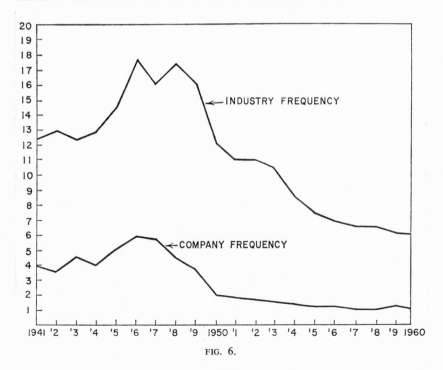

FIG. 6.

The use of charts and graphs should not be neglected. (A typical chart is shown in Figure 6.) These charts can be designed to show injury trends, comparisons between various departments, comparisons with national frequency, costs, and so on.

The use of data secured from accident statistics can be broadened almost immeasurably. Many companies prepare monthly reports on their accident situation, which are included in the company magazine. Other companies use the device of a letter signed by the president of the company to the superintendent of each department, pointing out the record of his department during the past month or six months, and either complimenting him on the report or questioning him as to the why of the situation, if the record is worse during the more recent period. The possibility of use of statistical data presented in graphical form in charts or posters on the bulletin board should not be neglected.

It is likewise desirable to write up the same type of information for use in safety meeting discussions. It will be found that the men in these meetings are intensely interested in the record made by their own group as it relates to other groups. Every possible avenue of getting this type of information back to superintendents from their employees should be used. This is all a part of the job of maintaining interest in the safety program. It might also be added that from a selfish standpoint it is advantageous for the safety engineer to point out the improvement that is being made from period to period as a result of the efforts being devoted to accident prevention. The successful safety engineer keeps in mind that in stopping accidents, a program which produces results must have as one of its fundamental principles the interest of everyone from top management to the lowliest worker. Failure to use original records or the accumulation of data from records for this purpose indicates a weakness in the over-all program.

Chapter Twenty-seven

First Aid

The purpose of an organized accident-prevention program is to eliminate accidents (and exposures) that may result in injuries by removing the hazards, by protecting the individual worker, and by promoting safe practices. However, no program yet designed has succeeded in eliminating every injury. Therefore, even those establishments that have come nearest the goal of complete injury elimination have found it necessary and profitable to provide carefully for the treatment of those injured. This preparation involves both first-aid facilities and first-aid training. The dictates of humanity require at least reasonably effective provision for the succor of those injured, but it has also been found that employee participation through training in first aid can be strongly stimulative of safety-mindedness.

Early in the safety movement, many individuals charged with the prevention of accidents organized extensive and continuing first-aid training programs in the belief that by this means the whole safety purpose could be accomplished. Actually, nothing could be further from the truth. A safety program contemplates the elimination of injuries. A first-aid program contemplates the most adequate possible treatment of all the injuries that occur in spite of the effort to prevent them. Today it would seem that a careful appraisal of relative values is in order, for numerous accident-prevention engineers appear prone to neglect first-aid training and perhaps even adequate provisions for first-aid treatment because of failure to realize their value in accident prevention.

First-aid facilities

Adequate provisions for the first-aid treatment of all cases of injury or illness should be maintained in every establishment. The scope of such provisions will, of course, vary widely. Many large plants maintain facilities that approach those found in the modern hospital and offer extensive health-preservative services, particularly dental, eye testing and fitting, blood and urine analysis, and nutritional advice. However, the usual practice is to limit the plant facilities quite closely to first-aid needs and to arrange for any other services needed through the usual professional practitioners.

The primary purpose of plant first-aid facilities is just what the term implies—to give prompt treatment to all who suffer injury at their work. Every other consideration is secondary to this. This purpose is twofold: to give prompt succor and relief in case of serious injury, and to prevent the infection of lesser injuries. Essential to the satisfactory functioning of first-aid service are:

1. Fully competent first-aid attendants.
2. Adequate quarters and equipment.
3. Proper organization and records.
4. Employee coöperation.

Competent personnel. The minimum fully satisfactory standard of competence is that represented by the full-time service of a trained nurse. In the very small plant, this is obviously impractical. The alternative is to select at least two responsible employees who, after having completed a standard course in first aid, would handle the first-aid work under the general supervision of a trained nurse or a doctor. These attendants should be allowed time to keep the first-aid room in order, check supplies and keep them up to date, and keep the needed records. They should be so chosen that one will surely be available during all operating hours. This is the minimum that is to be regarded as at all satisfactory. Anything less will in the long run almost certainly result in inadequate first aid, needless infections, needless suffering, and high injury cost.

Quarters and equipment. Every fixed establishment should have a first-aid room. It should be attractively finished, well-lighted, kept spotlessly clean and orderly, and be situated near toilet facilities. The minimum size for practical use is about 7 feet by 9 feet. Such a room will accommodate the following:

1. Hospital cot.
2. Stretcher—hung on wall brackets 6 feet above floor.
3. Writing table—to fold up to wall.
4. Stool.
5. Porcelain-top table.
6. Sterilizer—mounted on wall.
7. Medicine cabinet—4 feet 7 inches from floor.
8. Headrest chair with folding armrest.
9. Gooseneck lamp stand.

10. Corner lavatory.
11. Liquid-soap dispenser.
12. Sanitary can with cover.
13. File for medical records.
14. Floor lamp.
15. Telephone.
16. Treatment table or instrument cabinet.
17. Small office and surgical equipment, such as basins, pitcher, rubber gloves (sterile), scissors, tweezers, forceps, hot-water bottle, ice bag, etc.

The miniumum first-aid supplies should be:

1. Inelastic tourniquet.
2. Pair scissors.
3. Teaspoon.
4. Medicine droppers.
5. Eye cup.
6. Assorted safety pins.
7. Paper drinking cups.
8. Roll absorbent cotton.
9. Small covered absorbent-cotton dispenser.
10. Package of applicators.
11. One package of sterile gauze.
12. Roll of 1-inch adhesive tape.
13. 1-, 2-, and 3-inch gauze bandage rolls.
14. Castor oil.
15. Some burn ointment.
16. Tincture of iodine or mercurochrome.
17. 4 per cent aqueous boric acid.
18. Aromatic spirits of ammonia.
19. Bicarbonate of soda.
20. White vaseline.
21. Splinter forceps.
22. Supply of 1-inch compresses on adhesive in individual packages.

The nurse or doctor in charge will suggest additional supplies and equipment to meet the needs of the specific establishment. This person should have a good knowledge of the hazards of the plant. For instance, an inhalator should be promptly and unfailingly available if exposure to asphyxiant gases is likely. Special materials may be needed to prevent or to treat injury from chemicals, and so on. A foundry will require extra supplies for the treatment of burns, and so on.

Dependence upon a first-aid kit or kits is specifically not recommended except for small construction jobs, line crews, and other transient or short-duration jobs. The record of the first-aid kit in fixed establishments is not satisfactory. Perhaps the chief reason for this is that the management that does not regard first aid of sufficient importance to justify the modest expenditure necessary to furnish the above-described minimum quarters and equipment will not give adequate attention to the maintenance of first-aid kits and to the first-aid service itself. Often two or more small establishments in the same building or in closely adjacent buildings may establish a joint first-aid room and first-aid services. For satisfactory results in such cases, whole-hearted cooperation is essential. This, once established, may happily lead to a cooperative safety setup. Many such setups are functioning effectively.

Organization and records. Unless definite procedure in case of injury is arranged for and thoroughly understood, injuries may be aggravated by bad handling or by unnecessary delay or both. Every supervisor should be fully instructed, and preferably should take a course in first aid. Many plants include key men from each crew in such a course.

The importance of getting adequate treatment for every minor injury should be fully understood by every foreman, and each should be painstaking in passing this knowledge on to his men and in getting them to report all small injuries. Even though foremen and men know in a general way of the danger of infection, satisfactory reporting for treatment is ordinarily not obtained unless the management stresses the need, gives definite instructions regarding the procedure, and keeps sufficiently in touch to see that the instructions are carried out.

Definite records should be kept. These should be as simple as possible, yet contain the essential information. The essentials are:

1. Requirements imposed by the terms of the applicable workmen's compensation act.
2. Data needed by the insurance carrier.
3. Information helpful to preventive effort.

For further detail, see the chapters, Accident Records and Reports and Accident Investigation.

The management should keep as close a watch on the accident records as it does on any other important phase of production.

Employee cooperation. The problem of getting full employee understanding of the danger of infection and consequent unfailing reporting of all minor injuries for treatment is a troublesome one. It can be met adequately only by:

1. Insistent pressure by the management.
2. Continuous supervision, education, and instruction by the foremen.
3. A continuing informational campaign by the first-aid attendants.
4. The persistent use of available posters, literature, safety meetings, and other educational and stimulative means.

First-aid training

First-aid training has as its primary purpose the instruction of plant personnel so that when an accident occurs, its severity may be controlled through proper handling of the injured employee. A well-developed training program has a secondary, and from the safety engineer's standpoint, perhaps a more important objective than simply the treatment of injuries.

The very fact that employees are trained to be prepared for accidents reacts favorably on their interest in stopping accidents.

One of the basic requirements of every safety program is the maintenance of the active interest of each employee in his own safety, as well as in the safety of his fellow workers. Whenever this interest lags, the accident frequency rate rises. It has been demonstrated that a good first-aid training program has, in many cases, improved the safety mindedness of the group. The program provides for knowledge of different types of injuries, the effect of injuries on the individual, and the treatment required for each type of injury. In the discussions pertaining to these injuries, the tragic results that occur because of accidents are of course emphasized. The impression made on individuals in the class is excellent from the standpoint of safety psychology. It is this factor that has brought about marked changes in frequency rates immediately following intensive first-aid training. Records indicate that, in some cases, the improvement in frequency has been as great as 50 per cent during the months or year following such a program. These reports come from textile mills, steel mills, mines, and many other industries. The records also show that the rate of accidents among the employees who are being or who have been trained drops off sharply when compared to previous years, and that the frequency of accidents in this group is substantially below the frequency for the group of employees not taking such training.

A well-organized first-aid program will have as its by-products several factors that are of assistance to the safety man in maintaining his program. Experience shows that trained men give thought to their own welfare in terms of physically handicapped men. It is also indicated that individuals taking such a course begin to measure the cost of accidents, both in money and in physical suffering to themselves.

A first-aid program gives those who study it a much better understanding of the construction of the human body and its limitations, and, of course, such a program prevents added injury through improper handling of employees following an accident.

First-aid instruction has been made available in virtually every community throughout the entire United States through the facilities of the American Red Cross. Industry, governing bodies, colleges, and youth organizations have come to realize the significance of such training. In addition to the Red Cross, the United States Bureau of Mines has been active for many years in promoting and conducting first-aid courses in the mining industry. It has also done much of this work in industrial areas.

Out of this normal desire to protect oneself and family against fatal injuries have arisen certain benefits. Undoubtedly, there will be a more widespread safety mindedness as a result of first-aid training. As science continues to develop atomic warfare to even greater devastating degrees, medical science will continue to advance, and popular interest in the knowledge of first aid will keep pace. Although the over-all effects and ever-present possibilities of modern warfare are generally realized, a considerable sales job must be done to get workmen to take and follow through with what is necessarily a strenuous course of study.

Experience has shown that workers may become interested in the first-aid problem and subsequent training through several approaches. As in any effort to convince an individual that he should buy or sell or do a certain thing, appeal must be made to the benefits he will receive as the result of his action. The idea of possessing knowledge that enables one to act properly in an emergency, in the plant, on the street or highway, or in case of injury or danger to one's own family or loved ones, is an appeal that can be used to convince workers that they should, for their own good, take part in such a training program.

One consideration that must be given careful attention in introducing this type of training in a plant is the selection of an instructor. Much of the success of the program will depend on the knowledge of the instructor and on his ability to teach what he knows to those in the class. Both the Red Cross and the Bureau of Mines are ready at all times to assist in the furnishing or training of instructors for this work.

The question of the amount of training that should be given is also of prime importance. In some companies, it is a general policy to give a quite complete course in first aid to virtually all employees and to make this a continuing program from year to year. Other companies, feeling that this complete training is inadvisable for all employees, take instead a middle-of-the-road plan under which a limited group of employees in each department is given full training, and other employees are given fundamental training in the basic treatment of certain types of injuries. In this secondary training are included instructions for treatment of shock, instructions on how to locate the pressure points and on the application of tourniquets, and instructions in at least one of the methods of artificial respiration. It would seem that this latter course is generally most advisable, particularly in large plants. The difficulty of maintaining classes for all employees is hardly warranted by the benefits that might result. On the other hand, each employee should have a general knowledge of what to do and what not to do in case of injury.

In order to maintain interest in first aid and to keep small groups highly trained over a period of years, the development of first-aid teams has been an important feature of the safety and first-aid program in many plants, particularly in mining areas. These teams are trained to a high degree of skill, and in serious emergencies are able to function almost as well as a doctor or a nurse. The men on the teams are selected because of their ability to meet and handle emergency situations, and their instruction covers every possible angle of first aid following any type of injury. Interest is maintained for the team members through first-aid contests. Under pre-arranged conditions, teams are required to compete with teams of other plants or other departments, and to demonstrate their efficiency in the handling of problems that are presented to them at the time of the con-test. Judges for these contests are furnished either through the American Red Cross or the Bureau of Mines.

The use of bulletin boards, small instruction cards, and bulletins from time to time to stimulate interest among an entire plant organization is advisable. Many plants post regularly on the bulletin board a chart showing the pressure points, as well as instructions on artificial resuscitation. These are simply means of maintaining interest in order to create a consciousness for safety. Motion pictures and film strips on such subjects as infection, first-aid methods, and so on, are available, and will be furnished on request by the National Safety Council.

Resuscitation

Three methods of resuscitation for use with those who have ceased breathing due to electric shock, drowning, gas inhalation, etc., have been widely used. The prone pressure (Schaefer) method, first successfully applied by Dr. Schaefer of the East Pittsburgh Works of the Westinghouse Electric and Manufacturing Company, has received general acceptance in the United States. The back pressure arm-lift (Holger Neilsen) method, developed in Norway, has received wide acceptance in Europe. The oldest method of all, named after its originator, Dr. Sylvester in England, has been increas-ingly superseded by one or the other of the above methods. Recently, a fourth method in which the victim is put through a rocking motion as on a rocking horse has received a great deal of attention. It has the serious drawback for most situations, however, of requiring special apparatus. Currently, the so-called "mouth to mouth" method has come into use.

Detailed directions for resuscitation procedures are contained in manuals published by the U. S. Bureau of Mines, the American Red Cross, and others. The following references will be helpful in any detailed study of the subject:

Gordon, Archer S., Frank Ramon, Max Sadove, and A. C. Ivy: "Manual Artificial Respiration, Comparison of Effectiveness of various methods on Apneic Normal Adults." *Journal of the American Medical Association,* **144**:1447–1452 (Dec. 23, 1950).

Comroe, Julius H., Jr. and R. D. Dripps: "Artificial Respiration." *Journal of the American Medical Association,* **130**:381–382 (1946).

Gordon, Archer, S., D. C. Fainer, and A. C. Ivy: "Artificial Respiration." *Journal of the American Medical Association,* **144**:1455–1464 (Dec. 23, 1950).

National Research Council, "Ad Hoc Conference on Manual Methods of Artificial Respiration," October 1, 1951.

Chapter Twenty-eight

Occupational Health Hazards

This is a very big subject. Anything approaching a reasonably complete treatment would require a massive volume. However a text on occupational safety fundamentals should include at least the basics of the control of health hazards also. That is the purpose of this chapter. The bibliography at its end is purposely limited to material for use with this text. It is far too limited to meet the needs of the research student.

The progress made in cutting work connected injuries due to accidents has been briefly described in Chapter One. The progress made in the prevention of work connected health injuries has also been great but largely of a different sort. Certain very serious occupational diseases that formerly killed or ruined the health of large numbers have been eliminated, or nearly so, or brought under control. Phosphorous poisoning, "phossy jaw," once the scourge of the match industry, has been eliminated from that industry. The elimination of mercury poisoning in hat manufacture is another example. Lead poisoning, once characteristic in the painter's trade, is now a rarity among painters because of the use of factory mixed paints and the substitution of non-toxic pigments for lead. Silicosis, known for centuries to be connected with mining and stone cutting, is being increasingly reduced by dust control. Many other worthwhile gains could be cited but these will suffice for our purpose.

The gains in the occupational disease field have been primarily the result of extensive research to develop the tremendous volume of detailed information needed to prevent or control the nearly numberless health hazards associated with the complexities of modern industry. The "know-how" of prevention thus gained, has been carried to the industrial firing line and applied with the help and advice of highly trained technicians. Many large plants added such men to their staffs but, for the most part, this service has been, and is, rendered by technicians of the U. S. Public

Health Service, state health departments or, in a few cases, state labor departments.

Available data are far too sketchy and indefinite to permit a reasonably reliable estimate of either the year by year totals of work connected health injuries or the gains that have been made in reducing them. The reports of the agencies administering workmen's compensation laws do give enough data to permit a very rough estimate. This shows that in a number of heavily industrialized states, New York, New Jersey, Ohio, Pennsylvania and Wisconsin, less than four percent of the compensated injuries in a given year were due to occupational disease. Presumably in the less heavily industrialized states the proportion would be even smaller. It is emphasized however, that such ratios do not afford an adequate measure of the seriousnes numerically, or in any other respect, of occupational disease in this nation, because:

1. Many cases go unreported because of the limited coverage of the compensation laws of many states.

2. Certain toxic substances and some environmental exposures may cause health injuries that do not manifest themselves for months or years and therefore go unreported and uncompensated.

3. The occupational origin of some types of work connected health injuries frequently escapes detection.

4. New hazards are continually coming into being through the development and use of new chemicals and other substances, new uses for old substances, new combinations of substances and process changes.

Whatever the actual figure, it is certain that despite the great progress that has been made in their prevention and control, preventable occupational health injuries still cause a huge total of suffering and hardship as well as substantial wage loss and medical expense to the victims each year. The cost to industry is obviously very substantial and, of course, in the last analysis, to the nation as a whole.

Although health hazards exist in some degree in all branches of industry, the more serious ones are found in establishments that manufacture, use, or process the more toxic or otherwise harmful substances. In many such establishments health hazards are far more serious and more of a problem than are accident hazards.

The human body is an exceedingly complex mechanism. Healthy life depends upon the continuous orderly operation of incompletely understood and highly intricate chemical and physical processes. Anything that interferes with any of these processes in any way may be injurious in some degree. The human system has many defenses against the health hazards that ordinary living presents, but it has less defense against the toxic substances used in industry. Furthermore, industrial processes may intensify familiar exposures, such as heat, radiant energy, non-toxic dusts, and the like, to such a degree that without suitable control measures the bodily defenses to combat ordinary exposures such as these are overcome and injury results. Work with animal or vegetable products may involve exposure to harmful germs, insects or parasites.

Occupational health hazards are usually classified as:

Chemical.* For the most part these hazards are presented by substances that directly attack body tissues, as poisons and corrosives. They may be gases, vapors, liquids, solids or combinations of these.

Biological. These hazards include a long list of infective agents such as those causing anthrax, tuberculosis, pneumonia, and typhoid fever, such fungi as those causing athletes foot, and parasites such as that causing trichinosis.

Harmful environmental conditions or exposures. These include radiant energy, excessive noise, repeated vibration and shock, extreme temperature and humidity, rapid temperature change and abnormal air pressure.

Manner of Attack

Injurious substances reach the body and cause injury by:

1. *Inhalation*—breathing.
2. *Skin contact*—absorption through the skin, direct attack on the skin.
3. *Ingestion*—swallowing.

Inhalation

Inhalation is by far the most important means by which injurious substances enter the human organism. The great majority of occupational poisonings result from breathing air containing toxic substances in the form of gases, vapors, mists, dusts or fumes or mixtures of two or more of these.

Carbon monoxide, non-toxic in the usual sense, but commonly referred to as toxic because of its killing ability, is taken up by the red blood cells some 300 times more readily than oxygen and the victim soon succumbs to oxygen starvation. Carbon monoxide is formed whenever any carbonaceous substance is burned under conditions that prevent sufficient oxygen from reaching it to oxidize all the carbon to carbon dioxide. The ever recurring asphyxiations from inadequately ventilated fuel burning

---

* The term chemical is used here in a very broad sense to include all non-living substances that can act on the body to cause injury.

devices of all sorts bespeak widespread ignorance and neglect of the seriousness of this hazard. It has been with us ever since men learned to make fire. Undoubtedly many cave men were victims of carbon monoxide.

In a sense, asphyxiation from breathing oxygen-deficient air belongs under this heading. It is an ever present hazard when men enter tanks, wells, silos or other closed places in which oxidation may have reduced the oxygen content of the air. The fermentation of vegetable matter is an oxidation process, hence the hazard of silos and wells. Many farmers have died in them.

Breathing dust containing silica (SiO_2) is the cause of silicosis, a very serious and incurable disease of the lungs long known as miner's phthisis. The silica causes the gradual development of tissues resembling scar tissue thus progressively reducing lung capacity. It also greatly reduces the normal defenses against tuberculosis. Asbestosis is a similar disease caused by breathing air containing asbestos dust.

Substances that are or can become airborne are classified as dusts, fumes, mists, vapors and gases.

Dusts. Solid particles fine enough to become airborne. In industry, dusts are formed mostly by crushing, grinding, abrading and handling operations and by rock drilling and blasting. Dusts do not tend to agglomerate except under electrostatic forces; they do not diffuse in air but settle under the influence of gravity.

Fumes. Solid particles formed by condensation from the gaseous state, often including a chemical reaction, particularly oxidation. Particle size is an important difference between fumes and dusts; fumes being extremely fine. They are, of course, formed as individual molecules but these agglomerate.

Mists. Airborne liquid droplets formed by condensation from the gaseous state or by breaking up a liquid by splashing, foaming or atomizing.

Vapors. The gaseous form of substances that are normally in the liquid or solid state and which can be changed to these states either by increasing the pressure or decreasing the temperature.

Gases. Normally formless fluids that occupy the space of enclosure and can be changed to the liquid or solid state only by both lowering the temperature and increasing the pressure.

Skin contact

In the manufacturing industries, skin diseases (dermatosis) accounts for the great majority of compensation claims for health injuries because so many of the chemicals used, processed or made can cause them. In a number of the heavily industrialized states such claims run about two thirds of the total.

The problem of prevention is continually being made more difficult, not only by the ever increasing use of such substances, but also by the continual creation of useful new ones. For example, the introduction and rapid increase in the use of epoxy resins brought numerous outbreaks of dermatosis due primarily to the amine hardeners or catalysts. An older example is furnished by chrome plating particularly in the automobile industry. Contact with chromic acid or its salts can cause skin ulcers or dermatoses or both.

Many solvents, for example trichlorethylene, dissolve the natural fats the normal skin has, causing it to become dry and chapped and also reducing its normal resistance to bacterial infection. Bacterial agents can also gain entrance through minor abrasions and lacerations to cause bleeding or pain or both.

Corrosive chemicals, such as strong acids and alkalies, attack the skin directly. High concentrations can almost instantly cause chemical burns resulting in tissue destruction and permanent scars or disfiguration.

A few toxic substances can poison by absorption through the skin. If the area of contact is large some of them, aniline, carbon disulfide and tetraethyl lead for example, can cause death unless quickly removed from the skin. Some substances can cause chronic injury by continued absorption of small amounts through the skin.

Ingestion

Chronic poisoning can occur if even very small amounts of certain substances are ingested daily. Among these are lead, arsenic, mercury and some of the newer insecticides. When dealing with such substances as these, every precaution must be taken to prevent their entry into the digestive tract. Frequent washing of the hands, especially before eating or smoking, is important. Food should never be kept nor eaten where such toxic substances are used or handled or processed. Chewing tobacco is likely to become contaminated. All who work with such substances should bathe at the end of each shift and make a complete change of clothing. The work clothing should be kept separate from the street clothing and laundered frequently.

Biological agents

Health hazards associated with exposure to biological agents have not received attention at all comparable to that given chemical and physical agents. Probably the chief reason for this is that the illnesses these agents cause are so symptomatically similar to those of non-occupational origin that their true source is often overlooked. It is now known that certain bacteria, fungi, and parasites are the cause of much occupational disease. Workmen in slaughtering and meatpacking plants handling cattle infected with the bacteria of brucellosis (Bang's disease) may acquire it. Many workmen handling and processing unsterilized wool or hair from certain foreign countries have contracted anthrax. Athletes foot is a common fungal infection, but though annoying and sometimes painful, it is seldom disabling. Another fungus which thrives in chicken droppings, causes histoplasmosis, a disease that is difficult to cure and likely to involve serious prolonged illness. Parasites such as mites can cause dermatosis, "grain" and "cheese" itch, for example. While these diseases are seldom disabling, they can cause extreme discomfort.

Harmful environmental exposures

While the great majority of the serious health injuries in industry are due to work with poisons or other hazardous substances, a substantial total of health impairments are due to adverse environmental conditions. For the most part, these are cumulatively damaging rather than disabling. Some, however, can cause lingering disability or death; X-rays can cause cancer or sterility; excessive heat can cause heat stroke; excessive exposure to ultraviolet light can cause permanent visual impairment.

The environmental exposures that, when sufficiently unfavorable, can cause injury include:

1. Radiant energy.
2. Excessive noise.
3. Excessive vibration and shock.
4. Extremes of temperature and humidity.
5. Abnormal air pressure.

Radiant energy

Ionizing radiation. For convenience, radiation by discrete particles is discussed under this heading together with the highly penetrating forms of radiant energy (X-rays, gamma rays, cosmic ray photons), because all can cause tissue damage by ionization. Radiant energy is classified according to wave length and frequency.

The extent and seriousness of injury from exposure to such radiation depends upon the type and nature of exposure, the kind of radiation and individual susceptibility. The degree of injury may range from very slight to very severe, transient or quickly fatal. Only persons with special training in this field should attempt to evaluate or control exposures to ionizing radiation, because the measurement and interpretation is far too complicated and complex to be attempted without it. The continually increasing use of radioactive isotopes and X-rays in industry is correspondingly increasing the importance of this hazard.

Ultraviolet radiation. Ultraviolet light is the cause of sunburn. The degree of injury can range from a slight reddening of the skin to serious burns, blisters and inflammation as well as serious eye injury. In industry, the chief sources of ultra-violet radiation are arc welding and ultraviolet generators used in the inspection of castings for flaws and those used as sterilizers, in hospitals, for example.

Visible light. Visible light is not in itself a health hazard, but good lighting is so important to the safety and efficiency of workers that it is proper to mention it here. Lighting should be adequate in both quantity and quality to permit the efficient performance of each specific task without eye strain. The quality of light is as important as the quantity. Glare can reduce accuracy of seeing and contribute to eye strain. So can flickering and shadows.

Infrared radiation. Radiant heat is energy of wave lengths next longer those of visible light. Like light it can be reflected from certain surfaces, a property that is useful in limiting radiant heat exposures. It does not raise the temperature of the air it passes through appreciably, but does that of surfaces that absorb it. Thus the body heat of a worker is increased by exposure to such sources of infrared radiation as molten steel, heat treating furnaces and the like. Infrared radiation can also cause eye damage, necessitating suitable eye protection for work about such sources.

Microwaves. These (used in radar, long range communication, etc.) can, if sufficiently intense, cause tissue destruction through overheating. Since like gamma rays and X-rays, the intensity decreases in proportion to the square of the distance from the source, prevention is by shielding or isolation or both.

Noise

Although hearing loss has long been recognized as a concomitant of work involving continued exposure to high noise levels, as for example in boiler shops, it was only after a number of the states accepted such hearing loss as a compensable type of injury that serious attention was given to its prevention. Substantial progress has been made toward that end but much still remains to be done. Sound levels and exposures that can cause hearing loss have been fairly well established and means of control adequate for most industrial operations have been worked out, but these are not sufficient for such extremely intense noise as is produced in jet engine testing and in ammunition proving, for example.

Noise has been aptly defined as unwanted sound. Sound is a wave motion in the air causing small rapid variations of air pressure as it progresses outward from its source. Long continued exposure to excessive noise can cause temporary or permanent loss of hearing, nervousness or fatigue, separately or in combination. The degree of injury depends upon the intensity of the noise, its frequency range, the duration of exposure and personal susceptibility.

Sound beyond the range of the human ear (supersonic) can cause injury if intense enough. Research scientists working with ultrasonic generators have suffered hand and finger lesions, nausea, dizziness, loss of equilibrium and ear pain. Insects and mice have been killed by exposure to an intense ultrasonic beam.

Vibration and shock

Long continued intense vibration and repeated physical shocks can cause nerve injury and inflammation of tissues surrounding tendons, bones and joints. Example: dead fingers or stiff or sore joints often suffered by the operators of steam and air hammers.

Extreme temperature and humidity

This category of physical condition probably causes more complaints among workers than all others combined. Temperature and humidity extremes cause discomfort, increased fatigue and irritability and reduce the quantity and quality of the work output. Exposure to temperature that overtaxes the ability of the body's thermoregulatory system soon causes disturbances in the circulatory system, commonly known as heat stroke or heat exhaustion. They can be serious or even fatal. Frostbite is an ever present hazard in work in low temperatures, as in subzero food storage rooms and experimental test chambers. Sudden and abrupt changes in temperature and humidity can have deleterious effects on workers.

The more important factors that determine an individual's reaction to adverse temperature and humidity conditions are: dry bulb air temperature, wet bulb air temperature, radiant heat intensity, air motion, degree of exertion, type of clothing and acclimatization.

Abnormal air pressure

Some nitrogen is always absorbed by the blood from the air breathed in; the higher the pressure the greater the amount absorbed. This excess nitrogen is released again as the pressure is reduced and passes out through the lungs but if the air pressure drop is too rapid, it will form bubbles in the blood stream that may block the blood flow, particularly in the smaller blood vessels. This is the cause of caisson disease, commonly known as the bends. Symptoms are cramps, muscle and joint pain; in severe cases, even asphyxia and death. Prevention lies in limiting such exposure to workmen in excellent physical condition and in strict adherence to the standard schedule of decompression rates geared to air pressure and length of time under air pressure.

If, on the other hand, the air pressure is reduced sufficiently below normal atmospheric conditions, the blood cannot absorb enough oxygen for adequate oxygenation and anoxia, the so-called "altitude sickness," results. It may be acute when one ascends rapidly to high altitudes such as flying without supplied oxygen, or it may become chronic from long continued exposure to very high mountain altitudes. Tin mining in Bolivia furnishes a notable example of this.

It has long been known that persons with weak hearts should avoid high altitudes, the reason, of course, being that the heart has to work harder to meet the body's demand for oxygen. Another hazard of reduced air pressure is that it increases susceptibility to toxic gases, notably carbon monoxide.

Manner of attack

The factors that determine whether or not health injury may result from any given exposure can be stated fairly simply, but the making of an analysis adequate for an appraisal of the hazard and determination of the proper corrective action usually requires the services of an experienced industrial hygienist engineer. However, any person reasonably familiar with industrial processes and the kind of hazards they may involve, can readily learn to recognize conditions likely to spell danger. Also, he can learn to improve or correct many of these conditions by the use of well established procedures or by the use of devices of proved effectiveness or both. He can also learn to recognize conditions that make it advisable to call upon the specialist and also to maintain the effectiveness of the control measures prescribed by the latter. The purpose of this section is to present in briefest form the basic principles in the making of health hazard appraisals.

The nature and degree of any given potential exposure, whether or not injury results, will be determined by:

1. The nature of the substance or potentially injurious influence involved.
2. The intensity of exposure.
3. The susceptibility of the person exposed.

Nature of substance or exposure

The nature of the substance or substances involved is of first importance. A very large and steadily increasing variety of substances capable of causing health injury is being used in industry. The degree of hazard these offer varies from the mildest to the most acute, but adequate safeguards can be thrown about the use of any or all of them. To do this, however, it is necessary to know the properties of each substance and its manner of attack on the human system. That brings up the next point, before any new substance is brought into use, its properties should be thoroughly determined so that all necessary safeguards can be applied. The employer making use of a possibly hazardous substance new to him should obtain full information as to its potential hazards and apply suitable control measures. The responsibility is, of course, shared by the manufacturer of the substance and the employer who uses it. Close cooperation between these two is essential.

If the potentially harmful exposure is environmental (not due to some substance), the appraiser must still consider its nature. While there is no novelty in excessive noise for example, our ever developing industry occasonally creates new noise complexes requiring changes in control measures for best results.

Severity of exposure

The more intense the exposure, the more quickly injury will result. This applies particularly to air contamination. Practically every toxic substance can become airborne in some degree in the form of dust, vapor, fume or gas. Therefore it is vitally important when dealing with the more toxic substances, to maintain a close watch of their concentration in the air of the workplace and keep it at all times within limits known to be safe, or when that is not practicable, apply suitable safeguards, i.e., respiratory protectors. For many substances, severity of exposure is determined by their concentration in liquid solution. The factor of intensity is of major importance in such environmental exposures as sound, heat and humidity.

Length of exposure

Length of exposure is governing in two ways—for a single exposure and for repeated exposures. Some substances, for example, carbon monoxide in non-lethal exposures produce little or no lasting damage. With such substances the shortest exposure that may injure for a given concentration furnishes a fairly satisfactory guidepost for safety. This of course, assumes in addition a reasonable allowance on the side of safety to guard against errors of measurement. Most of the highly toxic substances are more or less cumulative in nature; that is, part of the substance taken into the body will remain for a time and if the rate of intake from daily or frequent exposures exceeds the rate of elimination, injury will occur that may be permanent even though the victim is removed from any further exposure. With substances of this type both the single exposure and the sum of a series of exposures must be considered in determining the hazard. Lead and Mercury are familiar poisons of this type.

Personal susceptibility

The resistance the body offers to specific substances varies as among individuals. Also for any given individual, it may vary from time to time. This variability is spoken of as personal susceptibility and is particularly important in the field of dermatosis. Some few individuals are very susceptible to certain substances or to extended exposures to others. Sometimes a single severe exposure will produce sensitivity in a person previously showing normal or even superior resistance. Rhus Toxica, the active principle in poison ivy, is a familiar example.

Measuring air contamination

It is obvious that the damage done by a given toxic substance will depend chiefly upon the amount of it taken into the system. Therefore the weight of it in a given volume of air will constitute a measure of the hazard involved in breathing air containing it. But for non-toxic dusts, notably silica and asbestos, the important factor is the number of dust particles tiny enough to get into the minute air cells of the lungs. Therefore, the hazard of such dusts is measured by counting the number of particles smaller than 10 microns (1/2500 in.) in size because those larger than this are relatively few; they settle quickly and if inhaled are, for the most part, caught by the tiny vibratile hair-like "cilia" that line the lung passages and are finally coughed out.

Dust counts are given in terms of millions of particles per cubic foot of air. Surprisingly large numbers of particles are present in even cleanest air. Counts of one half million or more are normal in homes and in buildings of ordinary occupancy; 100 millions or more are not uncommon in processes in which solid materials are being ground or crushed dry. Anything above 50 million particles per cubic foot of air is generally accepted as unsafe for even the most innocuous dusts. Five million particles is considered the maximum allowable for continuous exposure to dust containing over 40% free silica. Dust that is visible in the absence of a beam of sunlight, or a similarly intense ray or light, indicates a high dust count, hence the common saying among industrial hygienists "If you can see the dust there is too much of it." That is not an infallible guide, but safety is definitely on the side of eliminating dust that is visible without the aid of a ray of sunlight.

Gas and vapor concentrations are measured by means suited to the nature of the substance in question, for example, combustible gases. Instruments are available that give readings of concentration, their basis being the heat produced by the combustion of the gas or vapor. They must, of course, be calibrated for the substance in question. They will measure exceedingly small concentrations and can be made to give an alarm, operate furnace controls and the like. Carbon monoxide control systems in highway tunnels and garages use this principle to control the ventilating fans.

The health hazard survey

The obvious first step in appraising the health hazards in a given establishment is to determine which ones are likely or possible. Only technically qualified persons should undertake to make such a survey or determine the corrective action needed or advisable. Also such personnel should be available for overall guidance of at least the more difficult and highly specialized procedures where high hazard substances or exposures are involved. The survey normally involves the following steps:

1. Securing a complete list of the substances processed or used.

2. Making a study of operations and processes involved to find the hazard points.

3. Determination of the nature of each of the products, byproducts and wastes involved.

4. Analysis of the possibilities of explosion, fire breakout, or other untoward occurrences.

Purchasing department and stockroom lists will, in the well managed plant, include all materials and products brought in from outside. Sometimes however, such lists are not complete due to the retail buying of certain supplies. Retail purchases are likely to include paints, solvents, cleaners and the like for occasional use. The health hazard possibilities involved may be considerable and should not be overlooked. Any toxic substances should be labeled in accordance with the Standards of the Manufacturing Chemists Association.

The content of products sold under trade names, sometimes offers a problem. Frequently the list of ingredients is not given on the container or in the literature accompanying it. It is important to obtain it from the manufacturer however, especially in the case of such substances as paints, cleaners, solvents, inks, and pigments, whose use may expose workers to toxic, corrosive or irritating substances.

Full knowledge of the materials used having been obtained, the next step is to examine the processes and procedures for possibly harmful exposures. Wherever dust, gases, vapors, mists, or fumes are produced, injury is always possible if air contamination is not kept within safe limits for the substances involved. The handling and production involves the likelihood of spills, fuming, splashing, and vaporizing. Manual handling of toxic, corrosive or irritating substances offers specific hazards. The investigator should set down in suitable detail each hazard point found. With these located, the means of appraisal of the extent of the hazard and the determination of the need for correction will depend upon the nature of the substance or the type of the possibly detrimental exposure.

No analysis would be complete without consideration of all the by-products and wastes involved. Particularly in the chemical industries these may introduce hazards other than those connected with the source materials or their toxicity may be greater.

The possibilities of failure to maintain full control of processes and operations should be considered. This will include overheating, explosions, fire breakouts, failure of control devices, failure or reduced effectiveness of exhaust equipment, interrupted power supply, and any other factor that might unexpectedly make a normally safe situation hazardous.

Methods of prevention

Nine principal methods are used for the elimination or control of industrial health hazards, namely:

1. Substitution of less toxic material or change of process.

2. Enclosure of the hazardous process (with automatic operation).

3. Isolation of the hazardous process from the remainder of the plant with special protection for workers necessarily included in the area isolated.

4. Local exhaust ventilation.

5. General ventilation.

6. Wet methods.

7. The use of personal protective devices.

8. Decreasing the daily exposure through short work periods.

9. Medical supervision.

In many cases, no one method is adequate and two or more applied in suitable combination are necessary.

Substitution

The plant materials survey, if properly done, will have yielded a complete list of the toxic materials used, processed or produced. In each case the possibility of substituting a less hazardous substance should be considered. The elimination of the highly toxic white phosphorus in the manufacture of matches is a historic example. Other well known ones are the substitution of compounds of titanium and zinc for those of lead in white paints, the use of solvents of relatively low toxicity in place of benzol, and the use of steel shot in place of sharp sand in abrasive cleaning.

The reverse possibility should always be guarded against, namely, the substitution of a more toxic substance. This may come about through a desire to save expense or processing time without adequate consideration of the hazards possibly involved. A well publicized example was furnished by the fatal poisoning of employees of a daily newspaper due to the substitution of a solvent containing benzol for a less toxic solvent in order to shorten drying time. The exhaust system, adequate for the less toxic ink solvent was inadequate for one containing a substantial benzol content. The fatal mistake was failure to specify a low level of toxicity when the order for the quick drying ink was placed.

Sometimes a substitution of process or a change in process is practical to lessen the hazard. The application of paint or other protective coatings by dipping instead of spraying is one example; the use of factory mixed paints instead of mixing on the job is another.

Enclosure

Many processes involving the use of toxic substances can be completely enclosed during all or the more hazardous part of the operation to eliminate or greatly reduce, the escape of atmospheric contaminants. A slight negative pressure within the enclosure, where practical, will protect against leaks. Loading and emptying should be automatic or by mechanical means wherever possible. If this is not practical one or more, if necessary, of the methods listed above should be used. The approach should always be one of hazard elimination to the maximum possible extent before resorting to the use of personal protective equipment, an essentially defensive measure of limited reliability. For example, the fully enclosed fully automatic dry cleaning machine for clothing practically eliminates the factor of hazard from a formerly very unhealthful kind of work and at the same time enables a far wider choice of solvents.

Many processes require enclosure for efficient operation, for example a system of lines and tanks containing hazardous gases or liquids. Here the importance of preventing wasteful leaks works on the side of safety. The sand blast booth used for cleaning castings furnishes an example of the use of negative pressure to keep any leakage inward and thus keep the dust out of the workroom.

Many processes in which enclosure is not a necessity, or is not advantageous to production, should nevertheless be enclosed where practicable. In this class are many mixing, screening, and grinding operations, such as heat treating and cleaning. The test in each case is—does the process or operation give off, at any stage, any substance that can contaminate the workroom air harmfully. If so, can it be completely enclosed? If not can a partial enclosure combined with exhaust be applied? Examples —Dry grinding mills, rubber compounding mills, cyaniding kettles, plating tanks, lead pots, degreasers.

Isolation of process

Some types of hazardous processes may endanger workmen other than those directly concerned with the process or operation. Such processes can be isolated in a separate building or in a carefully sealed-off area with suitable specialized protection for the personnel required to operate it. Operations are made automatic as far as possible and the personnel are thoroughly trained in safe practice, not only for day by day operation but for emergency situations as well. That the thoroughgoing application of this approach can bring injury rates down to figures approaching zero in even the intrinsically most hazardous kinds of processes has been amply proved in the manufacture of, for example, explosives, prussic acid and tetraethyl lead.

Local exhaust ventilation

The survey will have located the sources of air contamination, if any, and identified the contaminants. If an escaping substance is of a highly toxic nature, for example, lead fumes, mercury vapor, or hydrogen sulfide gas, the aim should be to prevent *any* escape. If it is non-toxic, a nuisance dust for example, the comfort of the personnel, the prevention of damage to machinery and equipment and the maintenance of good housekeeping will be governing factors.

Where complete enclosure is not possible, local exhaust ventilation is next best. Since complete enclosure is either not practical or not necessary for the greater proportion of the processes and operations that yield air contaminants, local exhaust is by far the most widely used control method. Most air contaminants are given off by operations confined to relatively small areas, for example grinding and buffing, spray painting, plating and dip tanks, and many mixing and blending processes.

The almost endless diversity of such operations and the wide range of problems they present make the services of competent specialists particularly important. Failure to secure such services explains the frequency of faulty exhaust installations. Commonly found defects are, failure to trap and carry away all the contaminant, ducts subject to plugging or choking, incorrect air velocity, failure to design for ease of repair and maintenance without interference with operation, and unduly expensive operation and maintenance.

All such equipment requires systematic checking and maintenance if it is to continue to function effectively. Particular care should be given to this equipment; the health of all those it is designed to protect depends upon its faultless functioning. Any well managed plant maintains a system of preventive maintenance based on a definite inspection schedule. The frequency and detail of each inspection will be determined by the nature of the equipment, the basic purpose being to discover the evidence of wear and tear before damaging defects develop. A properly planned and efficiently operated system of preventive maintenance is always cheaper in the long run than one based on the idea of repairing breakdowns. Without preventive maintenance the first evidence of breakdown or other defects in an exhaust system is likely to be a case, or even an outbreak, of occupational disease among the plant personnel, particularly if the substances involved are relatively toxic.

While the design of exhaust equipment requires a high degree of technical competence, and should be undertaken only by qualified engineers, certain principles are so generally applicable as to justify their mention here:

1. To be effective, the air flow to the exhaust duct must include the entire area liberating the contaminating substance.

2. The shape and size of the hood (and baffles), its position in relation to the work and the air velocity used, should be such as to trap all the contaminants produced and carry them into the exhaust duct and away.

3. The air velocity over the area where the contaminant must be picked up is the significant velocity. In the case of dusts or other solids, the minimum velocity in the ducts must be sufficient to prevent settling-out. Sharp corners, irregularities, or other conditions that cause air turbulence reduce efficiency and should be avoided.

4. The air flow should be away from the breathing zone of the operator. For example, plating tanks should, in general, be exhausted at the back, the air pulled backward over the surface of the plating solution to the duct at the back.

5. Advantage should be taken of gravity, where practicable. That is, heavy dusts, fumes, and vapors should be exhausted downwards. When heated air is produced, as in cyanide pots, furnaces, etc., it should usually be exhausted upward and backward in order to get the benefit of the heat-induced draft. It should not be drawn directly upward unless the operator's station is far enough away so that the contaminants will not be drawn through any part of his breathing zone.

6. Stack (chimney) suction unaided by forced draft, because of its unreliability, is seldom if ever adequate when toxic contaminants are involved. In any given installation, the amount of suction produced will be affected by the velocity and direction of the wind, the barometric pressure, and the amount and temperature of the heated air produced. Every exhaust system should have at all times a margin of capacity above the minimum necessary to remove the maximum of contaminating substances. Only forced draft can assure this.

Air exhausted from productive processes should always be freed of any objectionable contaminants before it is discharged outside, either directly or through stacks, else it will contribute to atmospheric pollution, an already serious problem in many areas of this country. Also some contaminants may have considerable value if collected. These considerations have led to the development of various types of collecting equipment whose purpose is to remove the contaminant from the air exhausted and permit its recovery or harmless disposal. These collectors are of four types: cyclones, cloth filters, air washers and electric precipitators.

Cyclones depend upon the tendency of solids carried by air to settle out if the air velocity is reduced or its direction of flow changed. By carrying the main exhaust duct into a large chamber designed to slow the air down as much as possible and at the same time give it a whirling motion, the heavier particles settle into a collection space at the bottom which can be emptied from time to time. Cyclone collectors, however, are not effective for very fine particles and therefore are not adequate for toxic dusts. They are widely used in the wood and textile industries.

The *cloth filter* is what its name implies. The air is passed through filter bags much like those in the ordinary household vacuum cleaner. The bags hang with open end downward so that when the dust builds up sufficiently it can fall into a clean-out space below. Also the framework supporting the bags is, or can be, shaken periodically to loosen the collected dust. Frequent inspection and good maintenance are necessary as even a few very small holes in the fabric will reduce the effectiveness considerably.

Air washers remove the dust by thoroughly wetting it. The air is passed through a series of passages continuously drenched by a fine spray or mist of water. The dust is carried off in the stream of water or collected in catchment basins as a sludge. This method is most effective with soluble dusts and heavy dusts. Some dusts, for example, coal dusts, are very difficult to wet and hard to deal with by this means.

Electric precipitators depend upon the fact that dust particles that can be made to pick up a charge of electricity will thus be attracted to an oppositely charged surface. Electric precipitators are widely used in steam power plants and in the cement, paper, and chemical industries. They are also used to collect sulfurous and hydrofluoric mists.

Wet methods have been proved outstandingly successful in rock drilling. Water is forced through the drill bits, wetting the dust and keeping it from becoming airborne. In the Vermont granite industry where silicosis was traditional among drillers, this method has reduced average dust concentrations from 130 million to less than 2 million particles of dust per cubic foot of air. Wet methods are also used extensively in foundries, by cleaning castings with high-pressure water stream, by keeping the moulding sand moist, by wetting castings before shakeout and by occasionally sprinkling floors.

Personal protective devices

Personal protective devices have a serious weakness—they do nothing to reduce the hazard. They merely set up a defense against it and any failure of this defense means immediate exposure to the hazard. The fact that many protective devices can be or become ineffective without the knowledge of the wearer is particularly serious.

Despite its general availability and relatively low cost, protective equipment should never be allowed to supersede the elimination of the hazard. Employers who are not adequately safety minded are constantly tempted to rely on personal protective equipment instead of applying practical means of hazard reduction. This is particularly true in the case of air contamination.

Respiratory protective devices

These devices are discussed in considerable detail in the preceding chapter but a few points about their use are so important that, even though somewhat repetitive, they are briefly discussed below.

All respirators have two drawbacks in common; they are more or less uncomfortable to wear and they reduce the wearer's efficiency. If the lessened efficiency could be measured in terms of cost it would frequently, perhaps usually, show that very substantial expenditures would be justified if the hazard could thereby be eliminated.

It is vitally important that the respiratory equipment used be correct for the hazard involved. Deaths and near deaths have not infrequently occurred because of dependence in lethal atmospheres on respiratory protective equipment not suited to the hazard. Examples: the use of filter-type respirators in air containing carbon monoxide, depending upon a canister-type respirator when there is an oxygen deficiency. The fact that only respirators bearing Bureau of Mines approval for the specific hazard or hazards involved should be used is discussed in Chapter Twetny-nine. It is repeated here for emphasis.

In the event a hazard cannot be eliminated, an orderly procedure should be followed including at least the following steps:

1. Identify the substance or substances against which protection is necessary.

2. Obtain full knowledge of the hazards that each such substance offers and its significant properties.

3. Determine what, if any, personal characteristics and capabilities are essential for the safe use of the protective devices and procedures required.

4. Determine what facilities are needed for proper maintenance.

5. From these considerations, select the type respirator that will surely provide the protection needed.

The correct use of all types of respiratory protective equipment requires careful attention to many details and the unfailing observance of rules of safe procedure. Full details of approved respirators should be obtained from the manufacturers.

No matter how well a respiratory protective device is designed and made, unless it is maintained in good condition, it may fail to protect. Once the need for and type of equipment has been determined, provision should be made for careful and unfailing maintenance. This includes inspection, repairs, replacement of used filters, etc., cleaning and sterilization.

Since a respirator is uncomfortable when worn for extended periods, personnel must fully realize the need of the protection or they will not wear it faithfully. Important factors in getting full employee cooperation in this respect are:

1. Recourse to respiratory equipment only after every effort has been made to eliminate the hazard.
2. Explaining the situation fully to the workmen involved.
3. Careful fitting of respirators.
4. Adequate provisions for maintenance and cleanliness.
5. Careful instruction as to use.

6. Intelligent, fully informed supervision.

7. Sterilization of equipment before reissue.

Protective wearing apparel

In all work with substances that attack through the skin or attack the skin itself, protective clothing should be worn to prevent, or at least lessen, skin contact. It must be suited to the nature of the substance, the exposure involved, and the kind of work done. The material of which the garment is made must be resistant to attack by the substance in question, must not absorb it to any extent or be easily penetrated by it, must be cleanable, and have at least reasonably good wearing qualities. Comfort is of considerable importance and, for women wearers, appearance is also important.

Protective creams and lotions

There are a number of barrier creams on the market designed to protect the skin against substances that can attack or penetrate it. Their effectiveness varies, but properly chosen and correctly used they can be very helpful in preventing injury. They should never be relied on in lieu of positive means of preventing or reducing skin contact, but since some contact with at least the hands and arms is inevitable when working with any substance, whatever degree of protection they give is decidedly worthwhile.

In each instance it is essential that:

1. A cream or lotion effective against the substance or substances involved be chosen upon competent medical advice.

2. Each of the employees involved be carefully instructed as to the value of the protection and in the proper application.

3. Adequate facilities be provided for washing and for change of clothes necessary to eliminate any contact with the substance in question during off-time.

4. The workers practice careful personal hygiene; at the very least each one should wash thoroughly before eating and at the end of each shift.

Limiting the period of exposure

As a last resort, where other methods do not reduce or control the hazard sufficiently for safety, the daily period of exposure can be limited.

Work in compressed air furnishes an excellent example of this. Schedules of maximum permissible length of period under the air and corresponding decompression times have been established. The higher the pressure the shorter the permissible time under it and the longer the decompression period required. Close medical supervision is necessary coupled with careful selection of personnel.

The same principle is applied in work with certain toxic substances and with ionizing radiation both by limiting daily exposure and by rotating the workmen between hazardous and hazard-free jobs on a schedule suited to the needs of the work and the nature of the substance or exposure involved.

Medical supervision

Medical supervision is an essential part of any adequate program of prevention when such relatively high-hazard substances as lead, mercury, arsenic, benzol, and carbon disulfide are involved. In fact, it has become clear that a good degree of medical supervision is of substantial benefit to both employer and employees in at least the great majority of industrial establishments. While serious health hazards are limited to relatively few plants, milder hazards are widespread throughout industry and constitute a considerable drain on the health of large numbers of workers. Although in most cases these are non-disabling, a reasonable degree of medical supervision can eliminate most of them with substantial benefit to both employer and employees.

Maintenance, housekeeping and education

These three items are interdependent, for it is not possible to have an effective maintenance program unless the housekeeping is good and there is good worker cooperation. For example, if paint is allowed to accumulate on the blades of the exhaust fan in a spray booth, the amount of air exhausted will be reduced, perhaps below a safe level and probably increasing the fire hazard as well. If the thermostat on a degreaser fails or is broken, excessive concentrations of the cleaning fluid vapor may quickly build up in the work area, unless prompt repairs are made.

Housekeeping also is a very important control measure. Dust allowed to accumulate on floors, machinery, and beams may be disseminated to all parts of the plant. In the case of toxic dusts, such as lead, many more workers may be exposed to hazardous amounts with an inadequate cleaning schedule than there is any justification for. A well-managed plant will maintain a regular cleaning schedule using vacuum cleaning supplemented by wet methods where necessary; avoidance of stirring up dust being the prime consideration.

A definite program of worker education is essential to maximum results. Knowledge by the workers of proper operating practice is essential if the engineering controls are to yield the results for which they were designed. For example, improper loading or unloading of a degreaser will defeat the purpose of the controls and result in contamination of the work area. Workers should not only know the safe and proper procedures but also the reasons for each of them. This applies particularly to work with toxic substances and to the wearing of personal protective equipment where that is necessary or advisable.

Prevention fundamentals for management

The following items are offered to managerial personnel as being of fundamental importance in the prevention of occupational disease:

1. Know the nature of each of the potentially hazardous substances used in your establishment and the significance of each of the exposures that may be involved.

2. Set up and maintain the specific control measures indicated.

3. Make assignment of responsibility for all phases of the preventive program.

4. Establish contact with state, Federal, or other available technical services in the occupational disease field.

5. Make definite provision to insure that the disease possibilities involved in the use of new substances, changes in make-up of familiar substances, changes in process or work methods and the like, will in each instance receive adequate advance consideration.

Chapter Twenty-nine

Personal Protective Equipment

Equipment in great variety to protect any part of the body is commercially available and at moderate cost. In a sense, this is a hindrance to safety for employers who are not keenly safety-minded and are constantly tempted to rely upon the use of such equipment in lieu of hazard elimination. This is particularly apt to be the case with respirators. It is so easy and relatively inexpensive to provide respirators for men exposed to dusts, fumes and many other air contaminants that it is often difficult to get adequate attention given to the ultimately cheaper and sounder approach of contaminant elimination.

It is emphasized that personal protective devices should always be thought of as the "last thin line of defense." Both employers and workers should realize keenly that the failure of such a device, or failure to use it, exposes one immediately to the hazard in question. A point repeatedly made in preceding chapters is that the first step in injury prevention should be hazard elimination to the maximum extent practically possible. This applies with particular force to air contamination. Protective devices do nothing to reduce the hazard; they merely set up a frail barrier against it, and this must be constantly maintained, watched, and guarded. In light of this fact, even very substantial expenditures to eliminate the hazard will usually, in the long run, prove to be not only the safest way but also the most efficient and cheapest. All of this emphasizes the importance of developing the fullest possible employee cooperation in the use of the protective devices.

It is important too that the safety map (safety enginer if that be his title) have a thorough knowledge of the types of protective devices and equipment available for protection against each of the various hazards and exposures involved.

The appraisal of health hazards, briefly discussed in the preceding chapter, will disclose and evaluate the hazards, enabling decision as to the proper corrective action and, finally, will show where personal protective equipment must be relied upon to afford protection against the hazards that remain after all practically possible corrective action has been taken. Many safety men also conduct special surveys of eye hazards and in some cases, foot and head hazards also, especially after significant changes in operating methods or procedures. They not only find such surveys valuable in bringing overlooked hazards to light, but also in promoting employee interest and cooperation.

Personal protective equipment can be classified as follows:

Head protection.
> *Hard hats*
> *Hair protection*
> *Hearing protectors*

Face and eye protection.
> *Goggles and spectacles*
> *Helmets and hand shields*
> *Face shields*

Respiratory protective equipment.
> *Air purifying*
> *Air supplying*

Hand, foot and leg protectors.
> *Gloves and hand leathers*
> *Safety shoes*
> *Foot guards*

Protective clothing.

Head protection

Head injuries are of particular importance in certain branches of industry, for example, logging (falling branches), construction, mining, and ship-building. Even in these industries, however, near elimination of head injuries can be achieved by the unfailing wearing of the so-called "hard hat." Hats that will afford full protection against all but the heaviest sort of blow, yet are comfortable to wear, are commercially available. Getting their full acceptance by workmen has been, and still is, a problem in work where the degree of hazard is not obviously high. Coal miners, daily facing the hazard of falling rocks, gave them good acceptance as soon as they became convinced that such hats could in fact afford worthwhile protection. But in some other kinds of work, construction for example, it has been and still is, an uphill fight, partly because the hazard is less and partly because of the roving by construction workers from job to job and employer to employer.

The problem of how best to get a well-established habit changed is involved also. Men accustomed through boyhood and beyond to going bareheaded do not take easily to the wearing of any form of head covering. Others addicted to caps or western style hats do not want to change. Actually though, properly fitted protective hats are very comfortable to wear, particularly those made of plastic-impregnated fabric. They are neat in appearance, extremely durable, yet light in weight, well balanced, provided with replaceable sweat bands and adjustable as to fit. Air spaces between the sweat bands and the crown makes for coolness in hot weather.

Classes of head protectors

There are two types—hats with fullbrim and brimless caps with peak. There are three classes as follows:

Class A—*General service.* For protection against impact. They are used chiefly in mining, tunneling, shipbuilding, lumbering and building construction. They protect against voltages up to 600.

Class B—*Utility service.* For protection against impact and high voltages. They are in general use by linesmen.

Class C—*Special service.* For protection against light impact, such as bumping the head against a fixed object. They are usually made of aluminum, hence should not be worn where there is any electrical hazard.

Construction requirements

Purchasers should specify compliance with the provisions of ASA Code Z2.1-1959. Description and test requirements are:

Shell. The shell shall be of one-piece seamless construction designed to resist impact from falling materials.

Sweatband and crown straps. These when properly laced or assembled must form a cradle for supporting the protector on the wearers' heads. The crown straps help absorb the force of impact. They are designed to permit a clearance of not less than 1¼ inches between the shell and the skull of the wearer. Crown strap assemblies for use in Class B protectors contain no electrical conducting material. Protectors should never be worn with the cradle removed, for that greatly reduces the ability to absorb the impact force.

Insulation resistance. Although designed to protect against voltages of not over 600, Class A protectors are required to withstand 2200 volts, alternating current, for 1 minute with leakage current not in excess of

3 milliamperes. Class B protectors are required to withstand 15,000 volts, alternating current, for 3 minutes with leakage current not in excess of 8 milliamperes. Class B protectors when tested to breakdown must withstand up to 30,000 volts.

Impact resistance.   All three classes are tested by dropping an 8-pound steel ball on the crown from a height of 5 feet. Mounted on a standard head form, the protector must not transmit an average force of more than 850 pounds. The crown clearance for this test is 1½ inches for Classes A, B, and C.

Penetration resistance.   Protectors shall be neither dented nor pierced for more than three-eighths inch, when a hardened steel plumb bob is dropped squarely onto the center of the crown from a height of 3 feet.

Hair protection for women

The ease with which a strand of hair can be caught on a revolving shaft or other moving part presents a serious hazard to women working or passing near moving machinery. In such locations even the smallest shaft should be enclosed. Shafts well out of ordinary reach, as under tables or workbenches, have caused many partial scalpings when women workers who dropped tools reached or crawled in to get them. So have seemingly harmless small belts and the rotating spindles of small drillpresses and other small machines used on benches. Not only should particular attention be given to the guarding of all moving machine parts where women are employed, but they should also wear protectors to confine the hair and keep out dust, dirt, etc.

Various forms of protectors have been devised and tried out. Attractively designed caps have proved effective and have been well received. They should be made of fabric that will wear well, withstand repeated laundering or dry cleaning and hold their attractiveness well. The design should permit pressing by machine. A visor long enough and stiff enough to protect against a head bump is advisable. A range of sizes sufficient to assure a good fit is important.

Getting women to accept and wear hair protection faithfully is sometimes a problem. Usually the best approach is an informational one backed by firmness. A simple demonstration, using a wig, can be made very convincing. Scalpings are so painful and so shocking that once the women are brought to realize that the danger does actually exist the problem is solved.

Hearing protection

Modern engineering practice calls for the maximum practicable elimination of noise that is either harmful or noticeably disagreeable. Frequently usable methods include design revision, enclosure to baffle the noise, use of sound-absorptive materials, the substitution of a less noisy process and isolation of the noisy machine or process in a separate building.

Although no definite level of sound intensity that can cause hearing damage has been established it is generally accepted as on the order of 85 to 95 decibles. All persons exposed to higher levels of sound for substantial periods of time should wear suitable ear protectors. Protectors are of three types—ear plugs, muffs, and helmets.

Ear plugs. Stuffing the ear canal with absorbent cotton or cotton waste has been traditional practice in boilershops and similarly very noisy places, but manufactured ear plugs of rubber, plastic or other suitable materials are much more effective, more comfortable and more sanitary. Since close fit is very important, they are made in a range of sizes. Some persons even require a different size for each ear.

A reduction of the intensity of the sound that reaches the ear obtainable by the use of ear plugs varies from about 20 decibels for frequencies in the speech range to twice that in the higher frequencies. As a consequence, the intelligibility of speech in most such very noisy shops is usually improved by the use of ear plugs. A moderate additional attenuation of the noise level can be gained by adding muffs or helmets.

Such reductions are usually sufficient to prevent hearing loss in boilershops and shipyards and in the operation of such noisemakers as punch presses, riveters, drop hammers, etc.

Muffs. The muff type protector consists of cups to cover the ears and is held in place by a headband. Muffs may also be incorporated in a cap for continuous wearing.

Cups are made of rubber or plastic materials and are intended to enclose the ear without compressing it. They must fit snugly to the head to minimize leakage. Cups contain sound absorbing material or disks with perforations that discriminate against certain frequencies. The muff does not cover enough of the skull to reduce bone conduction materially.

Helmets are designed to cover as much of the bony parts of the head as possible to cut down bone conduction. Helmets may include muff type protectors and eye protectors. They are used chiefly against extreme levels of high intensity noise as in jet engine testing.

Selection of ear protectors

The intensity and frequencies of the noise must be determined, else any selection is little better than a guess. For intensities up to about 100 db., with most of the energy in the middle frequencies, plugs or ear muffs are adequate. For intensities of 110 db. or over and in the higher frequencies, it is advisable to add ear muffs or helmets. Above 130 db. it is necessary to do so.

Eye and Face Protection

In selecting eye and eye and face protectors, at least the following factors should be given careful consideration—kind and degree of hazard, degree of protection afforded, wearer comfort. Protectors are available in wide variety. They may be classified as follows:

Eye protective equipment.

GOGGLES.
> *Eyecup:* cup type or cover-cup type.
>> Chipper's model.
>> Dust model.
>> Welder's and cutter's model.
> *Flexible fitting goggles.*
> *Plastic eyeshield goggles.*
> *Foundrymen's goggles.*
> *Other goggles and spectacles.*

SPECTACLES.
> *Metal or plastic frame spectacles.*
> *Plastic eyeshield spectacles.*

Face-and-Eye protective equipment.

HELMETS AND HAND SHIELDS.
> *Helmets.*
> *Hand shields.*
> *Nonrigid helmets.*

FACE SHIELDS.

Goggles

Goggles consist of a pair of contour-shaped eyecups, or facial contact parts with glass or plastic lenses, worn over the eyes and held in place by a head-band for the protection of the eye and eye sockets. In general, the term "goggles" is also applied to spectacle-type protectors.

Eyecup goggles. Each eyecup is provided with a lens retainer bearing evenly on the lens and so constructed as to retain fragments in the event of lens breakage. The design is such as to permit ready lens replacement. Lens retainers for welder's and cutter's models are made to accommodate a filter lens, fiber gasket, and cover lens. The two basic types of eyecup goggles are:

Cup type—for those who do not wear corrective glasses.

Cover-cup type—for wear over corrective glasses.

Both of these two types are made in three models—chipper's, dust, and welder's.

Chipper's—to protect against objects that strike with considerable force, for example, hand or power chipping, breaking stone or concrete, machine operations likely to yield flying chips, etc.

Dust—for protection against dust particles or liquid splashes. Openings for ventilation are baffled or screened against the entry of dust liquid splashes. Dust goggles are used in light grinding and machining operations, in woodworking, etc.

Welder's and cutter's—for protection against glare and injurious radiant energy. The lenses are impact resistant. Cover lenses are used to protect the filter lens.

Flexible fitting goggles.   The flexibility permits a close fit for protection against fine dust, fumes, mists, splashes, etc. The lenses are set directly in the frame. It is made of a flexible, nonirritating, chemical-resistant, slow burning material.

Plastic eyeshield goggles.   For protection against light flying objects and with filter lenses, against glare or radiant energy of only moderate intensity. They are used in light chipping and grinding, woodworking, spot welding, babbitting, etc.

Foundrymen's goggles.   These amount to small face masks of flexible, nonirritating, flame resistant material carrying metal lens holders, lenses, and a positive means of support on the face. They are for protection against both impact and hot metal splash.

Other goggles and spectacles.   There are various other types of goggles obtainable commercially for special purposes but they are not covered by the ASA code.

Spectacles

Safety spectacles are similar to ordinary spectacles but more strongly made, with impact-resistant lenses and with or without side shields. Clip-on side shields are also available. Lenses may be clear or filter type, or of glass or plastic. Their lightness and neater appearance make them more acceptable to workmen generally, so they are usually regarded as preferable where they afford reasonably adequate protection.

Helmets and hand shields

Helmets and hand shields are designed to protect face, ears, neck and eyes also against radiant energy. They are used chiefly in arc welding and heavy gas cutting.

Helmets. The helmet body is made of vulcanized fiber, reinforced plastic, or other suitable flame resistant material that is opaque to light and to ultraviolet and infrared radiation and readily disinfectable. It covers the head and neck to well back of the ears and is supported by a headgear in such a way that it is never in contact with the face and can be thrown back above the head for examination of the weld. It has a window in front with a filter plate and cover plate.

Hand shield. Helmet mounted on a handle to enable a second person to watch the welding operation without donning full helmet with headgear.

Nonrigid helmet. Some helmets are made of flexible materials for use in confined spaces. Otherwise they are identical with the rigid helmet except for a closer head fit necessary to hold the window in proper position.

Face shields

Face shields are designed to protect the entire face against flying particles, splashings and, where needed, glare and radiant energy of only moderate intensity.

Lenses for eye protective devices

The lenses are obviously the vital part of the protection. Most lenses are of a good grade of optical glass but plastic lenses are also used. Lenses may be clear, impact resistant or filter type impact resistant. Either type may be ground to prescription. Each lens should be marked with shade number and manufacturer identification. All lenses should be made to meet specific identification. All lenses should be made to meet specific requirements as to prismatic and refractive power, haze, radiant energy transmissivity and breaking strength. Plastic lenses must also meet requirements for resistance to penetration and flame.

The shade number carried by the lens designates the kind and intensity of radiant energy it will protect against. The ASA standard contains a table of shade numbers recommended for various exposures. Users should consult this as well as the recommendations of the manufacturer.

Fitting and maintenance, correctly done, is important, for both effectiveness and wearer comfort. It should be done by someone with special instruction and training.

It is essential that protector lenses be kept clean. Dirty lenses constitute a temptation to lay the protector aside and can cause eyestrain as well, in time.

Pitted lenses can also cause eyestrain. Deep scratches can weaken lenses. Replacement policy should err, if at all, on the side of too often. Lenses are cheaper than eyes. Headbands that have become sweat soaked, inelastic, wornout or dirty should be promptly replaced or cleaned.

Personal protective equipment that has been used by one employee should be cleaned and disinfected before being issued to another. Equipment issued to the same employee for an extended period should also be cleaned and disinfected at regular intervals. Manufacturers should be consulted for their recommendations.

Respiratory Protective Equipment

The ASA standard describes in broad terms the kinds of exposures for which respiratory protection is needed, but it does not spell them out because of the extensive detail that would require plus the even more important fact that too many variables are involved to permit successful standardization.

However, the need for a guide for users was met by Congressional designation of the U.S. Bureau of Mines as the official agency for the approval of respiratory protective equipment. Out of the very extensive and thoroughgoing studies and tests the Bureau has carried out to comply with this assignment have come the standards and information needed to determine the effectiveness and suitability of each of the various types and kinds of respiratory protective equipment.

Any manufacturer can submit a protector for approval. If it meets all the requirements for approval, it is granted an approvals certificate bearing an approval number which also specifically describes the device approved and the exposures and uses for which it is approved. The manufacturer is required to mark indicated component parts with the approval number and also affix a copy of the complete certificate to each carton or package in which the device is marketed.

The Bureau of Mines approval certificate is the accepted standard for these devices, not only in the United States but also very widely abroad. Only protectors thus approved should be used for protection against the exposures described. Lists of approved devices and descriptive material can be obtained from the Bureau upon request.

Types of protectors

Respiratory protective devices are designed either to purify the air being inhaled by removing the contaminants or to supply the wearer with clean air from a source entirely independent of the atmosphere in which he is working.

The equipment that purifies the air is designated as *air purifying,* whereas equipment that supplies air from an outside or remote source is termed *air supplying.* Air-purifying equipment can be subdivided into two classes: (a) those that make use of mechanical filters for removing particulate matter such as dusts, fumes, and mists, and (b) those that make use of chemical sorbents for removing gases and vapors from the air. The air-supplying types can be subdivided into (a) types in which fresh air is brought to the wearer from a distant point through a hose or pipe, and (b) self-contained oxygen equipment in which oxygen from a tank of compressed oxygen carried on the wearer is supplied for breathing.

Air-purifying types. The simplest and commonest mechanical filter device is the dust respirator. It usually consists of a filter of treated paper or felt, which screens or traps the fine particles of dust from the inhaled air. This filter is attached to a half-mask facepiece (one that covers only the nose and mouth) and is shaped to fit the contours of the face. The part of the facepiece that rests against the face must be made of some resilient material such as rubber so that comfortable and sealed contact is provided. Adjustable headbands are necessary for holding the respirator securely in position on the face. The better types of dust respirators are equipped with exhalation valves which open to permit the escape of exhaled air.

Mechanical filter respirators approved by the United States Bureau of Mines are available for various classes of dusts, fumes, and mists. The chief difference between various types of dust respirators is in the design of the filter. Some filters are efficient against all classes of particulate matter while others are effective against only one group or class. In general, a filter designed for a particular dust such as silica will provide longer service life than a filter that will provide the required protection against all classes of dusts, fumes, and mists. However, where a variety of these contaminants is present in the same operation or plant, the simplification obtained through the use of one respirator and filter approved for all classes of particulate matter may outweigh the longer life and lower resistance advantages of filters specifically designed for one type of dust.

The inhalation or check valves which close the entry ports between the filter and the facepiece during the exhalation breathing cycle are very desirable and greatly aid in the efficiency performance of a filter-type respirator. Without these inhalation valves, a part of the exhaled air passes out through the filter in reverse and the contact of the warm, moist breath on the filter usually causes some condensation. As the paper or felt filter becomes wet, it readily clogs with dust and increases rapidly in breathing resistance.

Soft cotton facepiece coverings, commonly called facelets, are available for most styles of filter respirators, and their use is recommended, especially around irritating dusts such as lime or where the individual's skin is sensitive to the rubber facepiece.

Increase in breathing resistance, rather than deterioration of the filter, determines when the filter in a respirator should be changed. Dust particles removed from the incoming air by the filter clog the filter pores and it becomes more efficient as a filter, but breathing resistance increases in proportion. When breathing resistance becomes uncomfortable, the filter should be changed.

Chemical cartridge respirators are similar in design to dust-, fume-, and mist-type respirators and usually employ a half mask facepiece. However, in place of the filter there are single or twin cartridges containing a chemical, which remove certain gases and vapors from incoming air. These respirators are reasonably light in weight and have a low breathing resistance so that they can be worn continuously if necessary.

The chemical used in the respirator cartridges will vary with the type of gas or vapor from which protection is required. Most manufacturers supply one type of chemical fill for protection against organic vapors, such as benzol, carbon tetrachloride, and trichlorethylene, and another chemical fill for protection against acid gases such as chlorine, sulphur dioxide, and hydrogen sulphide. Special fills are sometimes available for protection against such gases as ammonia and metallic mercury vapors.

An important point to be borne in mind by the safety engineer in considering the use of chemical cartridge respirators is that they are not designed for emergency use or for use in atmospheres which may be harmful or toxic during a short period of exposure. These chemical cartridge respirators employ a relatively small quantity of chemical in order that they may be made light in weight, and the half-mask facepiece is not as secure as the full facepiece used on the regular gas mask. The limiting concentration will vary with the particular gas and with the type and quantity of chemical in the cartridge, but it is generally considered unsafe to use chemical cartridge respirators in concentrations of acid gases higher than .05 per cent and in concentrations of organic vapors higher than .1 per cent.

Where chemical cartridge respirators are used against solvent vapors in paint-spray protection, the use of an auxiliary filter in front of the chemical cartridge to prevent the paint pigment from coating and clogging the chemical cartridge is desirable. Such filters should be inexpensive since they must be changed several times daily.

Canister gas masks. New processes, new gases, new combinations of gases used in industry today are continually enlarging the fields in which gaseous hazards are encountered by the worker. Higher pressures create conditions in which leaks are more difficult to guard against and often more serious when they do occur.

Canister gas masks are similar in application to chemical cartridge respirators, but they afford protection against relatively higher concentrations of gases and vapors for longer periods of time.

Canister-type gas masks consist of a facepiece, corrugated connecting tube, canister, and harness. The facepiece provides protection for the eyes as well as the face and respiratory organs. The canister contains chemicals for absorbing or neutralizing gases or vapors from which it is designed to protect. Canister masks may be divided into two classes: the industrial type with canister for protection against one gas or group of gases, and the all-service type which, as the name implies, is designed for protection against all industrial gases, smoke, and fumes.

One precaution in the use of canister masks must always be kept in mind—they may only be worn where there is sufficient oxygen to support life. They should never be worn in any confined space, such as tanks or tank cars, manholes, or any place that is poorly ventilated. The canister does not provide oxygen, it simply removes poisonous gases from the air that is breathed. The atmosphere may be tested with a flame safety lamp or a Wolf oxygen-deficiency indicator. If the flame is extinguished, an oxygen deficiency is indicated. Hose masks or oxygen-breathing apparatus should be used whenever an oxygen deficiency may exist.

Canisters are approved for use in not exceeding 2 per cent of most gases and in ammonia, 3 per cent. A question commonly asked is, "How long will the canister last, and when should it be replaced?" The service time will vary with the concentration of gas present, the rate of breathing, humidity, and the age of the canister. When the mask is in use, the canister will give complete protection for a period of time, and when it nears exhaustion, only a slight trace of gas will leak through. At the first detection of this leakage, the wearer should return to fresh air and replace the canister with a fresh one. When the canister is first placed in service, the bottom seal should be removed. At the end of one year, even though the mask has not actually been used, the canister should be replaced because it deteriorates slightly in normal air over a period of time.

All-service mask. The all-service gas mask will protect against all industrial gases, smoke, and fumes. The canister of this mask is red in color and is larger in size than the industrial canister. As before mentioned, the warning that a canister is nearing exhaustion is the penetration of a slight trace of gas. This is true of all gases except carbon monoxide, which is odorless and tasteless. All-service canisters are designed to give two hours' protection against carbon monoxide. To provide a warning for carbon monoxide, all-service masks are equipped with a timer which records the time that the canister has been used, whether continuously or intermittently, and which indicates by one complete revolution of its pointer that the canister should be changed. The all-service mask should be used for fire fighting and wherever carbon monoxide is suspected or known to be present. It is also recommended for use in departments or areas where more than one gas or varieties of gases may be present, otherwise it would be possible for the wrong mask to be used. If there is any doubt as to the gaseous hazard present or the proper mask to use, the representative of a reputable manufacturer of approved gas masks should be consulted.

Aside from the hazards of industrial processes, all-service masks should be provided in every industrial plant for those responsible for fire and plant protection. Contrary to the popular belief, a large percentage of the lives lost annually from fires succumb to gases, not to flames. It has been found that the gases from fires contain toxic constituents in sufficient amounts to make breathing dangerous or even fatal in a short time. Because this is true of the burning of common industrial materials, the need for adequate gas-mask protection for fire fighters is apparent.

It is important that those who are expected to wear gas masks be thoroughly trained in their use and limitations, so that they may be thoroughly familiar with the mask when it is required for use in emergency.

The following schedule for inspection and instruction is suggested:

1. Be sure the seal is removed from the bottom of the canister when the mask is placed in service.

2. Examine the mask parts, connections, and fittings for leakage and wear.

3. Instruct in the proper method of putting on and adjusting the face-piece. (Follow the manufacturer's instructions that come with each mask.)

4. Test the mask for gas tightness. When the mask is in place, place the hand over the bottom opening of the canister or close off the corrugated tube by collapsing it and inhale. If the mask is properly fitted and there are no leaks, the facepiece will collapse against the face.

5. Have the workman wear the mask for a 15- or 20-minute period to familiarize himself with its breathing resistance, and so on.

6. After using, clean and sterilize facepiece and replace in its case.

7. Keep a card record of the date of last inspection and length of time the mask has been used.

8. Replace the canister with a new one after it has been in service for one year, whether or not it has been used.

9. If the mask is properly designed and fitted, it may be worn for relatively long periods of time with reasonable comfort.

Air line respirators. The most versatile of the respirators is the air line type. It is suitable for use as respiratory protection against all atmospheric contaminants in concentrations not immediately harmful to life or from which the wearer can escape without the use of the respirator. This limitation of use is made necessary because the air line respirator is entirely dependent upon an air supply which is not carried by the wearer of the respirator. Its failure would prevent escape from immediately deadly atmospheres.

The facepiece of the air line respirator is attached to a compressed air system by a hose of small internal diameter, and clean air from this source is fed to the facepiece in sufficient quantity to exclude from the breathing zone the atmosphere which surrounds the worker.

Accessory equipment such as pressure regulators, release valves, air filters, etc., must be used unless special clean air compressors are provided to supply respirable air.

In addition to being versatile, the air line respirator is the most comfortable and pleasing to wear of the respirators. There is little or no resistance to inhalation, and the surplus flow of air usually provides a cooling and refreshing effect. The only major disadvantage is the necessity of trailing a small diameter hose for connecting the facepiece to the air source. This limits the travel of the wearer.

Air line respirators are available with half mask type facepieces as well as those which provide full face coverage. The latter are to be used when the contaminant affects the eyes as well as the respiratory tract.

Another important distinction is the difference between "constant flow" and "demand flow" types of air line respirators. Breathable air is continuously fed to the facepiece on the constant flow unit. There is always a slight positive pressure present in the facepiece to assure against inward leakage. The constant-flow air line respirator is the most common and comfortable type, but it is suited only for operation on air compressor systems.

When it is necessary to utilize a cylinder of compressed oxygen or air, the demand flow type respirator is preferred. By inclusion of a small demand regulator, air is fed to the facepiece only upon inhalation of the wearer. The flow ceases upon exhalation. This conserves the air supply and permits one man about five hours of service from a standard 220 cubic foot cylinder of oxygen.

One of the most important precautions in the use of the air line respirator is to make sure that a clean supply of air is available at the proper pressure and in sufficient quantity. Most plant compressed air systems are operated with internally lubricated piston-type compressors. Oil and water mists, oil vapors and small amounts of foreign particulate matter are present in many compressed air supply systems. These contaminants should be removed by mechanical and chemical filtering and air line filters are available for this purpose.

When internally lubricated compressors run hot because of excessive friction, there is the likelihood of partial combustion of the lubricant along with production of carbon monoxide. A carbon monoxide alarm system should be installed near the takeoff for respirable air to provide the workmen with a warning should the deadly gas be fed into the air lines.

The pressure on the plant air line should be reduced to respirable levels as recommended by the equipment manufacturer. On United States Bureau of Mines approved air line respirators, the manufacturer is permitted to specify any range of operating pressures up to a maximum of 25 lbs. per square inch so long as a sufficient amount of air is fed to the facepiece within the range specified. In no case, however, can the operating pressure exceed 25 lbs. per square inch on constant flow air line respirators. Pressure reducing valves, as well as relief or blowoff valves, are used to control this factor. The same general type, but with a different capacity, is used to reduce high cylinder pressures to a low value suitable for use with demand-type air line respirators.

Certain types of air compressors are manufactured specifically to supply respirable air. These are usually called "clean air blowers." They utilize compression seal liquids such as water to prevent the friction of metal contact and to eliminate the necessity of internal lubrication. These devices furnish cool, clean, and properly humidified air at proper respirable pressures, and are available in various sizes depending upon the number of air line respirators to be operated at any one time.

The air line respirator is a good general purpose protective device for all industry. It is used on many operations in confined spaces, for paint-spray vapors and pigments, welding and cutting fumes, and gases and vapors. It should not, however, be used in circumstances in which the worker's life is immediately in danger should the supply of compressed air fail.

Abrasive masks and helmets. Abrasive masks and helmets are in reality modifications of air line respirators. They are designed specifically for use on the sand or shot-blast operation. The mask type consists of a tight-fitting facepiece which covers the entire face, a special lens assembly to reduce pitting of the lens, and a rubber-coated hood covering the upper part of the body to the waist. The helmet type is similar, but the tight-sealing facepiece is replaced by a rigid, loose-fitting helmet.

Sand or shot-blasting is a common metal cleaning or finishing process. Sand or similar grit is ejected from a nozzle at high velocities by compressed air. The nozzle is controlled by the operator or sand-blaster and is directed at the metal parts to be cleaned. The stream or spray of sand, in striking the metal parts, abrades and removes the exposed surfaces. The sand-blast booth or cabinet is found in most foundries, and the technique is also employed on operations such as the cleaning of metal in preparation for refinishing.

A highly contaminated atmosphere at the point of operation is inherent with sand-blasting. The particles rebound in the direction of the operator, and the air which immediately surrounds him is laden with harmful particles. They are unusually small because the high velocity impact of the sand or grit on the metal reduces both the abrasive material and the surface which is removed to a fine particulate state.

Small particles remain airborne for long periods of time and, therefore, exist continually around the operator during the job. Then, too, with fibrosis-producing materials such as free silica in the abrasive mix, small particles are of greater health significance.

The contamination at the point of operation is too great for use of mechanical filter respirators. Even with small allowable leakages of less than 2 per cent, the amount of dust which would pass through a mechanical filter on this operation would exceed allowable tolerances.

Certain desirable features should be considered in the selection of equipment for a specific job. Of course, worker comfort is desirable in all instances, and in this respect, weight, balance, and fit of the equipment are important. Equipment weight in excess of 5 pounds is considered burdensome, and several units on the market weigh as little as 4 pounds.

Good balance on the equipment is necessary because it is carried on the upper portion of the body. Of course, the need for perfect balance becomes less important with the decrease in weight of the equipment. Even so, equal distribution of weight over the head is a point which must be considered to eliminate excessive worker fatigue. Good fit is especially desirable on abrasive masks and helmets because they are worn for long periods on arduous work.

Some of the other features of operational importance are:

1. Adequate vision. The lens area must be large and/or close enough to the face to permit a wide angle of vision so that the operator can see his work and move about freely.

2. Protection against pitting of the lens. The rebound of abrasive ma-

terial pits lenses quickly. This action is usually retarded by use of a wire screen placed in front of the exterior lens. On jobs requiring intermittent and frequent inspection by the operator, a lift-front screen holder is desirable. This unit permits the operator to remove the screen from the visual area quickly and conveniently.

3. Protection from flying particles. The rebound of the abrasive material is discomfiting to the body of the worker and deteriorates any exposed metal parts on the safety equipment. A rubber hood of good quality is required to protect the face, shoulders, and neck of the worker, and some parts of the respiratory protective equipment. On many of the heavier operations it is necessary to utilize a rubber-covered coat and pair of pants for additional body protection. Gloves, of course, are essential.

4. Volume control for air supply. Because the volume of air required is, within limited degrees, a matter of individual needs and desires, a flow control valve to be worn on the body of the operator should be provided. This is a United States Bureau of Mines requirement. It should be so constructed as to prevent accidental change of flow, and to permit a minimum flow at the lowest setting.

Air supply equipment listed as accessory equipment for air line respirators in the section on this equipment is all applicable for use with abrasive masks. The same precautions for assuring an adequate supply of respirable air must be taken when abrasive masks or helmets are used because they are identical with air line respirators in basic design.

Hose masks. The hose mask is a respiratory protective device in which clean air from an uncontaminated source is supplied through a hose to a mask assembly worn by the person to be protected. With the mask adjusted so as to be gas-tight, the fact that the wearer breathes air coming from the remote end of the hose makes its operation simple and easily understood. Hose masks fill an important place in the field of respiratory protection. Workmen like them because of their simplicity.

Hose masks are used to furnish fresh air to the workman who must enter and work in highly concentrated gaseous or oxygen-deficient atmospheres within a short distance from fresh air—in places such as tank cars, oil storage tanks, sewers, and the like. Units are available for supplying as many as four men. Fresh air is taken from the outside and drawn or blown through the hose attached to the mask facepiece. The wearer is restricted in his travels to the length of the hose, which may, however, be as long as 150 feet.

Hose masks consist of a full gas-mask facepiece with corrugated tube connected to varying lengths of 1-inch-diameter hose, anchored to a body harness and usually a blower. They differ from air line respirators in that they operate independently of any source of compressed air and that, even when used with a blower, it is possible to breathe in the event of blower stoppage.

Hose masks possess many advantages where the extent of the space to be entered is definite and limited. They fully protect the respiratory system against gases, vapors, dusts, and mists. Since they do not depend on chemicals or compressed oxygen, they may be used over extended periods with low-maintenance costs.

Hose masks, however, have some limitations. The wearer is definitely limited by the length of the hose, which must not be in lengths too great for safety. He must emerge from the space entered the same way as he went in. He must also take care to keep the extension hose from becoming caught or fouled.

In selecting a hose mask for a specific job, the following conditions should be considered:

1. Blowers should be used on all outfits using more than 25 feet of hose. They assure coolness, comfort, effortless breathing, and maintain sufficient positive pressure inside to insure an ample flow of air to the wearer.

2. Hose should be suitable to resist action of any outside substance. For instance, in petroleum work, oilproof hose should be specified. Lengths selected should allow sufficient clearance at the blower end to insure fresh air.

Hand-operated blower hose masks are furnished with double outlet blowers so that two men can work on one assembly or, if it is only necessary for one man to do the work, the second mask assembly can be available for use in any emergency that may arise. This type of mask is limited to use with not more than 150 feet of hose on each blower outlet (150 feet is the limit for which Bureau of Mines approval is granted). All hose masks operate on the principle that the blower end be kept in clean, uncontaminated air at all times.

Motor-driven hose masks use the same facepieces, safety belt harness, hose, and blowers as the hand-operated type and are generally arranged so that they can be operated by hand if electric current is interrupted, or where electricity is not available. Motor-driven assemblies are available with four outlets on one blower, and any number of the outlets can be blanked off if not required.

Hose masks are available with 25 feet of hose (without blower), where this length of hose is adequate to reach fresh air. Masks without blowers are not recommended by the Bureau for use with more than 25 feet of hose.

Training in the use of hose masks should consist of the following:

1. See that gaskets are in place on all union connections.
2. Connect lengths of hose and attach to blower outlet if blower is used.

When only one hoseline is being used, close off the unused blower outlets with caps provided for that purpose.

3. Attach free end of hose to harness.

4. Connect corrugated breathing tubes to hose and to facepiece.

5. Adjust length of shoulder straps so that body strap falls in proper position around the waist. Adjust the body belt for a snug, comfortable fit.

6. Follow the manufacturer's instructions for putting on and adjusting facepiece.

7. Test facepiece for leakage by closing off the corrugated tube or tubes, and inhale. Collapse of the facepiece and lack of inward leakage are indications of a tight fit. Investigate and correct any leak detected.

8. *a.* On blower-type masks, *be sure the blower is placed in clean, fresh air*. Have the man wearing the mask indicate to blower operator when he is receiving the desired amount of air, and operator can continue to crank or operate blower at this same rate.

b. On masks without blower, *see that end of hose is anchored securely in clean, fresh air by means of the spike or hook.*

9. Have mask worn in fresh air for fifteen minutes so that wearer becomes familiar with its operation and gains confidence in the protection which it provides.

10. After use, clean and sterilize facepiece, clean hose if necessary, and see that mask is properly replaced in the trunk provided.

11. Store mask in a cool, dry place where it will be readily and conveniently available when needed.

Note: The same procedure recommended for training should be followed in actual use, except, at the end of Step 9, proceed with work required. Steps 10 and 11 should be followed after the work has been completed.

Self-contained breathing apparatus.   Self-contained breathing apparatus provides complete respiratory protection in any concentration of toxic gases and under any condition of oxygen deficiency. The wearer is independent of the surrounding atmosphere because he is breathing in a system in which no outside air is admitted and the oxygen or air supply of the apparatus itself takes care of respiratory requirements. Such devices enable man to work in places where he is, by nature, unfitted to live.

Self-Contained Breathing Apparatus is divided into three basic types which are again broken down into a number of variations. The three basic types are:

1. Oxygen cylinder rebreathing type
2. Demand type apparatus
3. Self-generating type

Oxygen cylinder rebreathing type apparatus in use today is almost without exception lung governed and consist of a relatively small cylinder of compressed oxygen, reducing and regulating valves, a breathing bag, a facepiece or mouthpiece, and nose clip, and a container with a chemical which removes carbon dioxide from the exhaled breath. The self-generating type also uses the principle of rebreathing, but functions in a much different manner since it has no mechanical operating components. The two types of cylinder rebreathing units now being manufactured are of one hour or two hours' duration under hard work. Since these apparatus function in the same manner, they will be discussed together. The high pressure oxygen from the cylinder is reduced in pressure to a breathing level by means of first a high pressure reducing and regulating valve and secondly an admission valve that delivers the required oxygen flow to the wearer through the breathing bag. The oxygen coming through the admission valve into the bag is delivered by means of a breathing tube to the wearer's lungs through a face covering. The wearer's exhaled breath then passes down another breathing tube into the container holding the carbon dioxide removing chemical, then through a cooler and back into the breathing bag, where the purified (carbon dioxide removed) exhalation mixes with the incoming oxygen from the cylinder.

The so-called lung-governed principle is one in which the wearer of the apparatus, by his own breathing, regulates his oxygen supply automatically so as to provide the exact amount required. Some earlier apparatus, particularly those made in Europe, employed a method of fixed dosage in which there was a constant fixed rate of oxygen flow regardless of the rate of work. This meant that the user might have to reduce his work level or risk collapse because no one flow rate is proper for varying work loads.

The rebreathing principle is one which permits the most efficient utilization of the oxygen supply. The exhaled breath contains both oxygen and carbon dioxide since the body consumes only a small part of the oxygen that is inhaled. As the user exhales into the chemical container, the carbon dioxide is removed by the chemical and the oxygen which is left is reused. This method of operation applies to all oxygen cylinder rebreathing type apparatus as well as the self-generating type. All oxygen cylinder rebreathing type apparatus operate in the same manner, but vary in service time depending on the size of the oxygen cylinder and the amount of carbon dioxide removing chemical used. These apparatus require that the oxygen cylinder be refilled and the carbon dioxide removing chemical replaced after each use. As is true of all respiratory protective equipment, training in proper use and maintenance is essential if the most efficient operation is to be obtained.

Demand-type apparatus all use the same principle of operation, but are available in a number of different models for specific applications. The various models can be grouped into three categories as follows:

1. Back mounted thirty minute duration apparatus.

2. Chest or side mounted apparatus.

3. Working apparatus which are attached to large compressed oxygen or air cylinders by means of a connecting hose for long duration use. The construction of this apparatus is such that it doesn't fall within the scope of any Bureau of Mines Approval Schedule.

In order to simplify the discussion of demand-type apparatus, the principle of operation common to all types will be discussed first. All of these apparatus consist of a high pressure cylinder of oxygen or air, a demand regulator connected either directly or by high pressure tube to the cylinder, a facepiece and tube assembly with an exhalation valve, and a method of mounting the complete apparatus on the body. In use, the wearer turns on the cylinder valve after putting on the facepiece, inhales, drawing oxygen or air through the demand regulator at breathing pressure to the facepiece, and then exhales through the exhalation valve in the facepiece to the surrounding atmosphere.

The demand regulator which is the heart of the apparatus operates as follows:

The high pressure oxygen or air from the cylinder is introduced into a reducing valve which reduces and regulates the high (about 1,800 pounds) pressure. As the wearer inhales, he creates a negative pressure which draws a diaphragm inward and opens a valve through which the oxygen or air flows to the facepiece. As the wearer exhales, the valve shuts off, thus producing flow only on inhalation. The term, demand regulator, comes from the fact that the flow is on inhalation demand, automatically regulating itself to the desired level to compensate for variations in breathing needs. All demand regulators should be provided with a bypass valve to be opened in event of failure of the automatic operation of the regulator. All demand apparatus are relatively inefficient when compared with rebreathing type apparatus, since the exhaled oxygen is released to the atmosphere instead of being reused.

The back-type apparatus uses a large cylinder of about 40 cubic foot capacity of either oxygen or pure air mounted on a frame held to the body bya harness and lasts for thirty minutes at hard work. It can be applied generally where complete respiratory protection is desired but is heavy and of short duration as contrasted with the rebreathing type of apparatus.

The front- and side-mounted apparatus use cylinders of either 11 or 22 cubic foot capacity and last about 8 and 15 minutes respectively. For special applications where short service time is all that is necessary such as escape from suddenly developing toxic conditions, these units are useful but must not be regarded as filling the need for a rescue or working apparatus.

The work mask type of apparatus is used for planned maintenance work. It is not an emergency apparatus as it requires setting up some auxiliary equipment for use and has a connecting hose which limits the free movement of the wearer to the length of the hose. This apparatus is actually a twofold unit being a self-contained apparatus with which the wearer can move freely about using a small (11 cubic foot capacity) cylinder to enter or to leave the toxic atmosphere, either routinely or on failure of the main breathing supply. There is a provision for connecting a hose to the demand regulator so that the wearer can breathe during the work period from a large cylinder which has a pressure reducing valve attached to provide low pressure for the connecting hose. Manifold assemblies can be provided to permit more than one worker to work from a common breathing source. It is imperative that the small emergency cylinder be used with this type of apparatus because otherwise a failure of the supply from the large cylinder would immediately expose the wearer without this protection to the toxic atmosphere in which he is working.

The self-generating type of self-contained breathing apparatus has a chemical in its canister which liberates oxygen on contact with moisture in the wearer's breath as it is carried through the closed system by the wearer's lung action. Check valves keep the flow unidirectional. The rates of evolution of oxygen is governed by the breathing rate. The exhaled carbon dioxide is absorbed by another chemical in the canister. A pressure relief valve is also provided.

Selection of respirators

The following factors should be considered in choosing a respirator:—
(a) nature of hazard, (b) severity of hazard, (c) type of contaminant, (d) concentration of contaminant, (e) period of time protection would be required, (f) distance of contaminated area from source of respirable air, (g) expected activity of wearer, (h) the characteristics and limitations of the respective respirators.

Nature of the hazard. Oxygen deficiency, gaseous contaminant, particulate contaminant or combination of two or more of these.

Severity of hazard. Immediately dangerous to life; if degree of severity doubtful consider as immediately dangerous.

Type of contaminant. If gaseous, identify—acid, organic vapor, ammonia, carbon monoxide or a mixture of two or more of these. If particulate, ascertain physical form—dust, fume or mist; a toxic substance type—as arsenic, antimony, lead, etc., fibrosis producing asbestos, free silica; neither—as flour or wood dust.

Concentration of contaminant. If gaseous, determine possible maximum—gas mask inadequate above 3% ammonia by volume, or above 2% by volume of other gases; organic—vapor chemical-cartridge respirator inadequate above 0.1% by volume. If dust, air-line respirator should be used where concentration is so high as to plug filter of filter type too quickly.

Period of required protection. Self-contained breathing apparatus, hose masks and chemical cartridge respirators protect for limited periods only. Hose masks with blower, air-line respirators, (including those for abrasive blasting) protect for unlimited periods.

Distance from respirable air. For self-contained breathing apparatus the wearer should obviously stay well within a distance from which he can return before the protection expires. Equally obviously this requires keeping a close watch of elapsed time. Air-line respirators and hose masks have no such limitation but the wearer must, because of the hose, go out the way he came in.

Activity of wearer. The necessity of trailing a line of hose along is a serious handicap in work among obstructions, in close corners or in situations in which quick escape might be necessary. This may so limit his freedom of action that self-contained apparatus is prerable even though it necessitates periodic returns to outside air to replace air supply. In such case the greater the activity of the wearer, the faster the air supply is used up. For example, a man walking at a rate of four miles per hour breathes about three times the volume of air he would standing still.

Characteristics and limitations of the respective respirators. It is obvious that a thorough knowledge of the available equipment is necessary for sound selection. The table on the following page, though by no means an adequate guide, should be helpful in such selection.

Care and maintenance

When the safety engineer has selected the most suitable type of mask or respirator for a particular hazard or type of operation, the most important part of his job is yet to be done—that of seeing that the devices are properly worn and that they are maintained in efficient condition.

At first, there is usually a reluctance on the part of persons to wear masks or respirators. This can be overcome by carefully explaining to each worker the hazards involved and the necessity for wearing the equipment to protect his own health. Next, he should be taught to wear the

Hazard	Respirator
Oxygen deficiency	Self-contained breathing apparatus Hose mask with blower
Gaseous contaminant: Immediately dangerous to life	Self-contained breathing apparatus Hose mask with blower Gas mask
Not immediately dangerous to life	Air-line respirator Hose mask without blower Chemical-cartridge respirator
Particulate contaminant	Dust, mist, or fume respirator Air-line respirator Abrasive-blasting respirator

Combination gaseous and particulate
  contaminant:
  Immediately dangerous to life
	Self-contained breathing apparatus
	Hose mask with blower
	Gas mask with special filter

Not immediately dangerous to life	Air-line respirator Hose mask without blower Chemical-cartridge respirator with special filter

equipment correctly and should learn the function of its various component parts.

The degree of training necessary for a particular mask or respirator will depend on the intelligence and experience of the wearer and also on the particular type of device. Filter and cartridge-type respirators are relatively simple, and only a few minutes' instruction may be necessary to demonstrate their fitting and use. The canister-type mask and the hose mask require more instruction and training, since these devices are usually worn in emergency conditions. The self-contained oxygen-breathing apparatus should be worn only by persons who have undergone thorough training in its use.

Failure to keep masks and respirators clean and in efficient operating condition is common in many industrial plants where such equipment is used. This neglect is responsible for much of the resistance of workers to wearing the equipment and thus for its failure to provide the protection intended. Neglect also makes it necessary to replace the equipment more frequently.

Respiratory protective equipment that is used chiefly for emergencies should be inspected carefully after each use in order to determine whether any of the parts have become damaged or the canisters exhausted. Furthermore, a definite system should be established for inspection at regular intervals.

The equipment should be stored in a clean, dry place where it will not be tampered with and will be conveniently available when an emergency arises. Definite responsibility for periodic inspection and checking after use should be given to one person, and a record should be kept of the date of each inspection and the condition of the equipment.

Such respiratory protective devices as respirators and abrasive blasting masks which are worn frequently or continuously in production or maintenance operations require special arrangements for regular cleaning, inspection, and repair. This should be the responsibility of one specially trained employee.

The following rules for care of respirators have been found to be practical and to produce the desired results:

1. Always give the same respirator or respirators to the same men.

2. Have a definite place to leave dirty respirators and pick up clean ones.

3. Establish a maximum length of time the respirator may be used before it must be serviced and cleaned, and keep a record of the dates inspected.

4. Establish a simple, effective method of sterilization at regular intervals.

The respirator can always be returned to the same man if it is numbered with his check number. If the respirator has a fair-sized metal part, numbering can be done with a steel stamp or an electric marking pencil. Respirators using plastic parts can be identified readily if the worker's name or number is typed on a piece of plastic magnetic tape and affixed to the part. The label will not be affected by water or other material.

The most suitable method for cleaning and sterilizing special protective equipment is somewhat dependent upon the materials used in its construction. However, almost all metal, rubber, and plastic parts will stand scrubbing with soap and lukewarm water. This method is most effective in removing dust, dirt, oil, grease, and perspiration. After the parts are cleaned, they should be rinsed in water and sterilized.

The factors to be considered in selecting a suitable sterilizing agent are the effect of the agent on the materials and parts to be sterilized, the effectiveness of the sterilizing agent in killing common bacteria, the effect of the agent as a skin irritant if small amounts remain upon parts which contact the skin, whether or not the sterilizing agent will leave an objectionable odor for some time after it is applied to the equipment, and its convenience to use, its cost, and its availability.

Hand, Foot and Leg Protection.

About three fifths of work connected injuries in American industry as a whole are to legs, hands or feet. Of these, hand and finger injuries run about half. If non-disabling injuries were included, hand, forearm and finger injuries would be the most numerous by far. This should be obvious with a moment's thought, for the hands and fingers are necessarily almost always in contact with or very close to the object or material being worked on or handled. Therefore, not only from the standpoint of preventing crippling or disabling injuries, but also to prevent minor injuries as well, careful attention should always be given to hand protection where the nature of the work is such that any injuries are at all likely without it.

Hands and arms

In operations involving the handling of hot or sharp edges or points, gloves, mittens, or hand pads should be worn. To most people gloves are a matter of appearance but in industry suitability to give protection against the hazards involved is the overriding consideration. Experience amply proves that gloves, where properly selected for a particular job, do much to reduce scratches, blisters, burns and so on. Mass production, and modern manufacturing methods have made specialized hand production necessary for certain hazards or groups of hazards.

For the severest work in the foundries, steel mills, and so on, the necessary protection for hands can only be obtained with gloves or mittens that are reinforced with steel staples and that are steel sewed. The leather base for the steel-reinforced gloves is usually chrome-tanned cowhide. This leather is ideal because it is flexible, tough, and of uniform weight. The steel staples are clinched into the leather over surfaces receiving the greatest wear, usually the entire palm, thumb, and, partially or entirely, the four fingers.

When flame and heat are a factor, aside from welding, where gloves made from chrome tanned cowhide, horsehide, or carpincho are used, gloves of asbestos only, or of asbestos combined with leather or wool, are used. Where heat is involved but wear is not severe, gloves made of asbestos only are suitable.

Where rough or sharp hot objects are handled, the asbestos gloves should be reinforced with chrome leather on the portions of greatest wear.

Where extreme temperatures are encountered, the glove should have an insulating lining of cotton fleece or wool.

An entirely different problem arises when the protection required is not from the handling of rough or hot materials, but to protect against acids,

alkalis, various types of oils, and solvents. Where acids only are encountered, rubber or plastic gloves usually will give protection, the weight,
length, and style of glove to be used being decided by the type of acid
and the amount of wear involved.

Where a combination of oils and acids is encountered, gloves made of
synthetics, such as neoprene, have been found to be satisfactory.

Where naphthas, oils, and solvents are encountered, rubber gloves should
never be used, because rubber will disintegrate rapidly in contact with
such materials. Gloves made of solvent-resistant synthetics are best.

Wrists and arms generally are protected by the glove gauntlet, shirt, or
jacket sleeve. Where gauntleted gloves are not used, and the ordinary sleeve
is too loose or does not afford sufficient protection special sleeves or arm
protectors should be worn. The type of material of which they are made
depends mainly on the degree of hazard involved.

For light splatters and sparks, sleeves of flame-proofed duck or of chrome
leather will be found to be satisfactory. In handling sharp materials, such as
glass, tin-plate, scrap, and so on, in addition to gloves, a leather arm protector reinforced with steel staples affords the best protection.

Since the shoulders are taken care of generally by the clothing that
covers the body, they seldom require special protection. In carrying sheet
glass or other sharp-edged materials, however, the shoulders should be protected by pads of heavy felt covered with chrome leather or by some
similar apparel.

Leg protection is available in various types of leggings, ranging from
waist length to those that reach only part way to the knees. The type to be
used will depend on the hazard involved. For foot protection against sparks,
spats are suitable, but these are not required where leggings are worn, because the flare of the legging affords this protection.

Where the hazard of foot injuries—from dropped objects, slipping, or
acid spills—is encountered, proper footwear should be worn. Shoes in-
corporating steel safety toes or metal foot guards should be worn to protect against injuries to the feet from falling objects. Wooden-soled shoes
are recommended where slipping hazards exist, and rubber boots or shoes
should be provided to protect against acids.

Although the foregoing information can in no sense be considered a
complete guide to all the numerous personal protective problems that are
continually arising in the vast industries of our country, it does set up a
procedure that should be of assistance in most cases.

Feet and legs

The great majority of foot injuries are due to dropping heavy objects on
them or getting the toes caught under them. Safety shoes that will protect

against all but the most severe of such hazards are commercially available at prices that compare well with those of ordinary work shoes. Moreover a sufficient range of sizes, shapes and styles is available to permit the proper fitting of all normal feet, also to give good appearance as well.

Many large plants maintain shoe departments through the cooperation of shoe manufacturers who train designated employees in the proper fitting of their shoes. Some retail stores render a similar service. Many employers report that this service has proved to be very worthwhile by improving employee cooperation in the wearing of safety shoes and by improving employee foot comfort as well.

There are five principal types of safety shoes identified as:

Safety toe.
Conductive.
Non-sparking.
Non-conducting.
Foundry.

Safety toe shoe. The vital point is the toe protection. The accepted standard for strength is that the toebox must withstand a weight of 2,500 pounds placed on it or the impact of a 50 pound weight dropped 1 foot without the inside of the toebox coming closer than ½ inch to the upper surface of the sole.

Conductive shoe. Designed to dissipate static electricity accumulating on the body of the wearer so as to prevent static sparks. They should never be worn outdoors for dirt may impair their effectiveness. They are used in hospital operating rooms and in certain operations in the manufacture or processing of explosives and explosive or highly flammable substances.

Non-sparking shoes. These are made without any ferrous metal except if with metal toebox the latter has a non-ferrous plating. They are used in explosives manufacture where there may be explosive gas-air mixtures as cleaning tanks that have held flammable volatiles.

Electrical hazard shoes. These are made non-conducting and without any metal except a well insulated toebox. They are for work on or about live electrical circuits where the hazard of contact exists.

Foundry shoes. These are of the "Congress gaiter" type. The snug fit gives protection against the entry of sparks or splashes of molten metal and also permits quick removal.

Foot guards. For protection against very heavy impacts, as in handling pig iron, toeboxes alone may not be enough. For such exposures high strength steel foot guards that clamp or strap on over toe and instep are commercially available.

Protective clothing

Many industrial exposures require more or less specialized wearing apparel that is worn in place of ordinary work clothing or over it. Many industrial operations and processes present such hazards as burns, abrasions, dermatosis, etc., and necessitate, or at least make advisable, the wearing of clothing of asbestos, flameproofed duck, rubber, neoprene and the like.

In selecting such protective clothing two points are paramount:

1. The garment must afford adequate protection against the hazard involved.

2. It must not interfere unduly with the worker's movements.

Chapter Thirty

Fire Prevention and Protection

Fire prevention, protection and control are sometimes thought of as separate and apart from routine accident prevention activities as carried on in industry. There may be some justification for this if one thinks of fire losses in terms of property damage only. But fires carry a serious injury potential. Fires in industry cause many serious injuries and deaths each year. Since this is the case, the prevention and control of fire should be a part of every plant safety program.

The annual loss of life and property from fire is tremendous. The National Fire Protection Association estimates that during the decade 1951-1960, fire killed more than 116,000 persons and caused over $11 billion property damage.

These estimates cover direct destruction by fire only. They do not include the numerous indirect losses that follow or are incidental to every fire of any consequence, such as interruption of business, loss of wages by workmen, loss of market, public expenditure for fire fighting, etc. Nor do they include forest fire losses. Conservative estimates place these indirect costs at not less than twice the direct cost, probably substantially more.

The constant danger of fire has made necessary the establishment and maintenance of well organized fire departments in virtually every community. It has also brought about the creation of many organizations devoted to the prevention and control of fire, the oldest and best known of which is the National Fire Protection Association. The existence of a local fire department in its own neighborhood does not, however, relieve the plant management of the fundamental responsibility for the prevention of fires on its premises, the maintenance of fire extinguishing equipment of suitable type and adequacy, and the organization and training of employees for control of fires in their early stages.

Although many branches of industry are faced by special problems of fire prevention and control because of the nature of the materials handled and processed and the operations performed, the great majority of plant fires are due to hazards and causes common to all branches of industry. Virtually all of these hazards can be eliminated or controlled. Practically all fire losses can be prevented by the proper application of sound engineering methods and through adequate provisions for early discovery and extinguishment of any fires that occur despite such a preventive program. Although some, a very few, fires are practically unforeseeable, the great majority are due to human failure. Perhaps fire preventionists should coin the term "fire prevention mindedness" to go along with the safety man's term "safety mindedness" because if everyone were imbued with the attitude of mind the term implies there would be few fires in industry or anywhere else.

Fundamentals of prevention, protection and control

The prevention of, protection against and control of fire is an extremely technical and complex subject. The literature relating to it is voluminous. The Fire Protection Handbook of the National Fire Protection Association is in its 12th edition, a huge volume; yet it attempts only to include "in compact form essential information on fire prevention and fire protection that time has crystallized into good practice." The similarly authoritative "Handbook of Industrial Loss Prevention" by Factory Mutual is voluminous also. Yet the fundamentals on which all this vast detail is based are relatively simple and easily understood. Stated in briefest form they are:

1. Prevent the start of fire.
2. Provide for early detection of fire.
3. Prevent the spread of the fire.
4. Provide for prompt extinguishment.
5. Provide for the prompt and orderly evacuation of personnel.

Prevention of start of fire

This fundamental has to do with measures designed to reduce to a minimum the possibility of fire start. They cover primarily, arrangement and layout, construction, control of operations, maintenance, housekeeping and the elimination of unsafe practices, or more positively, the development of the maximum in safe and adequate behavior.

Fire is a chemical reaction between a flammable or combustible substance and oxygen. It is often referred to as "rapid oxidation with evolution of light and heat." The oxidation of substances in general that goes too slowly to produce rapid heating with light are otherwise identical in nature as, for example, the rusting of iron. In an atmosphere of pure oxygen, iron, heated to a glowing temperature, will burn rapidly.

The N.F.P.A. has sought through the years to direct popular attention to the fact that if you have oxygen fuel and heat together you get fire. This relationship is usually pictured as a triangle, "the fire triangle," with fire as one side, fuel as the other and oxygen as the base.

Each combustible material will ignite and burn when raised to a certain fixed temperature, its "ignition temperature," in the presence of air. Ignition temperatures vary widely. Some are so low that they will ignite and burn on contact with surfaces, for example, steam pipes and furnace smoke pipes that would not ordinarily be thought hot enough to be a hazard. Some can undergo a chemical change that lowers their ignition temperature. Wood furnishes an important example of this. Long continued contact with steam heating pipes at temperatures far below the ignition temperature of the original wood may cause it to change to a form of charcoal whose ignition temperature is low enough for it to catch fire from the same steam pipe eventually. This hazard has caused innumerable fires and will continue to until fire prevention mindedness becomes far more widespread than it presently is. The same thing is true of many other hazards that are common throughout our civilization, as the following list of the six largest fire sources in numerical importance shows, namely:

1. Matches and smoking.
2. Heating and cooking.
3. Housekeeping and rubbish.
4. Electrical wiring and apparatus.
5. Open flames and sparks.
6. Flammable liquids.

Even a cursory consideration of these sources and the manner in which fires ordinarily start in each of them will emphasize the overwhelming importance of always keeping the first triangle in mind, that is, always keeping combustibles and heat safely separated.

Except for matches and smoking, the above order of listing should not be taken as order of importance either as to relative number or aggregate cost. If the list were limited to industrial fires, the six major sources would be the same still, but their relative importance would change. For example, heating and cooking fires are far more important numerically in homes than in industry. In industry, oil fires in oil processing or in heating it for other purposes frequently involves heavy losses. Also there are significant differences as between the various branches of industry. For example in industries making extensive use of electrical equipment, fires of electrical origin are likely to predominate; in hotels fires due to smoking are a

major source both in number and in loss of life; in restaurants heating
and cooking fires are numerous.

Matches and smoking

Year after year, over one-fourth of all fires are started through the careless use of matches and failure to extinguish cigar, cigarette and pipe ashes.
America has become a nation of smokers, and any serious consideration
of fire prevention and protection must recognize and deal with this fact.

The first step the safety engineer should take to meet this situation is
to make an analysis of all plant and yard locations where smoking would
be particularly hazardous. These areas should be designated as *no-smoking*
areas and signs prohibiting smoking should be so posted that no misunder-
standing is possible. It is imperative that once the signs are posted the
prohibition be strictly enforced. It must apply to supervisors and executives, even the company president and visitors just as strictly as to workmen. It should be enforced with strictness comparable to that by which the
goggle wearing rule has been so effectively and profitably enforced in the
areas of the Pullman Company plants that presented eye hazards, profitably
in that a once very high eye injury rate was reduced to near zero and has remained there. Once the worthwhileness of the wearing of eye protectors was
established employee cooperation grew to a point such that enforcement became almost wholly by employee action; for example, on a visit to the works,
the company president forgot to put on his eye protector upon entering an
area where it was required. Almost at once a workman politely but in-
sistently called his attention to the lapse. The president thanked the worker
and later praised his action publicly as that of a truly safety minded man.
Just as it takes only a single flying object to destroy an eye it takes only a
single match or lighted cigarette to cause a serious fire if conditions are
right, and they are always likely to be.

In very high hazard plants or operations, it may be advisable, even
absolutely necessary, to prohibit the carrying of matches or cigarette lighters
into the no-smoking areas or even the entire plant. A check of pockets of
all who enter is routine in many such plants, and is a major factor in the
remarkably fine fire and explosion record many of them have. If all employees understand fully the need for such a measure, few if any will fail to
cooperate. It must be made clear to every employee that a single slip could
mean a disaster with probable loss of life to say nothing of loss of job.

Similarly restricted areas are common where highly flammable or
explosive gas dust or vapors are likely to be present, as, for example, in
oil refineries, grain elevators, the manufacture of paints, enamels, varnishes
and the like. Although areas or rooms where such hazardous materials
are held in storage in tanks, cans, barrels or other closed containers would

seem to present little hazard, the record of fires and disasters in such places tells a different story. It is sometimes difficult to get employees to realize that a leak may exist and go unnoticed for some time; in the storing and removal operations a dropped container may break open, etc. A storage room or building may be an inviting place to sneak a smoke; altogether such places generally present a high hazard for smoking as the record shows.

Heating and cooking

The variety of types and kinds of stoves, heaters, ranges, furnaces etc., used in industry or in dwellings, or both, is practically endless. However, certain general principles should be unfailingly applied in the selection, installation and use of such equipment. Briefly:

1. Type and kind should be carefully selected to best meet the needs and conditions of the service for which it is intended.

2. All such equipment should bear the approval of a nationally recognized agency or be in full conformance with all requirements of the legally constituted agency having jurisdiction.

3. Installation should be in full conformance with recognized safety standards for such equipment.

4. Installation should be such as to provide, so far as possible, for safe, fault-free operation for extended periods of time.

5. Provide for and maintain safe clearance between any heating device and any combustible materials.

6. Make careful provision for the safe storage and handling of all fuels used.

7. Provide for the safe handling and disposal of ash and waste.

8. Provide safe connections to adequate chimneys or vents for all fuel burning equipment.

9. Make sure of adequate air supply to all rooms housing fuel burning equipment.

10. Provide for the unfailing maintenance of all such equipment in safe condition, whether in operating or standby status.

11. Make sure of the competency of the operating personnel in the safe use of the equipment.

Housekeeping and rubbish

Accumulations of combustible material of any kind, particularly rubbish or waste, although they may not ignite of themselves, constitute standing invitations to fire. A spark, a carelessly thrown match or cigarette, a short circuit, hot metal from a soldering or welding job, any such quick heat, combined with poor housekeeping, can cause fire and does in innumerable cases each year. Moreover, many waste products have relatively low ignition temperatures and ignite easily, particularly when in finely divided form, and flame high very quickly.

Poor housekeeping contributes greatly also, to the hazard of spontaneous combustion because spontaneous heating is favored by accumulation. Oily or greasy rags are well known offenders, particularly if allowed to accumulate in corners or other places that favor the retention of heat rather than its dissipation. Even materials used in maintaining good housekeeping can present this hazard because they may contain hazardous flammable solvents.

A definite program for the maintenance of good housekeeping should be set up and maintained, consisting of at least the following:

1. Announce the program to all employees and make sure they know the reasons for it and realize its importance.

2. Provide for the orderly and adequate disposal of all combustible wastes and rubbish.

3. Provide safe containers for all substances subject to spontaneous heating, and for regular disposal of their contents.

4. Where large amounts of combustible wastes cannot practically be removed from the building immediately, provide for their interim storage in fire-resistive rooms or vaults effectively cut off, fire-wise, from the rest of the building and sprinklered, if at all possible.

5. Prohibit storage in nooks, corners, or seldom visited rooms in plant buildings except for storerooms properly cut off from the rest of the building and sprinklered, if possible.

6. Provide for the systematic maintenance of good external housekeeping to prevent the accumulation of waste and rubbish around buildings and to keep down weeds, grass, etc. that could serve to spread fire.

Electrical wiring and apparatus

Fires that originate in electrical equipment, or in the use of electricity, constitute a very substantial proportion of total fires in industry; a major source both as to number and total cost. The National Fire Protection Association presents an annual summary of fires of electrical origin in industry. With minor variations, the cause relationships remain about the same year by year. For a typical year the major causes were:

1. Worn out in service............................28% of total.
2. Improper use of approved equipment.............14% ”   ”

3. Accidental occurrence......................12% " "
4. Defective installation.......................11% " "
5. Unknown or not reported..................35% " "

The breakdown showed further that the fires originated in:

(a) Appliances (including motors)................52% of total.
(b) Wires, cords, cables......................27% " "
(c) Terminal equipment......................12% " "
(d) Other .... 9% " "

Electricity, properly used and properly controlled, presents virtually no fire hazard. Investigations of fires of electrical origin show that in the overwhelming proportion of cases the spark or heat that started the fire resulted from a break in the insulation, partial grounding of a circuit, poor switch contacts, faulty splices and connections, overheating of equipment due to overloading, temporary wiring improperly installed or improper fusing. A few fires each year result from incandescent lights coming in contact with flammable materials but these are not properly electrical in origin. The Cleveland Clinic disaster in 1929 which involved a life loss of 125 persons resulted from an unguarded incandescent light coming in contact with the highly flammable nitrocellulose X-ray films in a film storage vault in the basement of the Clinic building. This disaster highlighted the unwisdom of storing such hazardous materials in a building of such human occupancy; storage in a separate fire resistive building for that purpose only, is of vital importance. However, some good did come of it for it led to the hurried development of the slow burning type of film.

It should not be necessary after a half century of general use of electrical equipment to explain herein why proper fusing of electrical circuits is so very important, yet the number of fires each year due to overfusing to say nothing of the frequency with which electrical inspectors discover this offense against safety, proves that the need for a better understanding of the hazard is widespread.

It is vitally important that every electrical circuit be properly fused. The fuse has a function similar to that of a safety valve on a boiler. Electric wiring is in each case designed to carry a certain load. If that load is exceeded by the addition of more or bigger equipment than it was wired to carry, the wire will heat up and eventually, if the overload is heavy enough, a fire will result. Furthermore, long continued overheating may cause deterioration of the insulation, thus presenting both a fire and a life hazard. Fuses and circuit breakers are placed in electric circuits and set to cut off the current at a point a little below the danger point. The practice of replacing a blown fuse with one whose current carrying capacity is greater than that for which the circuit was designed, or of using coins, nails or some similar metal object, or bridging the fuse with a piece of wire, is inviting disaster. It indicates on the part of the person who will do this sort of thing, not only surprising ignorance but also the lack of any sense of responsibility for the safety of others. When fuses blow repeatedly in a given circuit, an electrician should be called in to find and correct the trouble.

In rooms where explosive gases, vapors, or dusts may be present, special explosion proof electrical equipment must be provided. Such equipment is designed to prevent the entrance of flammable material or to withstand the force of an internal explosion without allowing flame or heat to escape and ignite the explosive room atmosphere.

Portable electrical equipment, particularly portable lamps and hand tools, are the source of many fires. The use of substandard equipment and poor maintenance are the chief causes, though misuse is also often a factor. The extension cord is the weakest link because it is so subject to abuse with resulting failure of insulation, particularly in the presence of moisture. A life hazard from electric shock is obviously involved also. No extension cord not bearing the approval of Underwriters Laboratories should ever be used. Also every plant should set up and maintain a thoroughgoing system of inspection and maintenance of all such equipment.

Open flames and sparks

It would seem that the hazard of open flames and sparks near or even in the neighborhood of combustible materials is so obvious that sensible people would always have it in mind and would govern themselves accordingly but the fire record strongly refutes this assumption. Except for a few totally unforeseeable occurrences, fires from this source are wholly preventable. Cutting and welding torches used without proper precautions are serious offenders because they throw so many and such hot sparks. They have caused many extremely heavy losses, for example, the burning of the French liner *Normandie* just at a time when it was urgently needed in our war struggle. Another was the destruction of the General Motor's automatic transmission plant which involved not only a very heavy direct cost but a staggering production loss as well. Both these fires were the result of the failure of responsible people to take even elemental precautions to keep the welding sparks away from highly flammable material.

If the following simple rules of general applicability were universally observed, fires from open flames and sparks would be rare indeed. They are:

1. Do not permit accumulations of fuels or other combustibles near where there may be open fires or sparks.

2. Where open flames are necessary, provide for their strict control in all phases of their use and supplement these control measures with the provision of suitable means of fire extinguishment.

3. Provide for safe clearances between combustible substances and flames or other high temperature sources.

4. Where safe clearance is not feasible, provide insulating, incombustible covering or other suitable protection for combustible substances that might be, or become, exposed by any of the operations involved. As the two examples cited above show, this is particularly important where electric or flame welding or cutting is to be done.

5. Bond and suitably ground all electrical equipment to prevent arcing and sparking.

6. Use only properly designed and constructed equipment.

7. Develop a safe procedure for the use and operation of all devices and equipment that might produce flames or sparks and train all employees involved, in the application of this safe procedure.

8. Set up and maintain an effective program of inspection and maintenance.

Flammable liquids

Presumably everyone knows that flammable liquids themselves do not burn; it is their vapors that do, and if the vapors are mixed with air in the right proportion, the burning is so rapid that it amounts to an explosion, even though the pressures that can be produced thereby are only a fraction of those characteristic of even the least powerful explosives.

The range of proportions within which a vapor-air mixture is explosive (explosive range) is different for each substance. For some it is narrow, for others very wide. For example, in ordinary gasoline vapor-air mixtures the range is about 1.3% to 6% by volume. Ethyl alcohol has a range of 3.5 to 19%, acetylene a range of 2.5 to 80%, a range that justifies treating it with the utmost respect.

It should always be kept in mind that the vapors of flammable liquids will collect above the surface of the liquid in a vessel or tank; if it isn't closed they will spill over its edge and be carried by air currents, will rise if lighter than air, will sink to the ground and seek low levels if heavier than air but will continuously be mixing with the air. Therefore, wherever such vapors exist there is always both a fire and an explosion hazard, and they must be handled and treated accordingly. Even relatively small amounts of such volatiles, vaporized and mixed with air in the right proportions, can do a lot of damage. For example, a gallon of gasoline can wreck a sizable building under optimum conditions.

The following precautions should be taken by users of flammable liquids:

1. Always choose the least flammable liquid that will serve the purpose in question.

2. Keep all flammable liquids in closed containers or in safety cans.

3. Limit the supply of flammable liquid in the work area to one shift's requirements as a maximum.

4. Develop and unfailingly apply work procedures that will hold to a minimum the possibility of fire or explosion.

5. Bond and ground all equipment that might otherwise produce a spark.

6. Use only approved electrical equipment installed in full accordance with the requirements of the agency having legal jurisdiction.

7. Prohibit smoking, open flames, spark producing operations or devices in the vicinity of flammable volatiles.

8. Provide for storage of flammables safely away from heat or spark sources of any nature.

9. Store any substantial amounts of flammables in special buildings or vaults, built to conform to recognized standards for such storage.

10. Provide ventilation for all operations involving the use or storage of flammable volatiles adequate so far as practically possible, to prevent any accumulation of vapors.

11. Provide effective venting of all storage tanks.

12. Provide suitable equipment and develop and apply safe procedures for the cleaning and repair of solvent tanks.

13. Provide for the safe disposal of flammable liquid wastes.

14. Provide sand or other incombustible substance for use in cleaning up spills.

Discovery and extinguishment

Each year, many fires discovered in their early stages become uncontrollable because of the failure of the individual who discovered the fire to turn in a proper alarm promptly; usually because he attempted to extinguish it himself. No worse mistake could be made, for if he fails, the fire will usually have become so big by the time help arrives, that even a well-equipped city fire department is likely to find it very difficult to bring it under control and heavy loss will have become inevitable.

The first principle of effective fire fighting, then, is to turn in an alarm at once when the fire is discovered. This applies both to the plant alarm system and the public alarm system. It is obviously far better to turn in an alarm and then have the fire under control by the time the professional forces arrive, than to delay turning in an alarm and run even the slightest risk of a serious fire thereby.

Virtually all industrial plants are located in areas serviced by the community or other fire department. However, the failure of plant management to arrange for close cooperation between the plant fire control program and public fire protection forces has in innumerable cases, allowed small fires to become big and cause heavy loss. Most of these losses could have been prevented had the leadership of the professional forces been called in to serve as advisers, instructors, and partners in developing plans for joint action as needed. The plant management should take the initiative, normally through the plant safety engineer. The plan should cover at least (a) access to premises, (b) special hazards if any, (c) coordination of plant and public protection, (d) inspection.

Access to premises. A fire department representative should inspect the plant to determine the best means of access and the preferable path the fire fighting equipment should take to reach each of the buildings, etc. Many heavy losses have resulted from night fires because of failure to provide for the prompt opening of plant gates normally kept locked at night. In other cases, the department equipment after gaining access was unable to turn a corner in a narrow passageway or was blocked by piled material. This is best taken care of by establishing the fire route, posting it with suitable signs, marking off clearly the areas that must be kept clear and providing for inspection to maintain them.

Coordination of plant and public protection. With the aid of professional advice, a plant fire department should be organized, first-aid fire fighting equipment obtained and the plant personnel trained and instructed in its use and in the proper procedure in case of fire. In this connection, knowledge by all concerned of the location of valves, standpipes, fire alarm boxes and the like is of vital importance. Special hazards, if any: the fire department, both of the plant and the public one, should be given full information as to any special hazards involved in plant operations. Should changes in process, expansion of operations and the like introduce new hazards, full information on them should be given to all concerned, preferably in the planning stage.

Inspection. Inspections by representatives of the local fire department should be arranged for, not only in the first instance, but occasionally thereafter on the initiative of that department as a check on the plant program, particularly its inspection service. It may seem surprising, but serious losses have occurred because management, even after calling the public department in, refused to take its recommendations seriously or even resented them. If a plant management has any doubt as to the validity of such recommendations, the obvious course is to call for a consultation with others of professional competence, much as a doubting patient does with his family physician, of course providing the recommended changes would involve much expense. If not, they should be complied with as a matter of principle.

Fire alarms

As already indicated, the first principle of effective fire fighting is to turn in an alarm at once upon discovery of fire. All plant personnel should know exactly the location of each of the fire alarm devices, both public and of the plant and exactly how to operate them.

The use of a watchman during "off" hours is the oldest alarm system. Utter reliability is the primary requirement, and of course, the ability to get around quickly and do what must be done promptly and effectively. A full-time watch is needed, not just a regular more or less superficial tour of the plant. The use of a clock, which the watchman punches at specific stations throughout the plant, offers some protection against indifferent service, but a system whereby each "punch-in" is transmitted to a central control station is much superior because any failure by the watchman to punch in can be investigated at once.

The best system of fire detection is the automatic alarm which turns in an alarm when fire starts in its vicinity. The two most familiar types are:

The Fixed-Temperature type. This type is designed to operate when the temperature in its vicinity reaches a predetermined level, for example, 135, 150 or 200 degrees.

The Rate-of-Rise type. This type is designed to operate when the temperature in its vicinity rises at a rate rapid enough to indicate fire.

Each of these systems has its advantages for particular situations and hazards. The determination of the type to choose should be made with the advice of competent specialists after careful analysis of conditions and possibilities likely to be involved. The automatic type of fire alarm can also be tied in to sprinkler systems or other automatic extinguishing equipment to sound an alarm when it begins to operate, whether near the seat of fire or not.

The essentials of an effective alarm system are briefly:

1. A reliable signal must be transmitted.

2. It must reach all those who are assigned specific responsibility for fire protection regardless as to where they are located in or about the plant.

3. It should never be used for any purpose other than to sound an alarm for fire.

4. It should, if possible, indicate the location of the fire.

5. If an individual must be relied upon to transmit notice of fire, the means for its transmission must be readily accessible and should require the simplest possible performance.

6. The alarm should be so loud that everyone in and about the plant can surely hear it, and of such a nature that everyone will recognize it.

Finally, it is important that each alarm unit be installed where it will most surely, and promptly, give its alarm, that is, each should be at a high hazard point. Also, should changes in plant operations add other high hazard points or change them in any way, the setup should be reappraised for advisable changes or additions. The extreme importance of a high standard of maintenance for such equipment is, of course, obvious, yet serious fires have been due to lack of maintenance of originally excellent systems.

Control of fire in early stages

The sounding of a prompt alarm is the first step toward control. The next step, of course, is the prompt use by those nearest the source of fire, of the first-aid fire fighting equipment immediately available. This can be vital, because under unfavorable conditions, such as an unexpected delay in the arrival of the fire fighting forces, even a very limited but prompt bit of fire fighting may make the difference between a heavy loss and little or none. In order to provide the proper equipment, it is necssary that there be a thorough understanding of the types of fires that may start at each given point in the plant, and a correspondingly good knowledge of the type of fire extinguishing equipment best suited to deal with each of the kinds of fires that might be involved. The locations and mounting or storing of this first-aid equipment must of course, be carefully chosen for easy accessibility, maximum security and easy inspection, remembering always that "out of sight is out of mind." Finally every employee anywhere in the vicinity of first-aid fire fighting equipment should be thoroughly trained in its proper use.

It is emphasized that practically all fires start as small, localized flames. The function of the plant fire fighters is to extinguish the starting blaze at once or, failing that, confine and retard it as much as possible until outside help arrives.

With this function in mind, it is usually not difficult to decide on the type of extinguisher that should be made available at each specific location in or about the plant. If, for example, the possibility of oil fires exists at certain locations, extinguishers designed specifically for oil fires should be placed at these locations. Although other types of extinguishers might be of some help, they would not be adequate to keep such a fire under control, because different types of fires require different types of extinguishers. Studies have been made by laboratories * maintained by the fire underwriters, and through these studies fires have been classified. These classifications are based on the types of extinguishing agents necessary to combat specific types of fires.

Class A fires. Under this classification are fires that occur in common combustible materials such as wood, paper, rags, and allied material. Fires of this type can be readily extinguished by water or solutions containing large amounts of water. The process of extinguishing this class of fire depends primarily on the cooling and quenching effect of the water.

Class B fires. Under this classification are fires where a blanketing effect, which will exclude oxygen, is necessary for extinguishment. Water should not ordinarily be used to combat this type of fire. Quite often water would tend to spread the blaze rather than control it. Fires which fall into this classification are oil fires and fires of flammable liquids such as gasoline or grease.

Class C fires. Class C fires are those that occur in electrical equipment, or in equipment that is in close proximity to electric circuits. Here care must be taken to use a nonconducting extinguishing agent in order to protect the individuals who are fighting the fire. Examples of this type of fire are transformer fires, switchboard fires, and motor and generator fires.

There are numerous styles and makes of first-aid fire appliances which are suitable for each class of fire. To list all of the types of extinguishers would take considerable space, but a brief summary of some of those commonly used for each class of fire is given.*

CLASS A FIRES

Fire Pairs (12 quart)	Calcium Chloride (2½ gallon)
Soda-acid (2½ gallon)	Foam (1½, 2½, 5 gallon)
Pump Tank (2½, 5 gallon)	Carbon Dioxide Cartridge—with plain water (2½ gallon)

CLASS B FIRES

Foam (1½, 2½, 5 gallon)	Carbon Dioxide Gas (2 lbs. to 20 lbs.)
Vaporizing Liquid, pump type (1 to 2 quart)	Dry Chemical (4 to 30 lbs.)
Vaporizing Liquid, stored pressure type (½ to 3½ gallon)	

CLASS C FIRES

Any extinguisher using only nonconducting substances.

* Underwriters' Laboratories, Inc., 207 E. Ohio Street, Chicago, Illinois. Associated Factory Mutual Fire Insurance Companies, 184 High St., Boston, Mass.

Too much emphasis cannot be placed on the advisability of consulting with the state or local Fire Insurance Rating Bureau as well as the local fire department before purchasing fire extinguishers. After the extinguishers have been purchased, the local fire department should again assist in determining the correct location for the placement of the extinguishers. Many factors must be considered in locating an extinguishing agent, and only those who have had adequate experience in fire fighting can give sound advice on this point. The problems are so complex that it would be unwise for anyone without wide experience to attempt to give such advice. There is another reason why the state Fire Insurance Rating Bureau should be called into the picture at this point. Fire insurance rates, which determine the premium to be paid for fire protection, are based not only on the hazard that exists but also on the protection that is available. Although industrial management might feel that, from their own standpoint, certain protection is sufficient, it is possible that the rating bureau would allow no credit for this protection because of past experience, which might indicate that this protection is not entirely suitable. The expenditure of the same amount of money for other equipment might conceivably result in savings in fire insurance premiums, which would more than pay for the equipment.

Construction, operation, inspection, and maintenance of extinguishers

Portable Fire Extinguishers. The importance of the correct use of portable fire extinguishers can hardly be overemphasized. Improperly used they may be of little effectiveness or none. Without adequate instruction and training misuse is very likely, therefore any protection program that lacks thorough training may easily spell disaster.

It is also important to consult with the state or local Fire Insurance Rating Bureau before purchasing fire extinguishers, also, the local fire department. After the extinguishers have been purchased, the local fire department should be asked for help in determining the correct location for each of them. Many factors are involved and only persons with long experience in fire fighting can give sound advice in this connection. The problems likely to be involved in a fire are complex and foreseeable only to the experienced eye.

The commonly used types of portable fire extinguishers are:

Soda-acid *Carbon Dioxide*
Vaporizing Liquid *Dry Chemicals*
Foam

Soda-acid. The soda-acid extinguisher contains a charge of sodium bicarbonate dissolved in water. A small glass bottle of sulphuric acid is held in a metal cage. This bottle has a loosely fitted stopper which falls out when the extinguisher is inverted so that the acid is dumped into the soda solution. The acid quickly combines chemically with bicarbonate, releasing carbon dioxide gas which quickly builds up the pressure necessary to expel the contents of the extinguisher.

Under normal conditions the chemical reaction builds up a pressure of about 75 psi. Its stream has a range of from 30 to 40 feet and a duration of about one minute. Standard requirements for the 2½-gal. size call for them to be so located that a user would not have to travel more than 50 ft. to reach the extinguisher. At least one extinguisher should be provided for each 2500 square feet of area.

This extinguisher has the advantage of simple construction, it is easily charged and its operation is not complicated. It easily reaches overhead fires in rooms with ceilings of ordinary height. However, since its stream is a water solution, it must not be used on electrical fires nor is it effective on oil fires, or with any flammable liquid. It may actually spread these.

Foam. The shell of a foam extinguisher contains a water solution of sodium bicarbonate to which a foam stabilizer has been added. The inner container is a long metal tube containing a solution of aluminum sulfate. It operates upon inversion just as does the soda-acid type. The carbon dioxide produced expels the contents in the form of a thick, tenacious foam filled with bubbles of carbon dioxide. Spread over the surface of the burning liquid, it excludes the oxygen and thus extinguishes the fire; unless of course, the burning is so vigorous that the erupting vapors break the foam blanket or prevent its formation. The volume of foam is about 7 to 8 times that of the original solutions. The range is about 35 ft. and its effective discharge time is about one minute.

Foam is best suited to extinguishing oil or flammable liquid fires. Once formed, the blanket persists for some time and prevents reignition. It is not effective for alcohol, esters or lacquer thinners because they react chemically with it. Special foam powders are available for such fires. Nor is foam of any kind effective with substances of especially low boiling points such as ether and carbon disulfide because their vapors are likely to penetrate the foam blanket, once it is formed, and burn on top of it.

Foam extinguishers freeze at approximately 27 degrees F., and must be protected against lower temperatures. It is not practical to add anti-freezing solutions because of the likelihood of damaging chemical reaction.

Vaporizing Liquid. Vaporizing liquid extinguishers are charged with specially treated nonconducting liquids, usually carbon tetrachloride or chlorobromomethane containing a freezing point depressant and anticorrosion components. When the liquid is sprayed onto a fire it produces a blanket of heavy inert gas that excludes oxygen. The cooling action is small. The freezing point is low, on the order of −40 degrees F. Their vapors are nonconducting so they can be used safely on live electrical equipment at voltages up to about 30,000. The range is from 20 to 30 feet, depending on size and type with a duration of a little more than a minute.

These extinguishers, useful though they are, have two serious limitations; namely, the vapors are corrosive and can do considerable damage to polished metal machine parts, and the vapors are toxic of themselves and when in contact with highly heated metal surfaces may produce the even more toxic phosgene gas. Consequently, it is inadvisable to use these extinguishers in confined areas unless they are well ventilated. If ventilation is not practicable, respiratory protective devices approved for this exposure should be used. Also, suitable steps should be taken to protect personnel who service the extinguishers.

Carbon Dioxide.   This extinguisher consists essentially of a cylinder of carbon dioxide held liquid by pressure which at 70 degrees F. is about 850 psi. A siphon tube, valve, and hose with discharge horn are attached to the cylinder. The valve is at the top since the correct position for operating is upright. Capacity is rated by weight of carbon dioxide each will take, running from 2 pounds up.

Carbon dioxide extinguishes fire by excluding the oxygen from the surface of the burning material. Its effectiveness is limited to the area of contact. The cooling effect is negligible. It has the advantages of not corroding, not deteriorating with age, not conducting electricity and not freezing. Its chief usefulness, therefore, is for fires in or about electrical equipment and with the more highly volatile flammable liquids such as alcohol, ether and lacquer thinners. Their short range, 2 to 4 feet, limits their usefulness as does their limited duration, 15 seconds for the smallest size to one minute for the largest.

Dry Chemical.   The dry chemical extinguisher consists of a strong container holding a charge of dry chemicals, a smaller container charged with carbon dioxide or nitrogen gas under pressure and a discharge nozzle equipped with a shutoff valve. The range runs from about 6 ft. for the smallest size to about 45 ft. for the 450 pound wheeled unit.

The dense stream of finely divided dust, properly directed, can blanket a relatively large area and extinguish or greatly slow down the burning by excluding the oxygen. Also it leaves a coating of the chemical dust on the surfaces it reaches, a point of particular value in fires of cotton or other textile fibres because it inhibits reignition. On the other hand, these extinguishers should not be used on equipment that would be damaged or its operation interfered with by such a coating as, for example, a telephone switchboard with innumerable relays requiring perfect contacts for effective functioning.

Fixed Automatic Devices

These fall into two classes, namely:

1. Automatic sprinklers.

2. Installations providing for the automatic release of extinguishing agents other than water. They are used in high hazard situations where water would be ineffective or undesirable as for oil tanks, certain chemical processes, electric generators, etc. They use foam or inert gases.

Automatic sprinkler systems

The automatic sprinkler is by far the most important of all fire protection devices the world over. The value of property protected by them in this country alone runs into many tens of billions of dollars and increases steadily as our industrial economy expands. The losses for sprinklered property as compared to those for unsprinklered property are remarkably low, only a few percent.

The effectiveness of automatic sprinklers in saving life has proved even greater than in saving financial loss. Loss of life in a sprinklered building is of rare occurrence, and when it does occur is usually due to an accompanying explosion or other high hazard occurrence or situation.

The failures of sprinkler systems to control fires are usually due to:

Water shut off.

Flash fires as from flammable vapors, combustible dusts, lint.

Explosions or other violent occurrences rendering the sprinkler system inoperative.

Obstructions or other conditions that prevent the water from reaching the fire.

In such places as schools, hospitals, sanitaria, department stores and hotels sprinklers should be considered a practical requirement because of their effectiveness in saving life.

As its name implies, the automatic sprinkler embodies the basic idea of having the fire turn on the water and thus put itself out. Obviously, it is necessary that the heat get to the sprinkler head quickly while the fire is small enough to be put out easily. The spacing of the sprinkler heads must therefore be such that wherever a fire starts in a room or building, it will be near enough to a sprinkler head to operate it promptly.

Water is supplied through a system of piping ordinarily run close under the ceiling with the sprinkler heads spaced evenly along the pipes and the pipe spacing such as to give complete coverage. The sprinkler head consists essentially of an orifice closed by a disk held in place against the water pressure by a device that releases it at a predetermined temperature by:

1. *The melting of a solder.*
2. *The melting of a chemical.*
3. *The breakage of a bulb by the expansion of contained liquid.*

Each sprinkler head carries a "deflector" or "distributor" whose purpose is to distribute the water in a manner that will cause it to cover its allotted area properly. The minimum flowing pressure for effective sprinkler operation is about 8 pounds per square inch. At that pressure, each head will discharge about 15 gallons of water per minute and cover a floor area of about 100 square ft. Well defined rules based on long experience have been worked out for all details of correct sprinkler installations. The following points are of major importance:

1. The water distribution must not be interfered with by any barrier, such as unsprinklered enclosures for tool room, or bins or platforms, etc.

2. Stock must not be piled close enough to sprinkler heads to interfere with the spray.

3. Sprinkler heads must be kept clean and free of loading, incrustation, paint, etc.

4. Floor openings of some size should be protected to prevent drafts of heated air that might open an unnecessarily large number of sprinkler heads, thus causing unnecessary water damage and perhaps lowering the water pressure in the system and reducing its effectiveness.

5. There should be no concealed spaces in walls or floors to which the spray cannot penetrate.

6. The pressure and volume of water must be sufficient to supply effectively the maximum number of sprinkler heads likely to open in any fire that might reasonably be expected to occur.

7. Maintenance of the entire system in proper working order at all times is an absolute essential.

Sprinkler systems are ordinarily filled with water at all times, but where freezing may occur "dry pipe systems," that is, filled with air under pressure, are used. Release of the pressure due to the opening of one or more sprinkler heads will operate a valve to turn on the water. Since this method involves some delay and also since dry systems cost more than wet and are more difficult to maintain it is usually better, and, in the long run, cheaper to heat the building.

For occupancies where the nature of the materials involved is such that very heavy sprays are essential as in processing or storing pyroxylin, cotton nitration etc., "deluge" systems are used, which as the term indicates, can discharge large volumes of water quickly. When controlled by rate of rise devices they can be made to wet down a large area almost instantaneously.

From the standpoint both of fire fighting and of holding water damage down, it is important that an alarm be given whenever a sprinkler head opens. This is easily accomplished by means of water flow detectors, that operate alarms.

The extreme importance of a high standard of maintenance of sprinkler systems has led to the development of supervisory services that are obtainable on an annual contract basis through centrally located stations manned by personnel trained to install and service sprinkler systems. Basic to this service is the automatic transmission of an alarm to both the central station and the public fire department when a water flow occurs in the sprinkler system, and also if any other significant change occurs in the service condition of the system, for example, the closing of the water supply valve.

Fire hose systems

Fires that are not extinguished either by sprinkler systems or first-aid appliances in their incipient stages become large and require great quantities of water to prevent further spread and to secure ultimate extinguishment.

Although dependency must be placed on community fire departments for the handling of large fires, availability of fire hose attached to outlets throughout the plant is of first importance in the reduction of the fire hazard.

Care must be taken in the selection of hose couplings and nozzles, and in the proper location of outlets. In purchasing hose, the advice of the local fire department or state Fire Inspection Bureau should be followed. The hose should always carry the label of Underwriters' Laboratories to insure proper functioning under pressure.

In general, rubber-lined hose should be used for outside protection, whereas unlined linen hose is most suitable for inside use. Most fire departments recommend hose not exceeding 1½ inches in diameter because of the difficulty inexperienced men have in handling larger types. Should larger hose be purchased, men must be trained in its use. Many serious or fatal accidents have been caused by the whip of the hose when the water was turned on.

Hose of any type should be stored so that it is quickly available in case of fire. There are a number of types of storage devices, the use of which will accomplish this purpose and will likewise keep the hose in good condition when it is not in use. Reels, swinging racks, and carts are available for this purpose.

The life of good hose varies from a few years to possibly 10 years, depending on the care given it and the protection from dirt, injurious chemicals, gases, and so on. Hose is generally damaged by mechanical injury or through contact with heat, oil, acid, or gasoline. It must also be kept in mind that linen hose may be damaged through mildew, and provisions should be made to prevent this type of injury. Maintenance of hose requires constant and thorough inspection and care. The hose should be checked periodically, changed on the reel or rack several times each year, dried thoroughly after use and before storage, and washed or brushed after exposure to dirt or oil. It should, of course, likewise be protected from mechanical injury both while stored and while in use. Rubber-lined hose should be tested several times a year. Unlined linen hose should not be wet except when needed for fire protection. More damage can be done to this hose through wetting and insufficient drying than through continued dry storage. Careful inspection will help maintain linen hose in serviceable condition.

Couplings

It is vital that all hydrant nipples and hose couplings match. A National Standard for 2½ in. and larger hose has been adopted and this should be used where possible. It is in use by the fire departments of most of the major cities. When equipment is to be purchased, the local fire department should be contacted to determine the hose specification in use. Many times each year equipment has been useless in an emergency because of lack of thread uniformity. If it is found that there are variations in existing equipment, adapters should be provided before the equipment is needed at a fire.

The preceding discussion of fire equipment and apparatus has given consideration only to types of equipment designed for conditions usually existing. Special hazards often require special equipment. The mere presence of extinguishers, hose, or other equipment does not afford full protection against serious fires. Many cases are on record in which uninformed employees have made available equipment ineffective because of lack of knowledge as to how the equipment should be used. It is essential that all employees have an understanding of the various first-aid fire-protection equipment and, wherever possible, training in its use.

In many plants one entire safety meeting each year is devoted to a display, description, and demonstration of the use of the various types of extinguishers located in each department. When the extinguisher must be discharged in order to check its condition, discharge under actual conditions of use should be made.

It has been deemed wise by many safety engineers to seal all extinguishers after inspection in order to prevent tampering with the mechanical equipment or discharge of the extinguisher for purposes other than fire. The sealing offers a positive means of visual check, because, whenever a foreman, a member of the safety committee, or a superintendent finds that a seal has been removed or broken, he immediately recognizes the need of checking and refilling an empty extinguisher. Time lost in attempting to get an ineffective or damaged extinguisher to work, or even in getting it to the fire, could be better utilized for other purposes.

Fire brigades

In larger plants it is desirable to have trained groups or fire brigades to handle equipment and to take charge of the situation when an emergency due to fire arises. Even in small plants a few men can be given complete instructions as to fire hazards, use of equipment, and procedure in case of fire.

The work of fire brigades in larger plants depends on many factors which are related to the physical arrangement of the plant, the size of the plant, and the type of operations. Regardless of the size of the plant, however, it should be recognized by management that the fire brigade and fire protection is an important part of the plant's operation.

Certain fundamental essentials must govern the work of any fire-fighting group, if it is to be efficient. First, rigid discipline must be established within the group itself. Second, the group must be provided with necessary equipment, which is maintained in usable condition. Third, the group must be trained under discipline in the use of the equipment and in the fundamental principles of fire fighting. The strength of the brigade, the amount of equipment, and the frequency of fire drills will depend almost entirely on the size of the plant and the nature of the hazards.

The men selected as members of the brigade should be intelligent, level-headed, and able bodied. Generally the foreman or superintendent, or some other person whose authority is recognized and who has a thorough knowledge of the plant and operations, should be selected as chief. This man should have the respect of all members of the brigade and should have had specific training in fire fighting, fire protection, and the use of equipment. A unit or a brigade should be a part of each work shift.

Every man on the fire brigade should know the location of each piece of fire equipment. He should be assigned specific duties in case of fire. Those duties will be dependent on the nature of the equipment available, the size of the plant, and the type of hazard. For instance, where hose is available, hose men, nozzle men, and hydrant men should be trained. Other members of the unit should be trained to direct the exit of employees, still others to use the chemical extinguishers, and so on. It is generally desirable to select men for this work who live near the plant. The value of the brigade will be proportional to the promptness and efficiency of each member under emergency conditions. It is, therefore, imperative that every individual in the unit have periodic instruction and practice in fire drill and fire fighting. Constant drilling cannot be overemphasized. The drilling and instruction can, in many cases, be done best by the chief or other officer of the local fire department. Not only will this procedure guarantee the proper training, but it will likewise develop full coördination between plant and city departments in case of fire.

Prevention of spread of fire

One of the fundamental objectives in fire fighting is to confine the fire that has started to as small an area as possible. Because of this fact it is essential that those who are charged with fire protection and extinguishment have some knowledge of how fires normally spread.

Ordinarily, fires spread in three ways. The most rapid means of spread is usually upward from floor to floor of the same building. Second, under certain conditions fires will spread from one part of a building to another part, or from building to building where they adjoin each other. Under adverse conditions such as high wind, sudden explosion, close proximity, and so on, fires often spread from building to building not adjoining.

Consideration should be given to the check of fire within single areas. Each floor should form a barrier to the vertical spread of fire. Careful examination should be made of floor openings such as chutes, elevators, stairways, beltways, lightwells, and the like. Such openings should be tightly enclosed in a standard manner wherever possible. Fire doors, closed automatically by heat, should be used for openings that cannot be permanently closed.

It should be kept in mind that in many cases, while the fire itself may not pass from a lower to an upper floor through any of these openings, the heat generated by a fire will cause a rapid rise of extremely hot air to upper floors unless some means is provided to prevent such a rise. The temperature of these hot gases or heated air is often well above the ignition point of materials on the upper floors. Many cases are on record where a fire, having started on one of the lower floors or in the basement, has caused a fire several floors above without any flame between the floors. It is, therefore, not just the spread of flame that must be considered, but the rise of gases that will cause explosion or fire at other locations.

Fire likewise will search out any weak spot in building construction, such as thin sections of flooring, cracks between floorboards, or openings caused by shrinkage. In case of a fire on any floor, a check should be made to be certain that the fire has not made progress and has not found its way into the concealed construction of the building. Many times fires that have presumably been extinguished break out some time later because of lack of thoroughness or lack of understanding on the part of those who extinguished them.

Another means of fires passing from one floor to another is through external windows usually located one directly above the other on successive floors. This is particularly true where windows on the upper floor are not protected or are open at the time of the fire. The best protection against this hazard is to use windows of wired glass in steel sash in all stories of the building. It is true that a fire may destroy such windows on the floor it is located on, but it is not likely that windows of similar construction on the floors immediately above will be damaged.

Although fire normally spreads rapidly within the building where it begins, under some conditions the spread will be from one building to another building which is adjoining. In congested areas, one wall often separates two buildings, and in many cases where there are two walls, these walls are in contact. In such cases, fires pass from one building to another, either through unprotected divisional wall openings, through the failure of fire doors, through fire doors partially or improperly equipped with hardware, over roofs or around ends of walls, or by heat passing directly through the single wall. In rare instances, a smoke explosion within the burning building may cause fires in adjoining buildings.

A few suggestions can be made for protection against the spreading of fire in the manners indicated above:

1. Where openings in walls are not necessary, they should either be closed through heavy fire-resistive doors or be permanently bricked up.

2. If fire doors are used to protect such openings, they should be placed on each side of the wall so as to give two lines of defense with valuable air space between. It is not sufficient to place but one fire door, because this will, in many instances, permit the spread of fire, especially if the entire building on one side of the floor is consumed.

3. A careful check should be made to be certain that fire doors close properly and that the doors, sills, door frames, and so on, are of such construction that they will not convey fire under extreme heat conditions.

4. Where large values are involved, it may be desirable to extend the division wall between buildings through the roof in order to form a parapet, especially if the roof is combustible on both sides of the wall.

5. In buildings of ordinary height, additional protection against spread of fire can be secured through the protection of windows with fire-resistive frames and wire glass.

Although the possibility of fire spreading from building to building where buildings are not adjoining is not as great as the spread from other causes, there are still many opportunities for the development of a fire of considerable extent and one that will involve numerous unconnected buildings. Generally speaking, such fires develop from the dropping of burning embers or other burning material onto combustible roofs of near-by buildings. Where roofs are made of asbestos cement, slate, tile, or metal, this possibility is of course reduced to a minimum.

A building near the burning building often catches fire through the heating and breaking into flame of combustible cornices. Wherever possible, such cornices should be removed. If they cannot be removed, the hazard can be reduced somewhat through the covering of such cornices with lock-jointed tin or metal lath and plaster.

The exposure presented by combustible exterior walls is serious. Such walls may be heated to the ignition temperature by flames as far as 15 or 20 feet away, even further if the fire is especially hot. Although local fire departments can usually prevent the spread of any but very severe fires to buildings not directly adjoining the building on fire, many owners have found it wise to install outside sprinklers to give protection against neighboring buildings, especially in high hazard areas.

Exit facilities

The record of loss of life in fires testifies eloquently as to the extreme importance of adequate exits suited to the type of building in question, the nature of its occupancy and the hazards involved. Building exits should always be established and maintained in full compliance with all of the applicable provisions of the N.F.P.A. Building Exits Code.

The following list of items for use in determining the adequacy of exit facilities, though by no means complete for every kind of building or occupancy, will serve as an effective guide:

1. Emergency exit needs depend on the construction of the building, the fire hazard of the materials or processes housed, the fire protection provided, and the characteristics of the occupants. Actually however, it is seldom practical to vary exit requirements much, chiefly because occupancy and use factors may change widely, in some cases, almost overnight. In general, the sound approach is to provide exit facilities adequate to meet the worst combination of unfavorable circumstances that appear reasonably possible.

2. The possibility of panic should always be taken into account. Panics usually involve heavy life loss. They can occur without fire. In fact some of the worst have resulted from an irresponsible yell of "fire," "fire." Particularly, in buildings housing meeting rooms or other places of group occupancy, it is vital to avoid any and all conditions that might block or seriously interfere with a panicky rush, specifically, narrow exits, narrow sections or sharp corners in passageways, winders and narrow landings in stairs, inadequate spaces at foot of stair flights or at exit discharge.

3. The provision of two exits so located as to render the cutting off of both at one time extremely improbable is fundamental to safety. This principle should never be violated in areas where any considerable number of persons congregate for any purpose.

4. Free travel of able-bodied persons in single file requires a width of 22 inches, which is, for that reason, used as the unit of exit width. A two-unit width is the minimum acceptable as satisfactory practice, though building codes commonly accept narrower widths for light occupancy in existing buildings.

5. Maximum travel distance from any point in a workroom or area to reach the nearest exit should not exceed:

High-hazard occupancy .... 75 feet
Moderate or low-hazard occupancy .... 100 feet
Moderate hazard sprinklered .... 150 feet

(*High-hazard* is defined as having contents likely to burn with extreme rapidity, or to give off poisonous fumes, or to explode.)

6. Exits should be readily accessible, unobstructed, the path of escape unmistakable and suitably lighted.

7. The minimum allowable clear stair width is 44 inches; tread width, exclusive of nosing, not less than 9 inches; riser height, not over 7¾ inches. Treads and risers should be uniform in width and height and so proportioned that the sum of two risers and a tread, exclusive of nosing, is not less than 24 inches nor more than 25 inches.

8. Stairways should be enclosed in fire-resistive walls with openings protected by fire doors.

9. All doors in exits should open in the direction of egress with the exception of sliding doors, which are permissible in horizontal exits through fire walls between sections of a building.

10. Outside fire escapes should consist of stairs substantially in accordance with the requirements for inside exit stairs. Unless so placed or protected that flames or smoke from windows or other openings cannot cut them off, they are of little value and may constitute traps instead of means of escape. The ordinary outside fire escape is not recognized as a safe means of egress in new buildings.

11. The rope or individual types of escapes or ladders are of value only for vigorous persons trained in their use.

12. Slide escapes properly maintained are useful for personnel under good control and drilled in their use.

13. Revolving doors and elevators are not desirable for emergency exit purposes.

14. Ramps having a maximum slope of 1 in 10 are acceptable in lieu of stairs.

Chapter Thirty-one

Ionizing Radiations Protection

As the term indicates, ionizing radiations are radiations capable of splitting orbital electrons off from ordinarily neutral atoms thus transforming them into positively charged and negatively charged ions. There are two kinds of ionizing radiations, (a) Electromagnetic, X-rays and gamma rays, (b) Corpuscular, discrete particles discharged from their sources at high velocity, alpha and beta particles and neutrons.

X radiation (Roentgen rays)

In terms of wave length, X-rays from X-ray machines occupy the place in the electromagnetic spectrum next below (shorter than) those of ultra-violet light. Their length range is from about 10^{-6} to about 10^{-10} cm. Their frequency range in cycles per sec. is from about 10^{17} to about 10^{21}.

X-rays originate in the field of force that surrounds the atomic nucleus and result from a loss of energy by the charged particles (electrons) surrounding the nucleus. They are produced by the impingement of high speed electrons on a metallic target. The X-ray machine is essentially a device whereby electrons emitted from a hot filament are accelerated elec-trically to high velocity in a vacuum and caused to strike a suitable target with, of course, means of controlling the resulting beam of X-rays. X-rays can also be produced in particle accelerators; cyclotrons, betatrons etc.; and are incidentally produced in certain high power transmitting and rectifying valves and in certain other vacuum type tubes, in television for example.

X-radiation is of a highly penetrating nature, the higher the electron velocity, the greater the penetrating power. Penetration also varies with the density of the material in question. That is the property that makes the X-ray so valuable a tool in so many areas, particularly in medical diag-nosis, in product inspection in industry and in research. In air, a direct beam of 200 Kv radiation with tube current of 10 mA, such as is commonly used in industrial radiography, would require a distance of about 120 meters to reduce it to a reasonably safe dosage level. The equivalent value for lead is about 4 mm.

The velocity of X-radiation is the same as that of visible light, gamma also. Both obey the inverse square law. Thus, distance can often be used in safeguarding both but in so doing, the fact that an X-ray machine is designed to emit its radiation as a beam must be taken into account. Of course the shielding of powerful sealed gamma sources is normally arranged to give a similar result.

On striking the target object, or any other matter, at least some secondary radiation is produced much as in the case of visible light, its intensity and penetrating power varying rather widely with conditions. In general practice, however, safety lies in providing half as much shielding to protect personnel against the secondary radiation as would be required for the direct beam.

X-rays and gamma rays, as well, ionize sparsely along their paths but their great penetration largely offsets their low specific ionization value. Both travel in straight lines.

Gamma radiation

As compared with X-rays from X-ray machines, the chief difference is greater penetrating power, as would be expected from the shorter wave length of gamma, ranging from about 10^{-10} cm down to 10^{-11} cm and below where they merge insensibly into the photons caused by the impingement of the tremendously energetic particles from outer space on particles in the earth's atmosphere. At least some of these photons have penetrating power far greater than that of the most energetic gamma.

Gamma radiation originates within the nucleus of the atom and carries its energy in a number of discrete frequencies instead of in a continuous spectrum as do X-rays.

The naturally occurring radioactive elements and many artificially produced radioisotopes, for example CO^{60}, NA^{24} and I^{31}, emit their excess energy in the form of gamma rays when their nuclei go through a rearrangement to reach a more stable state. Either alpha or beta particulate radiation is always emitted also.

Low energy or "soft" gamma rays can be attenuated to negligible intensities by about ½ inch of lead but a thickness of several inches is necessary to give a similar result with the more energetic of the "hard" rays.

The significant differences between X- and gamma rays are in their origin and their penetrating power. In theory, the only limit to the penetrating power of X-rays is the speed that can be given electrons. In the so-called atom smasher that might approach the speed of light. In practice, however, it is usually cheaper and easier to get great penetration by using gamma radiation.

Alpha particles

These are the positively charged nuclei of helium atoms, 2 protons and 2 neutrons each, mass number 4, charge positive 2, some 7000 times the mass of the electrons. They are emitted during the decay of a number of the naturally radioactive elements and their daughter elements as well as a few of the artificially produced radioisotopes and elements, for example, plutonium. The chief natural alpha emitters are radium, radium C, radon, polonium and thorium.

Alpha particles have little penetrating power, up to only about 9 cm in air, about 0.007 cm in human tissue; a thick sheet of paper will stop them. Thus they offer no external hazard beyond that of skin deposition by an alpha emitter such as plutonium, but their high specific ionization value makes them extremely hazardous once an emitter gains entrance to the body and especially so if it has selectivity for a vital organ or tissue.

Beta particles

These are high speed electrons emitted in the decay of many radioactive elements both artificial and natural. In some cases, gamma radiation is emitted also. The emission energy of the beta particles and therefore their penetrating power, varies considerably according to source, but is relatively low; a few meters in air, about 1 cm at most in human tissue, a millimeter or less in most common metals. Their ionization value per unit of length of path is intermediate between that of X- and gamma radiation and alpha particles but unlike X-ray and gamma, they follow tortuous paths in human tissue, being easily deflected because of their small mass. Externally, their hazard is limited to the skin and the tissues directly under it. Their chief hazard is to internal tissues from radioactive elements emitting them that gain entrance to the body, usually through inhalation or ingestion but in some cases through skin breaks. The hazard is particularly serious in the case of a beta emitter that tends to collect in specific tissue, for example, Sr^{90} in bone.

The beta particle has a positively charged counterpart of similar mass, the positron. It is produced in a limited number of disintegrations, for example, that of N^{24}. It disappears almost instantly with the production of two gamma ray photons each of energy 0.51 MeV. It is rarely met with in industry.

Neutrons

These are electrically neutral particles that exceed the mass of a proton by only the mass of the contained electron. They decay with a half-life of 10-30 minutes to a proton and an electron. Atomic furnaces are their quantity source, but cyclotrons produce them also. Neutron sources in the form of sealed containers of radium-beryllium, polonium-beryllium or antimony-beryllium are available from atomic energy establishments.

Neutrons ionize indirectly. High energy "fast" neutrons cause ionization by colliding with atomic nuclei and setting them into motion with sufficient velocity to ionize matter. "Slow" neutrons enter atomic nuclei and are captured with the emission of ionizing radiation. Neutrons have long ranges in air. They can pass through considerable thicknesses of materials, but unlike X- and gamma rays, their range is less in light materials, paraffin for example, than in dense materials such as lead. Because of the secondary radiation they produce, neutrons are up to ten times as effective biologically as are X- or gamma rays but because of their limited use in industry they are of limited importance to safety men in general.

Radiation measurements

Several different units are used to express quantity and intensity of radiation. The curie is the commonly used unit of quantity; it is an amount of radioactive material in which 37 billion disintegrations occur per second. The roentgen is the commonly used unit of intensity; the amount of X- or gamma radiation required to produce a number of ions equivalent to one electrostatic unit in one centimeter of air under standard conditions. One gram of soft animal tissue will absorb about 93 ergs of energy when exposed to one roentgen of gamma radiation.

To measure the dosage of alpha or beta particles in soft animal tissue, a unit called the "roentgen equivalent physical" (rep) was adopted. When soft animal tissue absorbs 93 ergs of energy per gram from alpha or beta radiation, it has received one rep of radiation. Later, the "rad" was adopted as the unit of absorbed dose for X- or gamma radiation, corresponding to an absorption of 100 ergs of energy per gram. The difference in value between rem and rad is not significant, so that the rad has come to be accepted as the absorbed dose for all kinds of radiation.

Since the different kinds of radiation vary in energy and ionizing ability, some are more biologically effective than others. Therefore, each kind has its own "rbe" (relative biological effectiveness) value factor. This factor multiplied by the dose in reps or rads results in a biological dose termed the "rem" (roentgen equivalent man). The rbe factor for X- and gamma radiation of up to three million volts of energy can be assumed to be 1 so that a dose of 1000 millirads of either type of radiation is approximately equal to 1000 millirems.

Biological effects

The mechanism by which injurious radiations work their damage in living tissue is exceedingly complex and imperfectly understood, but basically it is through a process of ionization. The primary event is the production of an ion pair, each ion then reacting with the complex organic molecules of the tissue content, resulting in denaturation of protein molecules, splitting of large molecules into smaller ones with different properties, inactivation of enzymes, etc., and the formation of toxic molecules such as H_2O_2 along the paths of the ionizing radiations. Obviously such changes are essentially injurious. The actual type or types of injury depends upon many factors, chief of which appear to be the kind of tissue, the particular molecular arrangements involved, the density of the ionization produced and the rate at which it is produced. Known kinds of cell injuries include inhibition of mitosis, cell paralysis followed by partial, complete or over-recovery, cell death, malignant cell proliferation, chromosome damage and genetic mutation.

The sensitivity of the various types of tissues to ionizing radiations varies widely. In general, tissues having a high state of proliferative activity and cell replacement are the more sensitive, for example, bone marrow, lymphatic tissue and reproductive cells. Muscles, nerves and certain glandular tissues are relatively insensitive.

The effects of irradiation can be conveniently listed under two main headings i.e.:

1. Those resulting from external exposure of the whole or a part of the body to the highly penetrating radiations (X, gamma, neutrons) and also, to the extent of their very limited penetrating ability, beta and alpha radiations.

2. Those resulting from internal radiation by radioactive substances that gain entrance to the body through inhalation, ingestion or through the skin by skin breaks or absorption.

Although as already pointed out, some tissues are far more susceptible to radiation than others, basically the amount of damage for any given exposure to the penetrating radiations is governed by two factors, intensity and time. For example, a dose of 400 roentgens received over the whole body within a few hours' time will be fatal to about half of those so exposed. Yet the same dosage spread thinly enough over a period of years will do no observable damage, though there is considerable evidence that there might be some long deferred effects attributable to such exposure i.e., cancer, shortened life, genetic damage. The mere possibility of such serious, long deferred effects fully justifies the accepted policy of always and in every way, holding exposure as far below the established permissible limits as is practicably possible.

In 1950 the U.S. Atomic Energy Commission published the following table giving the effects to be expected from X- or gamma whole-body radiation received in a period of a day or less:

Dose in roentgens	Probable effect
0-25	No obvious injury.
25-50	Possible blood changes, no serious injury.
50-100	Blood cell changes, some injury, no disability.
100-200	Injury, possible disability.
200-400	Injury and disability certain, death possible.
400	Fatal to 50%
600 or more	Fatal, probably to 100%

The term "threshold dose" has been applied to the dosage that will produce the minimum observable injury, but so many variable and as yet undeterminable factors are involved, that the established threshold values should be used with great caution and as guides rather than as levels that spell safety if not exceeded. Safety lies in keeping dosages as far below the threshold values as possible. It is certain, however, that with the exception of genetic damage and possibly some other kinds, the body can repair the damage if the dose rate is not too high, that is if it is spread out (protracted). Thus, "protraction" as it is termed, is often of great importance in protecting against external radiation, particularly in work requiring the use of extremely "hard" X- and gamma radiation. It is frequently impossible to eliminate exposure of operating personnel, partly because of scatter and partly because impossibly heavy shielding would often be necessary. So monitoring, discussed later, with protraction by limiting the hours of exposure is the accepted practice in such cases.

Personal susceptibility to ionizing radiations appears to vary considerably as between different people, but not nearly as widely as with many chemicals, drugs and the like, and contrary to many chemical exposures, individual resistance to ionizing radiations does not appear to be altered by repeated or severe exposures.

Since certain organs are more resistant to ionizing radiations than others, the amount of damage done in less than whole body exposures is largely dependent upon the part of the body irradiated. Also the degree of the body's response to external radiation is markedly affected by the fraction of the whole-body volume exposed. For example, if a finger or a hand received a dose of say 500 rads of X- or gamma radiation, the damage, except for some minor disturbance, would be confined to the part irradiated but a whole body dose of like amount would cause serious injury or death.

In brief, overexposure to ionizing radiation may produce one or more of the following kinds of injury:

1. Damage to superficial tissues.
2. Systemic effects, particularly of the blood and blood forming organs i.e., anemia and leukemia.
3. Induction of malignant tumors.
4. Other deleterious effects including cataract, impaired fertility and shortening of the life span.
5. Genetic effects.

Relating dosage to damage

Analysis of accumulated knowledge of human exposures and their sequelae, supplemented by extensive research with animal and plant life, have enabled the establishment of reasonably reliable permissible levels for radiation exposures. Since there still is, and probably will long remain, a very considerable "factor of ignorance," the approach in setting these levels has rightly been to err, if at all, on the side of safety. Even should additional information indicate that the presently accepted permissible levels could be lowered somewhat with reasonable safety, authoritative opinion would probably be slow to endorse such action because the experience of the Atomic Energy Commission and their contractors has shown that the current levels can be met without great difficulty or unduly serious expense. The currently accepted maximum permissible weekly doses are the series recommended by the International Commission on Radiological Protection. The various nations formulating their own standards have either adopted these or have used them as a guide.

The term "maximum permissible body burden" denotes the amount of a radioactive substance that can be present in the body without exceeding the maximum permissible radiation dosage.

The degree of injury depends chiefly upon the amount of dose, the rate and kind of radiation, the organ or part of body irradiated and the fraction of the whole body irradiated.

The human organism has considerable ability to repair most kinds of irradiation damage, though this varies considerably with kind of injury or organ involved; therefore, with some exceptions, if the dosage is not too heavy, the damage is repaired and recovery is complete. The important exception is genetic damage. The weight of evidence is strong that genetic damage is irreparable and in most cases, either genetically lethal or productive of abnormalities in the offspring; in other words, mutations. the great majority of which are harmful. This, of course, is of vital impor tance in the use of ionizing radiations that can penetrate to the gonads or ovaries, i.e., X- and gamma rays and neutrons and also any radioactive substances that should they gain entrance to the body might reach these organs. This constitutes a powerful argument for holding all such irradia tion to as near the zero level as possible, at least until middle age, rather than merely down to the generally accepted permissible levels.

The term "threshold dose" is used to denote the dosage required to pro duce an observable injury but this is a variable. Not only does the factor of personal susceptibility enter, but some injuries may be undetectable by presently known means or may appear only after years have elapsed, cancer for example.

The term "latent period" is used to denote the time that elapses between the irradiation and the appearance of symptoms. In general, the greater the absorbed dose the shorter the latent period. For X- and gamma radia tion, with dosages in the range of 100 to 1000 rads, the latent periods will run from several days down to several hours.

The term "biological half-life" is used to denote the time required for one half of a given radioactive substance deposited in the body to be excreted.

The term "effective half-life" is used to denote the time required for one half of a given radioactive substance deposited in the body to be lost through excretion plus decay.

Record of Atomic Energy Industry

The combined injury record of the AEC and its contractors has from the start been remarkably good, in fact, closely approaching zero rates. This proves that radiation injuries are as preventable as are those from the familiar accident and health hazards in industry. Basically, the principles essential for effective injury elimination in work with ionizing radiations is the same, i.e., know the nature of the hazard, reduce it to the minimum, develop safe and adequate procedures, develop safe work practices, de velop employee safety know-how and safety mindedness, develop super visory know-how, maintain close supervision and continually check results.

In dealing with workers and, incidentally, with the public as well, the mysterious (to the poorly informed) nature of ionizing radiation is likely to present a very difficult problem to overcome. Mystery begets fear and fear inhibits reason. The tremendous amount of half-truth, and, in certain outstanding cases, downright misinformation or entirely unwarranted assumptions that have been broadcast, particularly since the advent of the atomic bomb, has created an attitude of unreasoning fear on the part of many, perhaps most, of our people that will be difficult to overcome. Yet it must be overcome, for atomic energy in its myriad forms is, and increasingly will be, so useful a tool in so many ways that it will profoundly affect every phase of our economy.

The fact that radioactive substances and ionizing radiations in all their forms and all their uses can be adequately safeguarded must be driven home to everybody. Our inability to detect the presence of ionizing radiations by any of our five senses presents a mental obstacle because from childhood on we are accustomed to receiving warning of danger through one or more of these senses. But such radiation can not only be unfailingly detected by suitable instruments and devices but the kind and degree of hazard can be reliably determined and adequate safeguards can be thrown about it. It is absolutely essential, however, that every person using or working with ionizing radiations know and unfailingly comply with all of the procedures and practices necessary for their own safety and that of their fellow workers.

Industrial Uses of Ionizing Radiations

The first use of ionizing radiations was in research and in medicine. The first industrial use was in luminizing. The deaths by 1930 of some 20 workers who had been engaged in luminizing from 1918 on, attracted worldwide attention and emphasized the hazard of internal irradiation.

The discovery that certain serious defects in metal castings and forgings could be detected by X-radiation led to the development of extremely powerful X-ray equipment for this purpose, chiefly during the decade 1935-45. When the nuclear furnace made powerful gamma sources available, Co^{60} for example, powerful sealed sources came into such use competitively and curtailed the need and demand for ever more powerful X-ray equipment.

More important still is the fact that the nuclear furnace has made a very wide variety of radioactive isotopes available in plentiful supply and at a reasonable cost. This has led to a great expansion and proliferation in their use particularly in industry and research and no end to it is in sight.

Anything approaching a complete description of the uses of ionizing radiation in industry alone would require far more space than can be spared herein for that purpose. Moreover, their use is expanding so rapidly that such a listing would soon be out of date. However, the following list of current uses of major importance will be indicative.

X Rays

1. Radiographic examination of castings, forgings and fabricated metal parts to detect flaws, cracks, blowholes and other defects. X-ray machines for this purpose may be fixed or mobile. The voltages employed usually lie within the range of 100-400 Kv but they may run into the millions. However, where the maximum in penetrating power is required betatrons are used because they can impart far higher speed to the beta particles than is practicably possible with the X-ray machine.

2. The fluoroscopic examination of manufactured articles, for example, spark plugs, radio valve assemblies, golf balls, tinned or packaged foods, etc., the purpose usually being to check the assembly or alignment or to detect foreign material.

3. X-ray diffraction apparatus is used for the analysis of crystalline compounds, the determination of plane orientations in quartz crystals, stress analysis in metals and alloys and in the routine examination for physical condition following such treatments as rolling, drawing, annealing, etc.

Radioactive elements

Radioactive substances, both natural and artificial, are used industrially in a wide variety of ways. Some of the more important of these are:

1. In luminizing. Radium or mesothorium mixed with zinc sulfide is applied to instrument dial markings and pointers to make them self luminous.

2. Gamma ray emitters, particularly Co^{60}, Ir^{192}, Cs^{137}, Tm^{170}, and radium, chosen in each case according to the gamma ray energy required, for the radiography of castings, forgings, welds and fabricated parts instead of or supplementary to the use of X-rays.

3. Static elimination. The processing of such nonconducting materials as paper, many fabrics, plastics etc., particularly in passing over rollers or revolving drums or by friction against machine parts, can cause static of sufficient intensity to ignite flammable dusts or vapors or cause very disturbing shocks to workers. Also, such static can seriously hamper operations by causing the materials being run to stick to rollers, refuse to stack properly (newspapers), tangle warp threads (textiles), and in many other ways as well. The amount of ionizing radiation necessary to ionize the air in an area of static generation sufficiently to cause the static to leak away as fast as it is formed is very small, usually in only millicurie quantities.

Thus the health hazard to those who tend the machines is very small if relatively simple safe practices are followed.

4. Thickness control (thickness gaging). In the running of such products as plastic and rubber sheetings, floor coverings, metal foil and thin metal sheet, paper, etc., beta emitting isotopes are used, chosen in each case according to the energy and therefore the penetrating range of the beta particles. Highly ingenious devices detect very slight over or under penetration due to thickness variation and operate controls to make the necessary corrections automatically. Gamma emitters, similarly chosen, can be used in running heavier metal sheet and strip.

5. As tracers to gain an understanding of the mechanism of chemical, physical and biological processes.

6. In measuring wear of machine parts, bearings, cutting tools, etc., the erosion of refractory furnace linings, etc.

Protection against external irradiation

The following methods, used individually or in suitable combinations, are effective if properly applied:

> *Distance protection.*
> *Shielding.*
> *Using radiation of minimum penetrating power.*

Distance. Since electromagnetic radiation obeys the inverse square law, this method is both effective and relatively inexpensive provided conditions are such as to make its use both practicable and dependable. In general, the approach should be to keep all personnel as far from the radiating source as possible. In the case of X- or gamma radiation, because of scatter, this also applies to objects on which the radiation falls. Both of these radiations have such long ranges in air that it is seldom practical and adequate to depend upon distance alone, but even in such case, distance can often be used to supplement shielding and protect against scatter. For example, a distance of about 120 meters would be required to reduce a direct beam of 200 Kv radiation with tube current 10 mA as is commonly used in industrial radiography, to a permissible dosage level.

The means commonly used to exclude personnel from hazardous areas are enclosure, barriers, warning signs and guards. Obviously the effectiveness of this method will always depend largely upon unfailing compliance by all personnel involved with the limitations placed upon their movements. For X-radiation exclusion is of course necessary only when the machine is "on," but unless very positive and unfailingly enforced provisions for exclusion at such times are established, slip-ups are sure to occur.

There is a rather wide range in the energy of beta particles from radio-active elements and, of course, a corresponding variation in penetration. In air it is several meters at a maximum. Alpha particles ordinarily have a maximum range of only about 8 cm in air.

Shielding. This will range from thin sheeting to contain alpha and beta particles up to massive thicknesses of concrete brick or lead for protection against high energy X- and gamma radiation, portable with sealed sources where mobility is important, as when interlocking lead bricks are used to shield temporary operations requiring the use of radiations of high penetrating power.

The provision of adequate shielding for highly penetrating radiation at a minimum cost emphatically requires the services of the highly competent specialist. He will need to explore in full detail the purposes for which it is to be used, the procedures that will be followed and all conditions pertaining to and surrounding its use. His findings will be of major value in working out the day by day safety provisions and practices.

Radiation of minimum penetrating power. This can be very important. The variety of sources has become so great that usually there are multiple choices for any given job or piece of work. The unvarying approach should be to select a source whose radiation has the minimum penetrating power for the work in question. The same principle applies to the use of the X-ray machine. The setting used should always be the minimum that will accomplish the desired purpose.

The above should not be taken to mean that other safeguards, such as protective clothing, movable shielding, etc., should ever be relaxed because of confidence in the adequacy of these provisions. The policy should always be to maintain at all times and under all circumstances, the maximum practically possible margin on the side of safety in accordance with the apparently well established principle that even the smallest amount of ionizing radiation of human tissue is in some degree inimical. This approach is sound for another reason, i.e., it may help prevent forgetfulness that could result in serious exposures.

Protection against internal irradiation

Internal irradiation is not only by far a more serious hazard than external irradiation but it is much more difficult to prevent where unsealed radioactive substances are used or processed. Also medically, it is very difficult to deal with once the radioactive substance gains entrance to the body chiefly because:

1. Radiation continues until the radioactive material has been excreted or its radioactivity has decreased to a negligible level.

2. Often, the rate of elimination cannot be increased materially.

3. Alpha and low energy beta particles dissipate all their energy in a very small volume of tissue and therefore may destroy a vital part of a critical organ.

4. Accurate measurement of internal radioactivity is frequently not possible and, in such case, a reliable evaluation of the degree of hazard and probable damage is impossible.

5. Even when the amount of radioactive substance that has gained entrance to the body is approximately known, its distribution in the various tissues and organs may not be determinable.

Obviously, then, in dealing in any way with radioactive substances, the basic approach must always be to prevent the entrance of *any* of the material into the body by any means whatever. Once even the most minute amount gains entrance some damage is certain and although the body has considerable ability to repair at least some kinds of such damage, this ability is limited and little can be done to aid it. There is a very considerable factor of ignorance in this connection, however, and there is room for hope that as research and experience-won knowledge accumulates, the situation will be markedly improved. Meantime the only sound course is to seek by every possible means to keep such substances entirely out of the body.

The means by which injurious substances reach the body and cause injury and the methodology of prevention is discussed in general in the chapter on occupational health hazards. Basically the same methods apply to radioactive substances but adequate prevention is far more difficult to achieve because permissible body burdens are so minute and it has therefore been necessary to set permissible levels of air contamination so low and acceptable standards against other ports of entry so high that only the most unfailing and scrupulous attention to the protection of all portals of entry to the body—nose and lungs, mouth, alimentary tract, and skin— will suffice. Basically, it requires the installation in properly designed and equipped workrooms of adequate ventilation (local and general), the adoption of measures to avoid spillage or the spread of contamination by other means, the insistence that strict attention be paid to the cleanliness of the person and of working equipment, the absolute prohibition of eating, drinking, smoking, etc., in the workrooms concerned, the unfailing use of suitable personal protective equipment and clothing by all those at risk, and the institution and unfailing maintenance of regular monitoring procedures suited to the conditions involved.

Where there is any possibility at all of radioactive dusts, sprays, fumes, or gases being produced or radioactive liquids handled, the utmost use should be made of complete enclosures around the operations concerned, and each such enclosure should be adequately exhausted. In many cases small exhausted fume cupboards or cabinets equipped with rubber or other suitable sleeves, to give hand entrance, can be used. The effluent from such cabinets should be collected and harmlessly disposed of.

If proper provisions are made for the prevention of air contamination, respirators should not be necessary except in emergencies, such, for example, as cleaning up spillages. They should of course be of the supplied air type, and always kept in use condition.

Scrupulous attention must be paid to the avoidance of the spread of radioactive contamination. This requires the working out and faithful following of safe and orderly operating and work methods, the use of catch trays under all radioactive materials being handled, the prompt wiping up or cleaning up of any spillage that may occur and the collection of all radioactive waste, dust, rinse solutions and the like, and their safe disposal.

Working surfaces likely to be contaminated can be covered by disposable sheetings of treated paper or plastics and the like.

All cleaning of workrooms where inhalation and ingestion risks exist should be by wet methods only; the rooms should be designed to facilitate this. Vacuum cleaning may also be used if proper allowance is made for the safe disposal of the collected material. The portable vacuum should be used with great caution because very fine particles will pass through the best of such filters.

Instrumentation

Instruments to detect and measure ionizing radiations are commercially available in wide variety. A list of manufacturers of such equipment and devices is published by *Nucleonics* magazine annually.

Detectors fall into two classes: those that detect and count individual ionizing events, and those that integrate the total number of such events that occur in a unit of time. Geiger counters and photon-multiplier scintillation counters are in the first class. Ionization chambers and chemical detectors, such as photographic films and those based on color changes, are of the second class. In general, the indications of individual ionizing events may be integrated electrically.

Some instruments detect only one kind and level of radiation, for example, alpha. Others detect several kinds and at several levels.

Ionization chambers are commonly used for X-ray measurement in roentgens and for determining absorbed energy for particulate forms of radiation.

Counters are based on the fact that a high energy charged particle may produce ionization in a gas, fluorescence in a scintillating material, a change in electrical resistance in a solid or a latent image in photographic emulsions. They will detect single ionizing events under certain conditions. They can also detect the presence of uncharged radiations, such as photons and neutrons, by the charged particles, ions, that they produce.

Photographic films, usually in the form of film carriers or film badges, are used to monitor X- and gamma ray exposure doses and beta ray absorbed doses. They can be calibrated in roentgens for X- and gamma radiation exposures.

Air sampling outfits for the measurement of air contamination by radioactive substances are available commercially. The radioactive dust particles are caught on a suitable paper filter and counted by a counter suited to the type of radioactivity in question.

Monitoring

Monitoring is primarily a check on the effectiveness of the preventive program as a whole. In the last analysis, the monitoring program is not fully effective if it fails to discover *every* case of overexposure to ionizing radiations.

The extent and type of monitoring for the detection and dosage measurement of radiation exposures is determined largely by the nature of the radiation source or sources. For example, if the radiation intensity is known to be low and certain to remain so, film badges or dosimeters worn by the exposed personnel may be adequate.

For operations where radiation emission at hazardous levels is intermittent, fixed monitoring equipment that will both give a suitable alarm at each such emission and record totals per unit of time are used.

The amount and variety of monitoring equipment necessary will vary enormously according to the extent and variety of the possible risks. In an atomic energy establishment there will be need for the full complement of instruments. These will include ionization chamber radiation monitors to measure beta, gamma, proton and slow and fast neutron radiation levels in working areas; proportional counters for measuring neutrons and alpha particles, particularly alpha contamination on hands, feet and clothing or on bench surfaces; Geiger counters for sensitive survey work generally, especially for measuring radioactive contamination, and sometimes linked with alarms and mounted on laboratory doorways to give warning of contaminated persons passing through; scintillation counters for alpha or gamma contamination monitoring and for testing urine samples for alpha emitting material; and special portable instruments for assessing radioactive dust or gas contents of working atmospheres (including those downwind of reactor chimney stacks or in the discharge ducts of filter systems) to enable efficiency of maintenance to be assessed.

The measurement by film or dosimeter of the individual external radiation dosages received is of the greatest importance, for not only does it act as the basic check on his safety and health in so far as ionizing radiations are concerned but it is also a very effective way of educating him in safe practice as applied to his job. Only if the initial radiation survey shows that no worker can under normal operation ever receive dosage exceeding permissible values, is dependence on periodical personnel monitoring advisable. When, however, the safety of personnel depends upon unfailing adherence to a particular technique or the continued proper functioning of equipment rather than upon inherently low radiation levels, continuous monitoring should be carried on.

It is very important that records of radiation exposures be faithfully kept. Not only are they valuable as a part of the personal medical record of the worker should he later develop dyscrasia of a type possibly due to radiation exposure, but also to his employer for a similar reason.

Film badges may be worn in a breast pocket, pinned to outer clothing, strapped to a wrist or as a finger ring. They are normally carried for a week or two before being developed. They can be used for the measurement of both X- and gamma dosage, and if covered on both sides over half the film's area by a millimeter of lead, for beta at the same time as well.

The pocket dosimeter is very useful where records of accumulated exposures to X- or gamma radiation are required at daily or shorter intervals. One type consists essentially of a small highly insulated ionization chamber which discharges proportionally to the radiation received and is read by means of an electrometer. Another type is a fountain pen form of quartz fibre electroscope, charged before each using and after being worn for a suitable period, read by observing the position of the fibre on a scale calibrated directly in milliroentgens.

Small battery operated pocket alarm instruments that give an audible alarm when a maximum permissible dose has been reached are useful for emergency situations, where radiation intensities are likely to vary considerably or are unknown, or where the worker's attention is likely to be distracted.

Planning for the use of ionizing radiations

The use of ionizing radiations increases yearly both as to total amount and variety of uses and the end is not in sight nor is it likely to be in the foreseeable future. This means simply that ionizing radiations are becoming a common hazard throughout industry. It therefore behooves every plant safety engineer as well as every other person having any considerable degree of responsibility for employee safety to acquire a good working knowledge of the nature of ionizing radiations, the hazards they present and at least the basics of their control. He should also find out where help and advice of the requisite professional competence can be obtained in case of need.

When contemplating the use, or any substantial expansion, of the use of ionizing radiations, the management should secure the services of a competent specialist if that has not already been done. His services will include a thorough analysis of the proposed use or uses, a survey of plant and operations that will be involved and a working out of the procedures that should be followed throughout for safety.

Such competent and thorough advance planning is extremely important, particularly where highly penetrating radiations or certain highly hazardous substances are involved. Some of the more important matters to cover in the planning stage are:

1. Layout and shielding of the fixed sources both X-ray and sealed.

2. Layout, arrangement and equipment of labs and workrooms.

3. Provisions for holding to a minimum the number of persons likely to be exposed to radiation.

4. Providing for suitable and adequate instrumentation.

5. Provisions for the development and adoption of the necessary routine safe procedures and safe practices.

6. Provisions for the instruction, training and continual supervision of personnel involved.

7. Provisions for suitable monitoring and medical checking.

The basic principles of the prevention of injuries due to ionizing radiations are deceptively simple. Only two things are required. All who work with or about them must be protected against:

1. Radiations from external sources.

2. The entry of radioactive substances into the body.

The procedures and devices necessary are neither difficult to understand nor to apply. The outstanding and ever present difficulty lies in obtaining their unfailing observance and correct use by everyone involved. The nearly perfect record to date of the atomic energy industry dealing continually, as it must, with a multiplicity of lethal hazards, shows what *can* be done. Will the steadily increasing numbers of users of ionizing radiations maintain a similarly good record out of their relatively low hazard level? Or will the outcome develop much as it has in the field of accident prevention? The high hazard branches of industry (steel, for example) have achieved injury rates that approach elimination, while the low hazard branches of industry have lagged far behind and for the most part have relatively high injury rates. Most small establishments also have relatively high injury rates. Small establishments will naturally, because of their limited finances, be loath to make the expenditures so emphatically advisable in the planning and preparatory stages. They do not, most of them, take safety seriously enough. Will they do the same with this new and potentially hazardous tool? What will the picture be in, say, a quarter or maybe a half century? The author fears that it is likely to prove the toughest problem the atomic energy industry together with the safety authorities will be faced with.

Radiation safety program

There has been considerable controversy over the position in the administrative setup that the person with primary responsibility for radiation safety should occupy. In the opinion of the author radiation safety is no whit different in principle from any other phase of safety and therefore should be an intimate part of the plant safety program however that may be administered, by whatever title, and from whatever location on the organization chart. The important thing is to develop a program realistically suited to the plant conditions, both physical and administrative, and to maintain and prosecute it vigorously and unflaggingly. Injuries caused by exposure to ionizing radiations are as preventable as those caused by any other kind of hazard; the basic principles of prevention are the same, only the technical detail is different.

The importance of advance planning for the use of ionizing radiations has already been brought out. If properly carried out, this planning will have established many of the activities the safety program should include. The radiation survey, also urged as important, will have indicated the extent to which preventive inspection will be needed, will have located the "hot" spots and furnished an approximate appraisal of their relative hazard. Actually, the use of ionizing radiations, even on an extensive scale, will usually involve the expansion of existing safety activities far more than it will the addition of wholly new ones. Monitoring activities will be new. So will the highly specialized equipment, but it is no more difficult to master the correct use of this equipment than it is to correctly use much of the equipment and instrumentation now in wide use in the manufacturing industries. There is one very important difference, however, a difference of degree rather than of kind, namely, a failure of a radiation detector to function properly or a misreading of its message can spell serious or fatal injury; a similar failure with production equipment may also cause an injury but usually the only hurt is to production.

Activities that may be added or greatly expanded or modified or both are:

1. Monitoring.
2. Inspection for and appraisal of ionizing radiations.
3. Pre-employment and periodical medical examinations.
4. Keeping of personnel exposure records.
5. The transportation, handling and storage of radioactive substances.
6. Control of air contamination.
7. Hazard analysis of all new processes and work activities and changes in established ones.
8. Safe practices development and training including training in the correct use of the specialized equipment.
9. Education and instruction on ionizing radiation, what it is, the hazards it presents, how to detect and control them etc., its uses and the great promise it holds for the future of our civilization.
10. Provisions for safe waste disposal.
11. Control of contamination of clothing and special provisions for the control of skin contamination.
12. Prevention of fire, explosion and other high hazard occurrences, together with the development of suitable emergency action, assignment of responsibility for and training therein.
13. Control of smoking, eating and drinking practices.
14. Provisions for the cleaning up of spillages, the decontamination of equipment, walls, floors, etc.

Considerable detailed discussion of most of the above items would be included if space permitted. Since it does not, only the following comments on a few of them are offered:

Air Contamination.   The control of air contamination is, of course, a familiar subject in the field of industrial hygiene. However the amounts of certain radioactive substances that can do damage if inhaled are so minute that where they are used, handled, or processed, under conditions that may allow them to become airborne, a new concept of air cleanliness is necessary. The hazard survey, properly made, will have established the standard of air cleanliness required for safety in work with the substance or substances in question. An air sampling procedure and program adequate to insure the maintenance of this standard should be set up and strictly followed. The measures used in work with even the most hazardous of chemicals to prevent the escape of dusts, vapors, gases or fumes will usually have to be greatly refined and intensified for radioactive substances.

Hazard Analysis.   The technique described in the chapter on Job Hazard Analysis is particularly useful here, provided it is carried out with meticulous attention to detail, both as to the hazard points involved and the resultant safe practices and procedures. The point here is that in job analysis for accident hazards an overlooked hazard point is usually less likely to produce a serious injury than in work with ionizing radiations. An accident announces itself, an exposure to ionizing radiation does not. Then too an accident of no consequence otherwise, may in work with radioactive substances contribute to or cause dusting, spillage, skin contamination, skin breaks etc., all of which emphasizes the value of thoroughgoing hazard analysis in this field.

Placed last, by way of a summing up and emphasizing, is the assignment of responsibility. Specific assignments of responsibility for the correct and effective prosecution of the various elements and activities of the program must be made. Such assignments are routine in production. The author has in many cases found the lack of such clear-cut responsibility to be a major factor in poorly functioning plant safety programs. It can be a very serious matter in dealing with ionizing radiations.

Medical supervision

Pre-employment physical examination should be required for all persons who are to work with or about ionizing radiations, not only to prevent the placement in such work of individuals who because of significant pathological abnormalities of skin, bone, blood, gonad, lung etc., would be particularly susceptible, but also to enable control sets of blood counts to be made and recorded for future reference. Also all persons regularly employed on work involving any exposure whatever to ionizing radiations should be clinically examined at least yearly as a routine precaution.

Bibliography

The author is in disagreement with the practice followed by many text-book authors, of including extensive bibliographies, that sometimes run into a hundred or more items. Useful as such all-inclusive listings un-doubtedly are to the research student, they are of little value to the prac-ticing safety man or the beginning safety student, the people this text is designed to serve. In fact such personnel will rarely if ever, have either the time or the inclination to wade through an extensive bibliography, or, should they undertake to do so, would they have the knowledge neces-sary for its discriminating appraisal. Unfortunately, too, many of the widely quoted research findings in the field of safety are superficial and un-reliable at best, obviously because the researcher or research team in ques-tion had little or no practical knowledge of the subject. Therefore, this bibliography is purposely limited to those publications the author considers for the most part sound and valuable for use as supplementary to the content of this text. That should not be taken as unqualified endorsement of everything in any of the publications listed, for there is room for difference of opinion on a number of the subjects dealt with, for example, accident proneness, accident costs and accident distribution.

In the author's opinion, the practicing safety man under whatever title, should have, either in his personal file or immediately available, at least the following material:

Books on safety

1. *Accident Prevention Manual for Industrial Operations,* 4th ed., Chicago: National Safety Council, 1962

   This is by far the most comprehensive of all safety books. The material in it was drawn originally from the more than 100 safe practices pamphlets prepared by committees of firing-line safety men and published by the Council as a membership service. The highly competent professional safety staff of the Council has revised and added to it so that the current edition, the 4th, has 45 sections totaling over 1700 pages. It is rightly regarded as the bible of the practicing safety engineer.

2. Heinrich, H. W., *Industrial Accident Prevention,* 4th ed., New York: McGraw-Hill Book Co., 1959.

3. DeReamer, Russell, *Modern Safety Practices,* New York: John Wiley & Sons, 1958.

4. Grimaldi, J. V. and R. H. Simonds, *Safety Management,* Homewood, Ill.: Richard D. Irwin, Inc., 1956.

Safety bulletins

Agencies publishing safety material in bulletin form include:

1. American Standards Association, 70 East Forty-fifth Street, New York, N. Y.

2. National Safety Council, 425 North Michigan Avenue, Chicago, Illinois.

3. National Conservation Bureau, 60 John Street, New York, N. Y.

4. National Fire Protection Association, 69 Batterymarch Street, Boston, Mass. (*Handbook of Fire Protection*—the fire prevention engineer's bible—N.F.P.A. quarterly)

5. United States Government. Numerous agencies publish safety material. See Chapter 2.

Books on occupational health

1. Sax, Newton I., *Dangerous Properties of Industrial Materials.* New York: Rheinhold Publishing Corp., 1957.

2. Fairhall, L. T., *Industrial Toxicology,* 2nd ed., Baltimore: Williams & Wilkins, 1957.

3. Gafafer, Wm. M., Ed., *Manual of Industrial Hygiene.* Philadelphia: Wm. B. Saunders Co., n.d.

4. Swartz, Tulipan and Birmingham, *Occupational Diseases of the Skin.* Philadelphia: Lea and Febiger, n.d.

5. Johnstone, R. T. and S. E. Miller, *Occupational and Industrial Hygiene.* St. Louis: C. V. Mosby Co., 1960.

6. Hunter, Donald, *The Diseases of Occupations,* 3rd ed., Boston: Little, Brown & Co., 1962.

7. Dallavalle, *The Industrial Environment and its Control.* New York: Pittman Publishing Corp., n.d.

Ionizing radiation

The literature in this field is so volumninous and being added to so rapidly that only the nuclear physicist specializing in radiation protection is qualified to appraise reliably the new material as it appears. Therefore, this bibliography is limited to publications that will be directly useful to the student or other user of this text.

1. Blatz, Hanson, *Radiation Hygiene Handbook,* Princeton, N. J.: D. Van Nostrand, 1959.

2. Braestrup, Carl B. and H. O. Wycoff, *Radiation Protection,* Springfield, Ill.: C. E. Thomas Co., 1958.

3. Glasstone, Samuel, *Sourcebook on Atomic Energy,* 2nd ed., Princeton, N. J.: D. Van Nostrand Co., 1958.

4. *National Bureau of Standards Handbook.* Washington: Government printing office.

Handbook 51. "Radiological Monitoring Methods and Instruments."
　　　”　　52. "Maximum Permissible Amounts of Radiosotopes in the Human Body and Maximum Permissible Concentrations of Radioisotopes in Air and Water."
　　　”　　54. "Protection against radiations from Ra^{226}, Co^{60} and Cs^{137}."
　　　”　　57. "Photographic Dosimetry of X- and gamma rays."
　　　”　　60. "X-ray Protection."
　　　”　　62. "Radiological Units and Measurements."
　　　”　　65. "Safe Handling of Isotopes."

5. *Glossary of Terms in Nuclear Science and Technology,* American Standards Association, 70 East 45th Street, New York, New York.

Index